*B*irthing in the Spirit is about understanding one's inner wisdom, about learning trust, and about empowerment. It is much more than a "how-to" book. Extremely important issues that all pregnant women face such as fears and worries, concerns about pain, questions about medical and non-medical management, body and birth physiology, sleep, support people, and birth environment are all covered along with helpful suggestions and practical methods to help a woman birth her baby.

Birthing in the Spirit opens the world of pregnancy and birth in a unique way that can benefit a woman's health and her full potential to expand her mind, her body, and her spirit. With each subject, the book interweaves ancient wisdom with modern knowledge of the physiology and psychology of birth in a manner that leads a pregnant woman to a deeper understanding and trust of her own body's knowledge. Clear examples, beautiful metaphors, and well-studied concepts inspire and move one to a deeper appreciation of the true potential of birth and of the individual. From detailed descriptions of such areas as how to enlarge one's pelvis, expand one's lungs, relax into and "breathe" and vocalize "the baby out", to release worry and doubt, and achieve a sense of peace and calm, this book encompasses each significant aspect of childbirth.

The key theme in this wonderful book is to discover your true nature, and to tap into the deepest human values such as "Truth, Love, Peace, Right Action, and Non violence". Following the wisdom that flows from these values into the birth of a human being takes one into an experience of "happiness and bliss" and ultimately into "an experience of spirit."

MARSHALL KLAUS M.D. AND PHYLLIS KLAUS MFT, LCSW

*I*n a groundbreaking publication, Cathy Daub accomplishes in *Birthing in the Spirit* something that I have not experienced in any other childbirth related book that I have read. Rather than the how-to format of so many birthing books which often leave readers with the impression that birth is an ordeal that women must endure in order to get that baby that they want so badly, Daub's labor of love truly makes birth feel like a work of art, and an event ties us all together through our one common and timeless experience, birth. *Birthing in the Spirit* is as exquisite and unique as birth itself. This book touched my spirit and I'm sure that whether you are a birthing mother, or someone who works with them, it will touch yours as well.

MINDY TROGE, CCE, PCD

Birthing in the Spirit

by

Cathy Daub

Birth Works® Press
MEDFORD, NEW JERSEY

Birth Works® Press
Medford, New Jersey

This book contains information and stories that can help to empower women during their
pregnancy, labor, birth, and parenting. It is intended to give women and their families
a wider scope of options available to them and should by no means substitute for the
personal care of a qualified physician or midwife. The author and the publisher are not
responsible for any adverse effects resulting from the use of information
contained in this book.

Interior design and cover design by Larry Taylor
Interior typesetting by Kathy Ristow, Red Wing Typesetting

ISBN: 978-0-9724616-2-7
Printed in the United States of America

10 09 08 07   1 2 3 4

I dedicate this book to my mother,
Frieda Schifferli Wald,
who brought me into this world,

and

to my two children,
Heidi and Aaron,
whose respect and love
make my life beautiful,

and

to all women who have ever given birth and those yet to do so.

Contents

Foreword   ix

Acknowledgments   xiii

Introduction   xv

LAYING THE FOUNDATION FOR BIRTH

CHAPTER 1:   *The Journey*   1

CHAPTER 2:   *Birth Is Instinctive*   5

CHAPTER 3:   *Birthing in the Spirit*   9

CHAPTER 4:   *Education and Educare*   17

CHAPTER 5:   *Exploring Your Options for Birth*   25

CHAPTER 6:   *The Baba Yaga*   39

CHAPTER 7:   *Human Values in Birth*   49

HUMAN VALUES IN BIRTH

CHAPTER 8:   *Truth*   61

CHAPTER 9:   *Fetal Development and the Formative Years*   75

CHAPTER 10:   *The Physiology of Birth*   83

CHAPTER 11:   *Understanding the Self: The Five Human Sheaths*   101

CHAPTER 12:   *The Power Within: Positive Thinking*   109

CHAPTER 13:   *Intuition*   115

CHAPTER 14:   *Dharma, the Mind, and Beliefs*   127

CHAPTER 15:   *Pelvic Bodywork*   143

CHAPTER 16:   *Nutrition and Our Health*   151

CHAPTER 17:   *The Power of Sleep*   175

CHAPTER 18:   *Peace and Equanimity*   185

CONTENTS

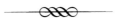

CHAPTER 19:   *Fears and Worries*   197

CHAPTER 20:   *Detachment*   219

CHAPTER 21:   *Interconnection of the Senses, Elements, and Human Values*   227

CHAPTER 22:   *Grieving and Healing*   237

CHAPTER 23:   *Our Mothers and Our Health*   249

CHAPTER 24:   *Love: The Foundation of All Human Values*   257

CHAPTER 25:   *Love Is a Verb*   269

CHAPTER 26:   *Respecting the Unity in Diversity*   279

THE PROMISE OF BIRTH

CHAPTER 27:   *Birth Times*   287

CHAPTER 28:   *The Full Potential of Birth*   297

CHAPTER 29:   *Parenting*   307

CHAPTER 30:   *Improving Birth in America and Around the World*   323

Endnotes   329

APPENDIX

Resource and Support Organizations for Childbirth   343

Overview of Fetal Development   347

The Ten Steps of the Mother Friendly Childbirth Initiative   350

INDEX   353

Foreword

Any book about childbirth—even a book on birth and transcendence—is read and interpreted in a particular technical and scientific context. This is why we must refer to recent advances that will speed up the history of human birth in directions it is still difficult to predict. We must contrast technical and scientific advances.

The particularity of technical advances is to spread out all over the world at a high speed. This is the case of the recent evolution of the cesarean technique. Since the simplifications suggested by Michael Stark in the 1990s, the cesarean has become an easy intervention that can be performed in twenty minutes: when I did my first c-sections half a century ago, we usually needed an hour or so. Today, in well-organized maternity units, the safety of the cesarean can be compared with the safety of the natural route…if one takes into account the only conventional criteria in use to evaluate how babies are born. For example, a recent study at the level of the whole Canadian population reported a series of 46,766 planned cesareans for breech presentations: there were no maternal deaths in this series. The simplicity and safety of this operation are two of the reasons why caesarean rates are increasing all over the world.

Knowledge of purely scientific advances, on the other hand, has a tendency to spread slowly. This is the case with the many scientific data I include in the framework of *The Scientification of Love.* Until recently, love was a topic for poets, philosophers and novelists. Today it is studied from multiple scientific perspectives. All these perspectives lead us to focus on the period surrounding birth. Among the spectacular recent advances we must mention what we have learned about the behavioral effects of the hormone oxytocin. Few people have already realized how important it is to have discovered that oxytocin—the hormone necessary for contractions of the uterine muscle and the subsequent birth of the baby and the delivery of the placenta—is also the main hormone of love. Furthermore it is important to understand that all hormones involved in childbirth have behavioral effects. This leads us to a new vision of what happens during the parturition of mammals—including human mammals: to give birth mammals must release a complex cocktail of love hormones.

The history of childbirth is therefore at a crossroads. On the one hand, technical advances might lead physicians to routinely offer cesareans to all pregnant women. On the other hand the "scientification of love" offers new reasons to avoid disturbing the physiological processes and to try to *rediscover* the basic needs of laboring women and newborn babies. "Rediscover" is the right word indeed, after thousands of years of culturally controlled childbirth: all societies we know about have dramatically disturbed the physiological processes, particularly via beliefs and rituals; we cannot rely on any cultural model.

This dilemma confronts us at the very time when physiology can help us interpret the specifically human handicap (where childbirth is concerned). It also confronts us at a time when we can understand the solution nature found for overcoming the difficulties inherent in the birthing process. These difficulties relate to the huge development, in our species, of the neocortex (i.e., the thinking brain): during the process of parturition—and during all sexual experiences as well—these inhibitions come from the neocortex. The solution found by nature is that the neocortex is supposed to reduce its activity during labor and delivery. Understanding this forces us to rediscover the harmful effects of language (and therefore the importance of silence), it makes us realize the importance of dim lighting, the need for privacy (i.e., having the feeling of not being observed), and at the same time the need for a feeling of security.

Not only is *Birthing in the Spirit* published at a turning point in the history of childbirth, it is also published at a turning point in the history of humanity. Until now successful societies have been those that have developed the potential for aggression. This was how it happened as long as the strategies for the survival of human groups were based on the domination of nature and on the domination of other human groups. All the beliefs and rituals that disturb the physiological processes in the period surrounding birth were previously evolutionary advantages that moderated the development of the capacity to love (including the respect for Mother Earth). These evolutionary advantages involved our developing the capacity to destroy life. The point is that we are in the process of realizing the limits of the domination of nature; we are beginning to understand the need for creating a sort of unity in our planetary village. Humanity now needs to rely on the energies of love in order to invent new strategies for survival. This is how the beliefs and rituals which disturb the physiological processes are losing their evolutionary advantages. We have to clarify what our new objectives should be. The main objective should be that as many women as possible in the world are able to give birth to their babies with the release of a "cocktail of love hormones." Questions must be raised in terms of civilization.

In other words it is urgent that we rediscover the basic needs of laboring women and newborn babies.

A simple rule of thumb appears as an appropriate aid to rediscovering the basic needs of laboring women. It can be summarized in one sentence: where labor, delivery and birth are concerned, what is specifically human must be eliminated, while our mammalian needs are being met. Eliminating what is specifically human implies that the first step should be to get rid of the aftermath of all the beliefs (inseparable from rituals) that for millennia have disturbed the physiological processes in all known cultural milieus. It also implies that the activity of the neocortex, that part of the brain whose huge development is a human trait, needs to be reduced. Furthermore, it implies that language, which is specifically human, must be used with extreme caution.

To meet these mammalian needs means first that we need to satisfy the need for privacy, since all mammals tend to avoid feeling observed when giving birth. It also means satisfying the need to feel secure: a female mammal in the jungle cannot give birth as long as there is a predator around.

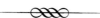

It is significant that when a laboring woman has complete privacy and feels secure, she often finds herself in typically mammalian postures, for example on all fours. People nowadays often say that childbirth should be "humanized." Instead the priority should be to "mammalianize" childbirth.

Access to transcendental mysteries is often considered a specifically human trait. In fact access to another reality than space and time reality is easier when the neocortex is at rest and when we accept our mammalian condition. Non-human mammals do not need to pray.

MICHEL ODENT

Acknowledgments

An undertaking of this magnitude would not be possible without the love and support of many people and I am grateful to all of them. I believe that when we seek guidance from the spirit, it sends the very people that are needed for the project. I am grateful to the following people, who I believe were guided by the spirit to be a part of the writing and publishing of this book, and also to those who paved the way in my life to make this possible.

I would like to thank the following people:

Heidi Daub, for format editing, photo choices, and keeping me on realistic timeframes for completion.

Elizabeth Frank, for the copy and format editing of my book.

Horatio Daub, MD, for providing medical consultation.

Nancy Wainer, for offering VBAC classes that gave me confidence to have a natural birth.

Mirel Orlofsky, who helped develop the Birth Works® International childbirth educator workshops.

Mindy Troge, for providing general editing, feedback, and marketing.

Suzanne Arms, Harriette Hartigan, Lennart Niellson, Mark Garlick, and Jan Wolfenberg, for their creative photographs.

Aaron Daub for photo choice consultation.

Gayle Peterson and Lewis Mehl Madronna, MD, for starting me on a journey in birth.

Susan Kaczinski and Judith White for their constant support and encouragement.

Soumya Sivakumar, PhD, and Audrey McDonnell for marketing and public relations.

The Birth Works® International Board of Advisors: Suzanne Arms; Raymond G. DeVries, PhD; Ina May Gaskin, CPM; Henci Goer, BA, ACCE; Barbara Harper, RN,CLD,CBE; Bethany Hayes, MD; Jean Sutton, TM; Marshall Klaus, MD; Michel Odent, MD; Jan Tritten, TM; Marsden Wagner, MD; and Nancy Wainer, TM,CCE, CHCE.

All those on the Birth Works® International Board of Directors past and present, who encouraged me to undertake this project.

The beautiful women who submitted their stories on what birthing in the spirit means to them.

All spiritual teachers Abraham, Jesus, Buddha, Krishna, Muhammad, Zoroaster, Sathya Sai Baba and Tich Nacht Han, and others not mentioned, who teach us the importance of living our lives with values and spirit.

And finally to the spirit, whose presence gives meaning to our lives,
if we but remember to seek it.

Introduction

BIRTHING IN THE SPIRIT: A STORY

Her baby was in a breech position and the doctor wanted to perform a cesarean two weeks before her due date, but she refused, saying, "My baby could turn in labor." She went into labor, and after nine hours, a power stronger than the contractions totally consumed her. Her baby's foot had slipped down into the vagina, causing an urge to push. It was useless to try stopping what felt like an elevator that wouldn't stop. She was amazed at the power inside her pregnant body. "Only six centimeters dilated," the doctor said. She thought, What if the baby's head gets stuck? I can't stop these powerful urges to push. It's not safe to try! Feeling she had done all she could, she surrendered to God and agreed to a cesarean. A short time later, her beautiful baby girl was brought to her. Looking into her eyes for the first time, the mother went beyond time and space in a moment of sheer ecstasy, connecting with the spirit. She felt respected by the birth team, who had honored all her wishes. And because she had made the choices and decisions, she felt happy.

Now, twenty-nine years later, I realize that this birth of my daughter, and the subsequent vaginal birth after cesarean (VBAC) of my son, paved the way for me to found Birth Works® International (BWI), whose purpose is to educate and empower women to have positive birth experiences. It is known for providing both an academic and emotional preparation for birth that emphasizes integration of the mind, body, and spirit.

Mystery surrounds questions relating to the spirituality of birth. Where does the individual soul come from? What is the spirit? How do we know it exists? What role does it play in childbirth? Is the spirit present in every birth or only in some births? Does it matter if the births are natural or surgical? How does a woman's body know how to give birth? Perhaps it is such mysteries that attract us to the spirit.

Women are curious and cannot wait to meet their new little baby or babies that have grown inside of them. I believe that although the mind and body play an important role in birth, birth is primarily

an experience of the spirit. What would birth be like if it was only about the mind and the body? It would lack that which brings love, compassion, understanding, and sanctity—some of the most meaningful aspects of life. My desire to further explore the role that the spirit plays in birth is what has led me to write this book.

WHAT IS THE SPIRIT?

I believe that the spirit is a conscious energy greater and wiser than ourselves. I believe it is loving, accepting, wise, and powerful beyond our greatest imagination. I also believe it is in everyone and everything—whether rich or poor, young or old—and that it is in every woman around the world, no matter how she gives birth. The journey of connecting with the spirit is called *spirituality,* which I differentiate from religion because religions set modes of behavior, rituals, and beliefs according to their leaders and/or books. I believe that spirituality is that which is both in and beyond religion, being very expansive in nature.

In this book I am referring to the spirit as a power that is selfless, pure, universal, loving, and unconditional, and that embraces the common bonds of humanity. People have their own beliefs about what exactly the spirit means to them. I believe that spirit is beyond definition and prefer to try and understand it through its action. I believe that the spirit unites instead of separates, and that it is concerned for the welfare of all. Just as a ray of sunlight expresses itself as colors of the rainbow through a prism, so are we all reflections of the spirit. While reading this book, I invite you to use whatever word you associate with spirit, whether it be life force, nature, source, higher power, God, consciousness, existence, Holy Spirit, or just spirit. One thing I believe to be true is that the spirit is always seeking that which is good.

HOW DOES THE SPIRIT RELATE TO BIRTH?

The purpose of this book is to show how we can connect more closely with the spirit through the practice of human values, thereby experiencing transformation and developing more of our full human potential. I believe that too many women in today's world have lost sight of the truth that their bodies already know how to give birth. This is reflected in the majority of births in our country today that are managed medically with anesthesia, analgesia, and other medical procedures. Birthing in the spirit means birthing with more confidence and love, and with less fear. It means opening one's view of birth to see it as a peak experience in a woman's life. It is my hope that the book will give a vision of the full beauty that birth can be, empowering women to give birth in love instead of fear.

What I have sought to explore are questions such as:

    How can we tap into the spirit as a great source of strength and recognize it more fully in our lives and in our births?

🔖 How can women feel closer to the spirit, receiving its guidance during pregnancy, labor, and birth?

🔖 How can the spirit empower women to experience birth with more love and less fear?

🔖 How can the spirit guide men and women during the years of parenting?

BIRTH PRACTICES TODAY

Women have been giving birth on their own for thousands of years—they never took childbirth education classes. I believe that all women are born with the knowledge of how to give birth, and that birth is instinctive. But I suspect that women have always been fearful of childbirth because it is one of the most intense experiences life has to offer a woman. The difference today is that obstetrical drugs and medical procedures are available to minimize or eliminate pain in labor. Thus, an increasing number of pregnant women are accepting modern technology to get through birth.

More and more women are opting for cesareans. Many pain-alleviating procedures such as epidurals are being used without a medical reason. As the number of medically managed births in which drugs and technology are used continues to climb, there is mounting evidence through primal health research (which covers the period in the womb through the end of the first year of life) that we are interfering with body physiology, bonding, attachment, and health in later life. What we are sacrificing and how serious are the long-term, adverse effects on women, babies, families, and society as a whole remains to be seen, but there are signs.

I believe we are in trouble because we are interfering with the body's internal system for giving birth that has developed over thousands of years, without fully understanding the workings of the human body. For example, we know that some studies are showing an increase in cerebral palsy in premature infants exposed to electronic fetal monitoring.[1] Questions unanswered include: What happens to hormones when the body is anesthetized? Are the chemicals used in inductions disturbing delicate connections in the fetal brain? Are these disturbances associated with autism and increasing rates of violence?

The trend towards medically managed birth is alarming, as shown by the results of the *Listening to Mothers II* survey.[2] In 2005, 76 percent of the 1,573 women polled had been given an epidural or spinal anesthesia while giving birth. In addition, 41 percent reported receiving inductions to start their labors, 94 percent had electronic fetal monitoring, 83 percent had intravenous drip, 75 percent had one or more vaginal exams, 56 percent had urinary catheters, 47 percent had artificial rupture of membranes, and 47 percent had synthetic oxytocin (Pitocin) administered to speed up their labors. In the polled population, 33 percent had a cesarean (which reflects the 30.2 percent national cesarean rate in 2005), with approximately two-thirds being medically unnecessary according to the Center for Disease Control (CDC).[3] The World Health Organization (WHO) recommends that a 10 to 15 percent rate is acceptable.[4]

Other studies report that primary elective cesareans (meaning that the surgery is performed for no reason other than a woman's request) comprise 4 to 18 percent of all cesareans and 14 to 22 percent of elective cesareans in the western populations investigated. Women in the study were afraid of losing their babies due to injury when the baby passed through the pelvis, or genital tract injury from pressure of the baby on the pelvic floor musculature.[5] In addition, in the *Listening to Mothers II* survey, many women felt they should have been informed of complications related to labor induction (78 percent) and cesarean section (81 percent) before having these procedures and said they were poorly informed or had incorrect knowledge about the risks.[6]

Women live with their birth experiences for the rest of their lives. My mother had a very negative belief about birth because when she gave birth in the 1940s and 1950s, she was forced to lie on her back and was given the drug Scopolamine, which has hallucinogenic and amnesiac effects. Thus, my mother remembered only parts of her births when she was thrashing around trying to get up. My father was not allowed in the room with her, and she had no other support. My parents had six children and never saw any of us being born.

A positive birth experience helps to facilitate bonding between a mother and her baby. A negative birth experience may increase the likelihood of post-partum depression and have adverse effects on their relationship. Many women, even those who are elderly, can tell you the about their births down to the most minute details. Birth is clearly an event of great significance in a woman's life.

Traditionally, women used to learn about birth by seeing, hearing, and experiencing other women giving birth. Today, 68 percent of those polled in the *Listening to Mothers II* survey said they learned about birth by watching television shows specifically created to depict childbirth.[7] Barely half (56 percent) of new mothers took classes for their most recent pregnancy, and only 9 percent of experienced mothers took childbirth classes.[8] Of these women, even fewer are taking consumer-oriented classes where they are more likely to learn about options and alternatives.

Hospital classes tend to teach about standard procedures, protocols, and routines established by the hospital for labor and birth. As one woman expecting her first baby recently told me, "I know they [the hospital] are doing unnecessary things, but I have to pick my battles." Another woman said, "In the hospital classes we were not presented with alternatives and choices in labor. I just went along with everything they said because I was so scared." A recent study showed that the more personal control a woman feels about her birth experience, the more satisfaction she will have about her birth.[9]

WHAT THIS BOOK COVERS

Much of the current literature describes birth as a mind-body event. Therefore, books and articles in magazines have typically been written about how to plan your birth, the birth team, comfort measures and positions for labor, all aspects of nutrition, and risks and benefits of medical procedures. Because birth is associated with loss as well, many books have been written about grief. Although

this book covers some aspects of the mind and body, it is primarily about the spiritual aspects of birth. It represents the beginning of a fascinating journey into understanding more about who we are and the way in which this impacts how we give birth.

Birthing in the Spirit is not as much a technical "how to birth" book as it is one that promotes a philosophy of birth that involves examining our self-perceptions, how they influence our actions, and how they contribute to our sense of well-being within ourselves and toward others. It is not about persuading all women to have a natural, medical intervention-free birth, but rather, for women to change their own viewpoints about birth so they can approach birth with more confidence and have more empowering experiences. It is my hope that this book will transform the way in which women decide to give birth, making it the peak experience in life it was meant to be. This is an inward journey of discovering more about the self, which will ultimately be the most helpful preparation a woman can have for birth.

We tend to be good at seeking happiness, knowledge, and consolation in the external world, but how often do we recognize and contemplate the knowledge within us? How often do we depend on our internal faculties to bring us lasting contentment versus the transient ephemeral joys of the external material world? Those who are able to recognize the spirit in their daily lives find a source of great comfort and strength that gives them a sense of empowerment and connection to a greater good. It is what helps many women find the courage and strength to work through contractions in labor.

There is actually a state beyond happiness that can be experienced, and in this book I will refer to this state of being as "bliss." Those who have experienced bliss can tell you that at that moment, time seems to stand still. Some also call it ecstasy. In his book *The Path to Love*, Deepak Chopra refers to ecstasy as a spiritual release. He writes, "Spiritual ecstasy is not a feeling or an idea, but a shift of perception in which direct contact with spirit is made."[10]

In *Birthing in the Spirit*, I will address the concept of spirit and its relationship to childbirth during the pregnancy, labor and birth, postpartum, and parenting periods. The book has three parts: Part 1 (chapters 1-7) lays the foundation for birthing in the spirit; Part 2 (chapters 8-26) discusses the five human values, with each value having its own chapter; Part 3 (chapters 27-30) shows how current birth practices are interfering with birth times, how a good birth lays the foundation for parenting, and what is being done in America and abroad to improve birth experiences. The stories within chapters are based on real-life events, but names have been changed to protect the privacy of the women who have shared them. For the stories at the end of each chapter, I have kept the real names.

A TRANSFORMED BIRTH AND LIFE

It is my hope that as you read this book, you will feel a strong connection and shared bonding with all women giving birth, for birth is cross-cultural, timeless, and ancient. Birth is also an experience greater than ourselves that has transforming power if we take the step of looking more deeply inside.

After all, isn't that what a woman needs to do when in labor? It is also my hope that you will feel touched at some deep level with inspiration to make changes in your life for the better.

People often become opinionated, resistant, and rigid when faced with information that challenges their assumptions. Instead of going to previous experience or knowledge, I ask you to go to your heart and draw on the deepest source of your inner strength, using your common sense when feeling a need to change a belief. I ask you to open yourself to the possibility of new perspectives. Remember that the journey into the spirit is one of expansion, not contraction. It is my hope that you will find this journey into the inner self and human values as empowering as I have found it to be.

It is with much humility that I've written this book. I constantly prayed to God for guidance, seeing myself as a vehicle through which the spirit works. It is my hope that as you read this book, you will find something that is helpful to you in your own life and your births. When you read something in the book that goes home to your heart, that resonates with your inner being, pay attention to it and see if you can begin putting it into practice, for what good is knowledge if it is not practiced?

Medical intuitives—people who can diagnose diseases based on energy—tell us that the soul is the oblique side of the mind and body and that it communicates with us indirectly. Upon reflection, I found that events of great significance in my life did, indeed, begin as small thoughts. But these small thoughts took hold of me and I flew with them, sometimes not knowing why initially and only understanding after many years had gone by. Founding the BWI program was one of those experiences.

I received a little postcard from Nancy Wainer in 1981 asking for help in chairing the first VBAC conference in the country. I remember holding that postcard and thinking, "If I do this, my life will never be the same." I was a co-chair for the conference, and indeed my life has never been the same. It was at this conference that the International Cesarean Awareness Network (ICAN)—formerly the Cesarean Prevention Movement (CPM)—was founded, and I became a founding member. It was through ICAN that Birth Works® International was developed into a teacher certification program. It has now become my life's work, and it all began with a postcard.

I have written this book for anyone connected with childbirth. I hope that it helps birthing parents have more beautiful and positive birth experiences. I hope that it helps caregivers, doctors, midwives, nurses, and doulas (birth assistants) to encourage women to embrace and not be afraid of their own power when giving birth, and that it helps the birth team be more sensitive to the physiological and spiritual needs of a birthing woman. I hope that it helps anyone in contact with a pregnant woman to realize the importance of keeping her happy during pregnancy, labor, and birth, as this affects hormone production with direct results on the health of the fetus. I hope that families reap the benefit of positive birth experiences, keeping the same intimate and close connection throughout their lives that was felt at their births.

I am also setting forth ideals and values which individuals can strive to make a part of themselves. These ideals may seem lofty for some readers, but I have complete faith that during the process of

beginning to use these values in daily living and birth, the changes in your life will begin to become apparent immediately. It is my hope that as you begin this journey, you will find yourself being transformed in a very deep and meaningful way. I hope that it will bring you closer to knowing your own full potential and that of birth. I know these things are possible because it is a journey I began thirty years ago that continues to this day.

LAYING THE FOUNDATION FOR BIRTH

CHAPTER 1

The Journey

At the very beginning, there was no you.
Like a seed in a soft round pod,
a tiny egg lay in an ovary deep inside your mother's body.

SHEILA KITZINGER IN *BEING BORN*

I remember a visit to Yosemite National Park, where I watched a slideshow about the moon presented by the astrological society from San Francisco. One slide was of the night sky filled with thousands of stars visible to the naked eye. Next, a slide was shown of the seemingly empty space between two of the stars, and to our astonishment, hundreds more stars could be seen. In between those spaces, again with more magnification, there were hundreds more stars.

In what looks like nothing, there is always something.

In one of my favorite books, *The Powers of Ten,* images are shown of the inside of the hand, with magnifications by powers of ten.[1] Quickly, the hand becomes a landscape that is unfamiliar to the eyes. Unexpected details appear, and one loses orientation. The inside of the hand becomes as unfamiliar as the distant stars. Going even deeper at 10^{11} magnification, it looks like empty space— verily, the inside of our hands is just that...space. But in that space there is something, and this something is everything, for at 10^{12} magnification, a little speck begins to appear—and it is an atom, the beginning of all life.

In a journey, at first there is complete darkness, stillness, quiet. There is no past or future. It seems there is nothing; but in that nothing, something is incubating. And then, where there seems to be nothing, there is a quiver, a tiny impulse of energy. Out of seemingly nothing comes something. It may be the birth of a new idea, or in childbirth, an embryo. The tiny egg starts out as small as the period at the end of this sentence. Called an *ovum,* it is packed with all the food and energy needed to make a baby. Its journey from the ovary to the uterus takes approximately three days and nights. It arrives in the uterus, waiting . . .

Although on the outside it appears nothing is happening, something *is* happening within. It is a process that is full of mystery, awe, and wonder. Many sperm are traveling quickly toward the egg because they only live about forty-eight hours and it takes ten hours to swim up the vagina, through the cervix, and into the fallopian tube. Out of the thousands of sperm, most never make it to the egg because temperature is critical to survival. Those that make it to the egg have to pass through many layers of the egg, each protected by hormones and specific temperature gradients. The sperm

THE MILKY WAY GALAXY

swim around the egg and keep trying to penetrate it. Then, wonder of wonders, one gets through.

Without the sperm, the egg can never grow into a baby. For any sperm to make it through so many layers of the egg is the miracle of conception. At first, the egg looks like the sun, bright and effulgent with the potential for creation. In the next moment, conception occurs and it begins to transform. There is immediate, organized cellular division. The energy increases and becomes more organized with every moment, and suddenly the egg begins to spiral, taking on an appearance similar to our own Milky Way galaxy.

Looking directly at the Milky Way galaxy, one can see a hundred billion stars, mutually bound by gravity, encircling the central region in a spiral. Looking at an egg just after penetration by a sperm is like seeing a miniature spiral galaxy. This connection shows creation inside a woman who has just conceived.

More and more energy develops as the embryonic cells continue to divide and begin early organ formation. By the time there is a missed menstruation, the embryo already has a beating heart that will work tirelessly the rest of its life whether the body is awake or asleep. What makes the heart start beating? How do the cells know what to do? These are all mysteries of the spirit.

CONCEPTION

As the embryonic cells continue to differentiate and mature in the early weeks of gestation, the embryo grows into what looks more like a sprouting bean than a human being. At one month or so, it has already grown fragile projections that will become arms. At two and a half months, it can open and close its mouth; and at three months, it can already make facial expressions while weighing only as much as a hen's egg in its shell. Its legs and arms are moving and stretching in a little amniotic ocean, but still its mother cannot feel any movement. Now it looks more like an extraterrestrial creature than a human, but tremendous potential is present, and it continues to transform.

At twenty-eight weeks of gestation, ultrasounds have shown that twins are already playing purposefully with each other, reaching out to touch each other's amniotic sacs. Fetal development grows and expands with rapid cell division and differentiation into various organs. The baby has learned how to push against the uterus to "swim" in its amniotic ocean, and the mother feels it kicking. By six months or earlier, the fetus can begin to hear its mother's voice.[2] By seven months, it opens its eyes.[3] Development continues with the presence of fingernails and a layer of fat under the skin to keep the fetus warm, preparing it for birth.

Even more energy is required now as the baby reaches full gestation. And then one day, the baby signals its mother with hormones that it is ready to be born, and labor begins. Even greater surges of energy help birth the baby into the world. With wide-open eyes, the baby looks at its mother for the first time and takes its first breath. The energy required to birth the baby has reached its peak.

The baby was drinking its amniotic fluid before birth and could smell it. Colostrum—the specialized secretion from the mammary glands that is high in proteins, antibodies, vitamins, and minerals, and that is produced before a mother's milk comes in—smells like amniotic fluid. The baby follows that smell to find its mother's breast. Life-giving colostrum and then breast milk nourish the newborn baby in the days, weeks, and months after birth. When the baby sucks on its mother's breast, it helps stimulate the mother's uterus to return to its original size.

The uterus has done its job of growing a baby, and after birth, as it returns to its original size—about the size of a fist, which is also the size of the human heart—the idea of growing a baby quiets and becomes still again. But just like the waning and waxing of the moon and the ebb and flow of ocean tides, out of that nothing *something* will come again with a fresh burst of energy, creating something new—just as a bud blossoms into a beautiful flower, giving off fragrance and delighting all who pass by. This something might be another baby in the womb, or it might be the birth of a new project that has its own cycle of beginning and ending.

Just as the earth passes through cycles, so do we pass through cycles. For when there is darkness and all is quiet and still—when you think nothing is happening—know that there is something starting to germinate, gathering energy along the way. All we have to do is wait and have patience, and it will come. Having trust and faith in the process of cycles brings equanimity and wisdom.

Birthing in the Spirit

Human beings have access to two realities. One is the space-and-time reality. The other one is an out-of-space time reality. It is the feeling that we belong to a whole. Access to the latter reality is easier in specific situations, such as during the period surrounding birth. Once a mother told me: "As soon as my baby boy was born I first touched him, and soon after, I became more audacious and I took him in my arms. Then I saw the whole universe in his eyes."

—MICHEL ODENT, MD

CHAPTER 2

Birth Is Instinctive

All I have seen
Teaches me to trust the creator
For all I have not seen.

RALPH WALDO EMERSON

The moon rose slowly over the South China Sea off the coast of Malaysia. My husband, Raysh, and I were in our third year of a backpacking trip around the world; eventually we would travel through forty-eight countries before returning home to the United States. We had heard that giant turtles laid their eggs here, and we had come to see them. We were told to come at night. The sandy coast was long and the waves lapped lazily at the shore. Moonbeams sparkled over the ocean waters. I thought our chances of seeing a turtle over this long coast were fairly small, and knew I might be up most of the night.

Raysh and I sat on a mound of sand back where the grasses grew and breathed in the ocean air deeply. I reflected on all the countries we had visited in South America, Europe, Africa, and Asia, and all the memories we would have with us for the rest of our lives. I reflected on my childhood, growing up in the foothills of the Appalachian Mountains in Pennsylvania where I used to ride horses. Though I didn't live on a farm, there were many farms around us. Strangely enough, I had never seen a live birth—not even a chicken laying an egg—even though I was a country girl.

My eyes kept scanning the waves for a turtle's head. Even though these turtles weigh 700 to 1,000 pounds, they are still small in comparison to the great waters of the ocean. The moon was rising higher in the sky now and becoming brighter. It was the early hours of the morning, and I was getting tired.

I looked at the waves again, searching for a little head. My eyes caught a glance of a piece of driftwood at the top of one of the waves crashing to shore. Was it a piece of driftwood? No, it was moving purposefully towards the shore.

Excitement began to mount inside of me. Fatigue left in an instant.

Gradually, the shell of the great turtle became apparent as she "rode" the waves in little by little. The buoyancy of the water moved her easily. And then there she was, beginning to grab hold of the sand with her fins, slowly pulling herself forward. We moved closer to see more clearly, yet keeping some distance.

We could hear her breathe now as she began her way up the sandy bank. Each breath sounded like

air coming out of a rubber tire. "Ahhhhhhh. Ahhhhhh." Every step she took involved tremendous effort. Every step moved her only a few more inches up onto the beach.

We watched for nearly two hours as she labored to move just halfway up the beach. Then suddenly she arduously turned around and spent another hour heading back to the sea. We wondered why she was doing this and what would happen next.

Very slowly, once at the water's edge, she turned around again and another hour went by until she had moved up the beach to where the grasses began. It seemed she was looking for those grasses. Her breathing was very labored with the great effort to move her body weight. Throughout, what looked like tears streamed from her eyes, making little dark pools on the sand. We realized this was her body's secretions to keep her eyes moist while out of the water, but I also felt the labor of love she was carrying out to birth her eggs on land.

Now she began to dig a hole with her large hind fins. We quickly moved back as sand went flying more than ten feet in all directions. When the hole was made, we watched as she laid about

nine eggs that looked like off-white ping-pong balls. To my astonishment, some local Malaysians climbed onto her back as she was laying the eggs. They pounded on her shell while laughing. *How rude and disrespectful!* I thought. I wanted to tell them to get off her but didn't feel I had any authority to say that, being a stranger in a foreign country. To them it was just a game. But I felt a deep respect for this turtle, the work she had done to find a place to lay her eggs, to dig a hole in the sand, and to lay her eggs. It felt sacred. How could anyone show such a lack of respect for this time of birth?

TURTLE LAYING EGGS IN MALAYSIA

It was sheer relief when she was finished laying her eggs. As she began to cover the hole with sand, everyone jumped back, for the power in her body could be felt by the force of the moving sand. *Good!* I thought. *Now this will make them stay away from her.* Her giant fins covered the eggs completely with sand. She paused for awhile as if to make sure everything was okay and then began to turn around.

TURTLE RETURNING TO THE SOUTH CHINA SEA

Now began the long trek back to the ocean. Every step forward made us feel like we wanted to help her, but she had to do this herself. It took a little less time to get back to the water since it was downhill. A feeling of joy and relief swept over me when she finally reached the waves and the buoyancy of the water helped her to feel light again. And then she was gone.

Two weeks would go by, after which time the little turtles would hatch and make their way back to the sea. Their greatest risk would be from the sea gulls who feed on them

as they try to make their way to the sea, or from humans who dig up the eggs and either eat them as a delicacy or make money by selling them. That is why the Malaysian government had set aside an area on the beach where egg poaching was prohibited. Those babies that made it to the ocean would grow into giant turtles and swim from the Arctic to the Antarctic. But when they were ready to lay their eggs, they would return to this very same beach.[1]

How do these little turtles, who have never seen their mothers, know where to find the same beach on which they were born? How do they know what to do once leaving the water's edge, and how to swim from one end of the earth to the other? At first this seems a mystery, but then we are left with the realization that it must be instinctive. The knowing is instinctive. It doesn't have to be learned. This is true for all animals, and we, as humans, are no different.

As I watched the dawn begin to appear, I thought about the mystery of life and our existence on the earth. I thought about how the earth speeds through space at 18.5 miles per second, and yet standing there by the China Sea, all appeared gentle and calm as creatures of the earth gave birth (and will continue giving birth for thousands of years). The earth is billions of years old, yet our individual lives are but a drop in the bucket of time.

Millions of women have been giving birth for thousands of years with no preparation other than watching other women give birth. They lived in close communities and became familiar with pregnancy, labor, and birth simply by being together and helping each other. Birth was simply a part of life for them. They knew that if they were to give birth one day, doing the work and feeling labor pains was just part of the process. They lived close to their instincts and trusted them.

Birth is instinctive, and what is instinctive cannot be taught—only experienced. Just like the turtle knew how to give birth, and her little turtles when they grow up will also know how to give birth, so the knowledge about how to give birth is born in every woman. This is innate knowledge that can be trusted. In that moment on the beach, I felt very connected to the turtle that had just laid nine eggs with nine little turtles inside. The same instinctive knowledge about how to give birth was in both of us.

I had been up all night. The sky was getting lighter. Yet I didn't feel like sleeping. I had just witnessed an event I would never forget, for it was the first birth I had ever seen.

Birthing in the Spirit

Some people are trying so hard to remove God from aspects of our lives they are forgetting where He does exist. People need a reminder of all that birth was made to be, and all the connection that can come with it.... Reminding people what they instinctively know about birth and how spirit is an intricate part of it may help people remember there is more to birth than we experience as a whole in this nation. That memory is buried deeply for many.

—JULIA WELSH, MOTHER FROM OHIO

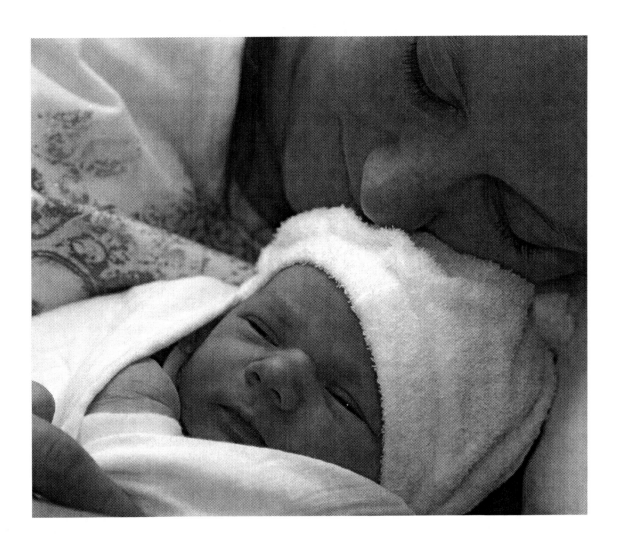

CHAPTER 3

Birthing in the Spirit

*When you are in spirit, you are inspired and
your mind transcends limitations and you become a greater person
than you ever thought to be. It is all about moving into spirit.*

WAYNE DYER IN *INSPIRATION*

Valorie was laboring in a warm pool of water. Dim lights gave the room a soft glow. The contractions hurt but the water felt good. The midwife asked every now and then, "How are you doing?" Valorie nodded okay. Her husband would look at her and smile and give a thumbs-up. As she lay in the tub, she wanted to know, *What is making it hurt? What is this incredible force and power that is in me?* She was feeling huge—not in her belly, for the physical body was such a small part of this experience. She was experiencing something much larger—a space, a connection with all women who had ever given birth.

Valorie was in her body, but a larger part of her was at one with all women before her who had ever given birth. What she was experiencing was so much more than what it looked like to her husband. And then she went deeper inside, and the more deeply she went, the more expansion she felt. Inside, it felt huge, as if all women who had ever given birth were inside her. She felt a kinship with all women worldwide.

Now, all around her felt distant. Without realizing it, she had moved into the "zone," as if on another planet in another space and dimension of time. The contractions came like waves. She went still deeper inside, into her consciousness that was beyond body and mind. She was in the spirit.

When we are in resonance with the spirit, we are in rhythm with our own nature. Resonance is like two keys of a piano being tuned to sound the same note. If they make different sounds, there is discord and confusion. When there is one sound, there is clarity and focus.

Valorie could "see" beyond herself as she bonded with all other women who had ever given birth, because she was "in tune" with her destiny of giving birth to the soul inside her. When we have clear vision, we are more in touch with what is real and profound in our lives, and this helps us to be more in touch with understanding our true nature. We are more than just a body and mind; the body contains the spirit. When that sense of purpose is awakened, we come into touch with who we are. Then, just like two instrument strings being in tune with each other, we resonate in rhythm with our own nature and have clear vision.

The Latin root of spirit is *spiritus*, which has the meaning of "breath or life force" and also "soul, courage, and vigor."[1] In Hebrew it is *ruach,* and in Greek, *pneuma*, with both having the meaning of "breath."[2] In Sanskrit it is known as the Atma, One with the Absolute, as its radiation,[3] and is differentiated from the jiva-Atma, which are individual souls. Soul and spirit are often used interchangeably, but spirit usually has a more expanded connotation than soul, as in, many souls come from one spirit just as many colors come from one light. Soul is referred to as the part of a person that cannot exist without the person, whereas spirit is viewed as the breath that brings life to the soul of the person.[4]

For the purpose of this book, I am suggesting the definition of soul as that which is central to a person's "beingness," and spirit as that which gives breath and life to the soul and which has intelligence, consciousness, and sentience. Something that gives breath to the soul must be from the creator Himself.

We use the word spirit in everyday language, as in "team spirit," "with us in spirit," having a "generous spirit," and "singing with spirit." In all of these connotations, the essence of spirit is to add vigor and vitality to something, and so spirit represents that which is good. When used in a more spiritual sense—as in a higher power, life force, consciousness, Holy Spirit, or God—spirit is an essence that goes beyond mind and form and is that which fills us with wonder, awe, and beauty, such as being moved when hearing a beautiful song, watching a dazzling sunset or sunrise, or looking into a newborn baby's eyes.

I like the definition given in *Webster's Dictionary* for spirit, which is "The vital principle in man coming as a gift from God and providing one's personality with its inward structure, dynamic drive, and creative response to the demands it encounters in the process of becoming."[5] This definition supports the idea that it is the spirit that knows how to bring the soul into a pregnant woman and grow a baby. It views the spirit as that which is responsible for what we call the miracle of birth.

The spirit is always associated with the characteristic of expansion. It is associated with that which is bigger than ourselves and which fills us with awe and wonder. This is in contrast to ego or self-centeredness, which is contractive in nature. Spirit is that which takes us beyond the borders of ourselves. It is that which allows us to think of the welfare of others before ourselves, such as in a woman giving birth being prepared to sacrifice much in her life to take care of her baby. There are some general characteristics I believe to be true that pertain to the spirit and that provide a dimension to its characteristic of expansion.

- It cannot be confined; its quality is that of expansion
- It is much larger than the body
- It is pure, pristine, effulgent, unsullied, everlasting
- Its nature is that of unity and not duality
- It is fresh, clear, and eternal
- It is mysterious and all-knowing

- It is powerful beyond our imagination
- There is love without boundaries that instills in us a sense of awe and wonder
- It can never be diminished or depleted
- It gives of itself freely and yet remains full
- It has no self-centered ego
- It serves others without expecting any reward in return

Though spirit has the aspect of expansion, it can appear as small initially. In this sense the spirit often has an indirect aspect to it, with its full impact not fully understood until later. It seems to "slip in the back door" and only then, in its own time, becomes a wonder in our lives as it manifests itself more fully. Take, for example, a woman who becomes pregnant. Initially she may think, *Ah, I'd like to have a baby.* She becomes pregnant, and then when she first feels her baby kicking, she realizes, *This is really happening.* Finally, towards the end of gestation, the multitude of changes she needs to make in her life become apparent and she may think, *Ah, what have I gotten myself into?*

The question of "When does life begin?" remains a mystery to this day. Historically, the Hebrew scripture relates a belief that a soul pre-exists and enters its mother's womb at conception. God is seen as being responsible for the process that develops the embryo into a human being. The idea of a pre-existing soul was presented by both Plato, who believed "the human soul lives before the body,"[6] and his student Aristotle, who described the fetus as having a "vegetative soul" associated with nutrition, then a "sensitive soul" when sensory organs were developed, and that this then evolved into an "intellective soul" as the fetus developed parts of the body and the ability for intellectual thought and animation.[7] The debate continues as to when life first begins—from the time of Aristotle, who believed life begins with first movements, to some who suggest the fetus is not alive until it is thought to be viable, to others who believe the infant does not receive a spirit or become human until its brain function is present or until it is born. For the latter, the life of a fetus has little importance or significance.[8]

Women are known to communicate with their babies before they are conceived or born. Tibetan women compose a song to invite a soul to them before it is conceived. Some women have dreams during pregnancy of a white bird or light that they believe to be a source of communication between their unborn baby and themselves when it enters their body in early pregnancy.[9] Such women feel it natural to continue communicating with their unborn child during the rest of pregnancy through prayer, singing, and reading to it.

There is a rising awareness in birth of the need to provide holistic care for a baby and its mother.[10] Holistic means providing care for the mind, body, and spirit and recognizing the needs of each. It means that in order to provide complete care to a baby in the womb and its mother, their spiritual needs must also be attended to. This is based on a belief that the baby is capable of having memories of early-life experiences. I believe this to be true because of my personal experience with my daughter.

When she was about three years old, she approached me one day holding her baby doll as I was playing piano. She said to me, "My baby just got born." I had not started teaching childbirth classes yet but had read about children remembering their births. It was suggested that only broad, open questions be asked. So I looked at her and said, "Oh, do you remember when you were inside me?"

"Yes," she replied.

"What did it feel like inside?"

She answered, "Warm and comfortable."

"Did you want to come out?"

"No," she replied.

"When you came out, did you see any colors?" I asked.

"Yes, red," she answered.

"What was red?" I asked.

She answered, "I was covered all over with blood."

"Did you hear anything?" I asked.

"Yes, many words," she said.

"What were they saying?" I asked.

"I don't know," she answered.

When she was born, I had wanted to know everything they were doing and was asking many questions. I also had remembered reading that children often see light at the end of a tunnel, but she was born by cesarean, so I was curious what she remembered seeing. There was no light at the end of a tunnel because she never came out that way.

Whether or not children have early memories in the womb, birthing in the spirit means treating both mothers and babies gently and with respect. Pregnant women often view birth as a sacred event and feel a need to become more spiritual during this time by attending a church, temple, or mosque on a regular basis, and praying more often and perhaps more earnestly. They develop a spiritual bond with their baby by talking to it, singing songs to it, and massaging their growing abdomens. A powerful connection between them grows, and what affects one affects the other. Any concerns about the pregnancy may delay this prenatal bonding.[11]

I was very surprised about an early memory I experienced while attending an Omega conference in New York City. The speaker took us through a multi-sensory visualization back to the time before we were born that helped me understand my soul in a way I never had before. I sensed a "me" that I cannot put into words, but which I know is the same now as it was then. Even though my physical body has changed, this "me" or "beingness" has remained unchanged. Intuitively, I know I experienced my soul, and to this day it remains a comforting feeling.

Birth is an integrated experience of the mind, body, and spirit. We know it is an experience of the body because we can see the body, feel the body, and hear the body. We see the abdomen grow in a woman as her fetus approaches full gestation. A pregnant woman can feel her baby kicking inside. These are tangible experiences.

Birth is an experience of the mind, and even though we can't see the mind, we believe it exists because of all the thoughts and emotions that surface during pregnancy, labor, and birth.

When it comes to the spirit, there is more ambiguity because the spirit means different things to different people. But the energy driving the creation of a soul taking birth must come from somewhere, and this remains one of the mysteries of life.

I believe love and spirit are synonymous with each other and that they cannot be separated. Love is in spirit and spirit is in love. I consider spiritual love as being distinct from attachment love.

Attachment love is the love one has for parents, children, or possessions. It is temporary because things of the world are temporary. Love for a car ends when it is no longer working. Attachment to a parent dissipates in time when he or she passes away. Spiritual love, in contrast, always exists in its permanence, so that connecting with someone on a spiritual level transcends the body's form. It has no expectations and gives only of itself, seeking nothing in return. Its actions are carried out from the goodness of the heart.

From the time of conception to the end of our lives, the body serves as an instrument of the spirit. The more the body can be viewed as a vehicle through which the spirit works, the more smooth the process of birth is likely to be. At birth, a part of the body has now become separate from it and a baby is born with its own personality, inclinations, and tendencies. This process can be likened to a flower. The flower can be viewed as a vehicle for the fragrance so that it can be expressed. This fragrance brings us joy. In the same way, the body can be seen as a vehicle for the spirit bringing joy. The sweet fragrance could not be enjoyed if it weren't for the flower. The spirit could not be enjoyed if it weren't for the existence of the body. Just as fragrance is in the flower, so the spirit is in the body. Both the flower and the body are material and can be seen. Both the fragrance and the spirit are nonmaterial and cannot be seen.

When a woman in labor views her body as a "vehicle" through which the spirit can flow, she is more likely to surrender to the forces of labor, welcoming contractions as they become stronger and more intense. Focusing on the awe and wonder in the power of such birth-forces can bring a woman inner strength that will serve her well as she progresses into the unknown of labor.

In addition to the characteristic of expansion, spirit also has the characteristic of attraction. This attraction is magnetism. The heartfelt connection of the spirit is like the pull of a magnet. The human body is full of electricity and thus also has magnetic power. Few of us are conscious of our magnetism, and few realize its tremendous power. The intense desire of a mother to protect her baby is magnetism. You may remember being around people who literally "draw" you to them, and you may perceive it as a gesture of affection, warmth, and love. This is magnetism at work. We use magnetism in our daily lives, often taking it for granted. Without magnetic power we cannot succeed in any endeavor; it is just that we don't realize its full potential. Love has the characteristic of attraction via magnetism.

Another example of magnetism is a mother holding her newborn baby. We cannot help but feel mystery and wonder when gazing into the eyes of a newborn baby. What makes us feel this way? Is

it the complete innocence, dependence, and fragility of the baby? Or is it marveling at seeing such a tiny human being? A mother who gazes into her baby's eyes for the first time begins a process of bonding and attachment that is so powerful that she will do anything to protect her baby. For most mothers, the joy is immeasurable.

MAGNETIC FIELD EXERCISE

You can experience another person's magnetic field by blindfolding one person or simply asking her to close her eyes and remain stationary. Stand about fifteen feet away, and slowly and very quietly walk towards her. Tell her to let you know when she begins to feel your presence. This is a direct experience of magnetism and also of feeling the boundaries of our own energy fields.

I believe that this positive energy of magnetic power is what provides a loving atmosphere around a woman in labor, helping her to feel more safe and secure. The implications of this for members of the birth team are important. If all members of the birth team were to do their work with love, respect, and compassion, feeling guided by the spirit in them, the way birth is typically practiced in today's world would change dramatically. Women would feel more respected and would experience a level of bliss in birth that they didn't know was possible.

Though labor is hard work, depending on a woman's beliefs, she will perceive it as either threatening in some way or empowering. The more she is in touch with her own spirit, the more empowering it will be.

Connecting with the spirit within us helps to make our actions speak with power. Rather than entering the birthing process unaware of what will take place and why, women have a right to receive a balanced perspective of the risk-benefit ratio of obstetrical drugs and medical procedures. Rather than entering pregnancy, labor, and birth with fear of the unknown and feelings of wanting the medical system to "do it for them," women have a right to receive adequate emotional preparation that empowers them about the beauty of birth and increases confidence in their bodies and decision-making abilities.

The spirit can be considered as our best friend, whose presence is always with us and who is completely dependable. All we have to do is call out for the spirit and it will be there—if we just remember. It is the spirit within us that reaches out to another with compassion, giving selflessly without any desire for reward. It brings forth a heartfelt connection with another. Allowing this friendship to grow and become stronger with every breath strengthens faith and brings courage especially to challenges in life such as birth. Birthing in the spirit means coming into rhythm with our own deeper nature. It is not an outward journey, but rather, an inner journey. Our only barrier is our readiness.

Birthing in the Spirit

"Birthing in the spirit" is the birthing of our ancestors. Before birth in the western world became mechanized and dehumanized, women and men honored the sacred ability of women to create and bring forth life. Birthing in the spirit is reconnecting with those natural, primal beginnings. More than just relaxing and letting go, birthing in the spirit is moving through the portal of birth to the transcendent place that birthing takes women; the place of connectedness to every being and to the earth. It is feeling life itself pulsing through your veins with the simultaneous power of a volcano and the peaceful silence of snowfall. It is loosing yourself entirely and only then knowing the core of who you really are. Birthing in the spirit is what women do when we are honored, cared for compassionately, and deeply trusting of our bodies' ancient wisdom moving us to that sacred space. Birthing in the spirit is the ritual of motherhood; it is through the intensity of the experience of birth that women find the power and the compassion to give all of themselves, and then to give more, to their babies. It is in that place that we become mothers.

—JACQUE SHANNON-McNULTY, MOTHER FROM ILLINOIS

Education and Educare

Your vision will become clear only when you can look into your own heart.
Who looks outside, dreams; who looks inside, awakes.

CARL JUNG

Educare can be described literally as education with care. The word *educare* comes from the Latin root *educare* (pronounced *edu-car-ay*), which means "to bring out that which is within." This means bringing out the knowledge that is already inside of us and putting it into practice in our daily lives.

There are two kinds of knowledge. The first is knowledge that can be thought of as worldly knowledge, which is external, such as that learned from books or other means. The second kind of knowledge is our internal "software" that we are born with—the creative knowledge that tells us how to live life.

Educare speaks about this internal knowledge which, if acknowledged, will lead us to peace and happiness and a fulfilled sense of purpose in the world. Educare is a journey into the inner consciousness and thus is an internal, not an external, experience. Without educare, words are said and actions are performed without care or love, and are like a barren landscape without life or the night sky without the moon and stars.

The practice of educare leads to a fuller expression of the spirit. Relating this to childbirth, the worldly knowledge of birth can be thought of as the "how to" books that teach about comfort measures in labor, the physiology of birth, the anatomy of the pelvis and how it moves in labor, risks and benefits of medical procedures and obstetrical drugs, and preferred positions for birth. They teach us other related topics such as good nutrition and the importance of exercise. Worldly education represents that which can be *seen*. This type of education is important because knowledge is empowering.

On the other hand, educare represents education in the spiritual sense and is the process of going within to find the primal place that contains the knowledge of how to give birth. All a woman in labor needs to do is focus inward, and after recognizing this knowledge, to build her faith and confidence upon it. Educare is values-based and represents that knowledge which *cannot be seen*. It guides us to act in a loving or compassionate way, gives us courage to speak up for ourselves, and provides the energy to do what our minds may tell us is impossible. It gives women confidence as they connect with other women who have given birth, but at the same time allows them humility to accept unanticipated events that may occur, such as the need for medical support. Educare is the voice that urges us to act with a high standard of character, putting our internal value system into practice.

As the following diagram illustrates, the "whole" cannot be experienced unless both kinds of education are present. Worldly knowledge (science) represents only one half of the circle. The other half of the circle represents education in the spiritual sense (educare). For an optimal birth experience, the circle needs to be whole. Both kinds of education work together to bring us a balance in life.

To give a better understanding of the differences between worldly education and educare and how they complement each other, the following chart has been developed with regard to pregnancy, labor and birth, and the postpartum period. You will notice that the column under educare is based on values.

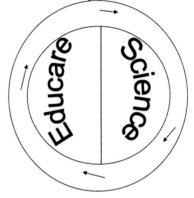

EDUCATION AND EDUCARE

Someone who pursues worldly knowledge . . .	Someone who pursues educare or knowledge within . . .
Researches the risk-benefit ratio of obstetrical drugs and medical procedures.	Has faith in her body that it contains the knowledge of how to give birth.
Observes birth settings to decide location of the birth, i.e., hospital, birthing center, or home.	Feels safe in the location she has chosen to give birth.
Meets with doctors, midwives, and doulas and looks for someone who is well trained and open to her ideas.	Has trust and faith in the caregivers she has chosen, feeling empowered by them.
Studies good nutritional concepts for pregnancy and the postpartum period.	Has determination to put good nutritional concepts into practice during pregnancy and the postpartum period.

18

Becomes knowledgeable about pelvic bodywork (advantageous pelvic positioning), ensuring there will be plenty of room in which the baby can move.	Puts concepts of pelvic bodywork into practice, knowing it helps her baby to have more space in which to move and descend.
Takes a childbirth class to learn more about birth and fetal development.	Is discriminating about her own sense of what feels right for her despite outside influences (talking to friends, etc.).
Decides on a particular method to give birth.	Sees birth as a process, staying in the present moment and trusting herself to be open to any eventuality that becomes necessary, knowing each labor is unique unto itself.
Explores options of how scheduling will work out (staying at home/returning to work) after giving birth.	Follows her intuition after the baby is born and makes changes in schedule as needed.
Reads about parenting and adheres to prescribed methods.	Trusts own instincts about what feels right and stays heart-centered.

The principles of educare can be put into practice regardless of the type of birth a woman has. These two hypothetical births show what educare would look like in practice.

NATURAL BIRTH

Jane's husband worked hard to keep her happy during her pregnancy, knowing that she would then produce oxytocin, the hormone of love, which they had learned would give their baby an optimal start in life. They sought a certified professional midwife in the area who had a good reputation and who would be with them at their home birth.

During her labor, Jane's husband, her mother, her doula, and her midwife were present. She felt safe in the comfort of her own home, eating and drinking as she wished. The contractions quickly became stronger and longer. She walked up and down steps, danced with her husband, labored on knees over a birth ball, and frequently sat on the toilet. Her birth team kept silent during contractions and kept the lights dim. Her husband gazed into her eyes and silently communicated to her his love and his belief that she was a strong woman and could birth their baby. Jane felt very safe and was able to open and dilate fully. At moments of panic when the contractions became too strong, she was reassured by a smile from her doula and midwife that all was okay. They simply said, "This is the way it is supposed to be."

It was work, hard work; but after awhile she realized there was a pattern to the contractions and Jane learned to work with each one as it came. She went deep inside and found a place where she was neither here nor there, as if on another planet. All around her sounded far away. She was connecting with her primitive brain that already knew how to give birth. She followed her body and listened to what it needed to do as contractions came one on top of the other. She kept moving her body wherever it needed to go.

Fully dilated now, Jane enjoyed the "rest and be thankful" stage as her body prepared for the final descent. The burning was intense, and she was in awe at the way in which her body knew how to open to give birth. Her baby emerged with wide-open eyes. There was peace, as if time stood still. Silence. Jane stroked her baby's body, picked her up, and held her close to her breast as the baby began to latch onto her breasts for the life-giving milk. The way in which Jane gave birth was empowering and would be remembered the rest of her life. She gave birth normally and naturally. There was only deep love, awe, and wonder at creation.

CESAREAN BIRTH

Mary's husband knew how important it was to keep her happy during pregnancy. He wrote her special love letters and even brought her flowers from time to time. She decided to give birth at a birthing center with midwives. It had a homey atmosphere, and she looked forward to laboring in their warm pools of water. Labor contractions began slowly, and Mary stayed home working on her scrapbook. Gradually the contractions became more intense. She sat on a chair in the shower and let the warm water flow onto her back, soothing her. She knew her baby was in a head-down position and felt certain she could birth it.

At home, Mary worked with the strong contractions and her husband supported her in various positions. Eventually they decided to go to the birthing center. The midwives were there waiting for her. Mary walked, ate, and drank as she wished. As dawn came, she lay down on her left side to rest awhile and then continued walking. By afternoon she was eight centimeters dilated, but the baby wasn't coming down for some reason. She assumed many different positions, but nothing seemed to be working and she was very tired. Her baby's heartbeat was fine, but the midwives realized that she needed to be transferred to the hospital.

After more hours of labor in the hospital without progress, she instinctively knew something was not right and agreed to a cesarean, even though the baby's heartbeat was fine. Mary requested a spinal anesthesia for the cesarean. To everyone's surprise, it turned out the umbilical cord was wrapped around her daughter's neck four times! No wonder her baby couldn't descend into her pelvis.

When Mary's daughter came out, she held her right away. Throughout the entire birth, all Mary's needs were met and all decisions were her own. She had experienced labor and knew the cesarean had saved her baby's life, and she was grateful. She knew what the contractions felt like and so could connect to all other women who had ever given birth. It was a beautiful birth.

In both births, the women believed that the knowledge about how to give birth was already inside them. They had trust and faith in their innate ability to give birth. The values of patience, determination, self-confidence, perseverance, respect, love, kindness, and compassion were present. Most importantly, they both did the work of giving birth. It was their experience and they "owned" it. Their birth memories will be positive ones.

Balancing worldly and educare knowledge applies not only to women who will be giving birth, but also to the birth teams of doctors, midwives, doulas, and/or family members who may be with a woman before, during, and after her birth. A doula's primary role in birth is to provide encouragement and comfort measures, help the woman in labor to feel safe, and assist her into various positions as needed. It is not her role to make decisions for the mother or significant other. Praise goes a long way in empowering a woman in labor to keep working through contractions and not give up. A doula can say, "Your body has its own time clock," or "Keep riding those waves [contractions] to shore," or "It is hard work, but you can do it, just like thousands of women have before you," or "You are so strong!"

When a complication is present, the woman in labor needs to know what is happening (worldly knowledge) and then needs to make a heartfelt decision (educare) that is respected, helping her to feel loved and supported. Balancing worldly and educare knowledge promotes actions with high moral standards that bring peace, regardless of the situation.

It is through the practice of human values that the internal knowledge of educare can be put into practice. These values include, but are not limited to, truth, patience, right action, determination, peace, compassion, love, kindness, and nonviolence. Practicing these values brings positive feelings. Knowing that women's bodies are designed to give birth is truth. Staying with contractions and working with them one at a time requires patience. Not giving up in the hard work of labor involves determination. Where there is love, we feel safe. A universal connection with all women who have ever given birth serves to empower women through strong contractions in their labors.

Anger, jealousy, envy, and pride are emotions that have negative consequences in time. Birth gives every opportunity for such qualities to manifest themselves. A birthing woman may feel angry at her doctor for performing a cesarean to suit his schedule or when she didn't dilate fast enough. Women may feel jealous of each other because of the kind of labors and births they experience or the sex of the baby. Many women experience anger down to their inner core when they are separated from their babies at birth.

I truly believe that every woman in any circumstance is doing the very best that she can at that moment in time. What more can we ask of ourselves than that? There is no place for blame or judgment in the practice of educare. When one feels judged, self-esteem is affected adversely and confidence is weakened. On the other hand, praising someone increases self-esteem and self-confidence. Practicing educare, speaking words with love from the heart and saying only good things, is empowering and inspires a feeling of trust and faith.

Educare is not just for birth—it is for life. When a conscious effort is made to practice human

values, you will find all aspects of your life changing for the better. Your relationships with people will improve; you will have more peace of mind, and therefore a steadier mind; you will feel healthier; and you will age more slowly. Most importantly, no matter what you do, you will simply feel better about yourself. Your perspective of the world will change and you will have a deeper understanding of why you are here on the earth. There will be more clarity in decision making and you will feel peace. All of these changes have a direct, positive impact on those involved in childbirth, from the pregnant woman and her family to the members of her birth team.

The goal of educare is to further the development of good character. In today's world, many people believe the ultimate goal of education should be to earn a living and satisfy the senses, when the goal should really be to develop character. The current system of education serves primarily to develop a more active intelligence, but not always to instill the qualities and virtues that are useful in life and essential in birth. Most hospital-based childbirth education classes, and even many consumer classes, are based heavily on the mind-body approach only. Worldly education becomes fairly useless if it is not accompanied by morals and ethics. I believe that the educare aspect of birth is what is missing in birth preparation today.

Often, what is important is not just what is said, but how it is said. Educare shows compassion for our fellow beings. When words are communicated with kindness, compassion, and understanding, and without hatred, jealousy, or ego, they will be received with sincerity, and those speaking will have an honorable reputation wherever they go. The reputation of such a doula, childbirth educator, midwife, nurse, or doctor will spread quickly and they will be in great demand, for the love within one attracts the love within another like a magnet. When we realize that the human values within all are the same regardless of race, creed, culture, or profession, a sense of unity is perceived. Feeling this unity in diversity is a hallmark of educare.

Direct experience is the best teacher, and so doing our own work instead of having someone else do it for us provides the best learning. This requires focus and concentration. Birth has the potential to teach us much about ourselves. It is hard work, and requires perseverance and determination along with a belief that the knowledge about how to give birth is already inside every woman. When worldly knowledge is combined with educare, a woman is more likely to feel safe and have the courage to face any situation that birth and life have to offer. Together, they can help women have beautiful, positive birth experiences with birth teams that understand the principles of educare. Women deserve no less that that.

Birthing in the Spirit

I really feel that birth is a timeless connection—a way for all of womankind to connect with the true essence of being female, the power of creation. In birth we have the chance to reach

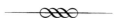

alternative levels of consciousness, the same levels as our sisters from millennia ago reached, and we become part of the collective Great Female.

Birth is a challenge—but a challenge spiritually... if we open to the occasion, we can be sure that our "spiritual DNA" will change; how may be more subtle, yet because we have birthed and have opened to a power greater than any force a human can know, we as women have an incredible, wonderful opportunity to elevate our consciousness. The fact that birth is a unique experience to the female animal cannot be ignored. If only our culture accepted the gravity of this fact, perhaps womankind across the world would be more honored, treasured, and revered. For in the process of birth, we women truly possess the ability to touch the hand of God.

—BETH CURTIS, CCE (BWI)

CHAPTER 5

Exploring Your Options for Birth

It is impossible for a man to learn what
he thinks he already knows.

EPICTETUS (WESTERN GREEK PHILOSOPHER, AD 100)

In today's world, women are giving birth either naturally without medical intervention, or naturally with varying degrees of support from obstetrical drugs and medical procedures, or by cesarean surgery. Sometimes women may want a natural birth without medical interventions, but end up needing them due to complications. Other times a woman may think prior to labor that she wants a medical intervention such as an epidural, but once in labor realizes she is coping well with contractions, perhaps being in a pool of warm water, and ends up giving birth naturally and even in the water. Other women may need a cesarean for either maternal or fetal complications, and still other women may request a cesarean without medical reasons. Each woman and her birth are unique, and the way she works with her body during labor varies as well.

NATURAL BIRTH WITHOUT MEDICAL INTERVENTION

In a natural birth without medical intervention, a woman goes into labor in her own time frame. She chooses to experience labor in its entirety and works with her body through each contraction by moving into various positions that help the baby to move down into her pelvis. If she has taken Birth Works® childbirth education classes, she knows the principles of pelvic bodywork so that with good positioning, her baby can pass in front of her pelvic floor musculature, helping to avoid harm to those muscles. She may labor in a pool of warm water and even decide to give birth there. Using gravity in upright positions or other positions that keep her pelvis forward, her baby has a better chance of moving into an optimal position down into her pelvis. She has confidence in her own body that knows how to give birth.

The baby will be born at its true birth time, as no procedures will have been used to speed up or slow down her labor. She will have people with her in whom she has trust and faith and who know how to help keep her neocortex quiet, thus facilitating labor. Silence will be respected, and the baby will be awake and alert without side effects from drugs taken by the mother. Natural instincts will be preserved as the baby finds mother's nipple, feels her skin, and has its first experience in the world as intimacy. The father or significant other will be alone with the mother and the baby in the first hour of birth, bonding as a new family. Within a short time after birth, the woman can be up walking around if she wishes, and will be able to take care of her baby.

Barbara Harper, a nurse and the author of *Gentle Birth Choices*, is the founder of the Global Maternal/Child Health Association that promotes water birthing in large tubs of warm water. She is a strong advocate of natural birth and writes in her book, "When labor is left alone and not medically managed, the majority of women will birth instinctively with power and dignity,"[1] and "One of the most important components for all methods of childbirth preparation is a healthy attitude."[2]

NATURAL BIRTH WITH MEDICAL INTERVENTION

An induction may be the beginning of a natural birth with medical intervention and is often used if a woman has not begun labor within two weeks past her due date. Sometimes practitioners offer inductions a week before or after a due date, but a woman must realize that normal due dates are based on phases of the moon and are *two* weeks before and after the due date. In such cases patience is required by the pregnant woman and her birth team, so long as there is no medical reason to interfere.

During her labor, when a woman reaches a point where contractions are getting very tight and long, she may request an epidural, which numbs her from the waist down so she can no longer feel her abdomen or legs. She will be unable to walk, sit on the toilet, or change positions on her own. A catheter is inserted into the urethra to help empty her bladder. Backlying, supported sidelying, or other positions will need maximum assistance and support to be changed and maintained. Pitocin (synthetic oxytocin) is often administered to keep her uterus contracting. Typically, an external fetal monitor will be strapped around her waist to record the baby's heartbeat, and an internal fetal monitor is often applied as well, with a little wire on the tip that is screwed into the baby's scalp to give an even more accurate reading of the fetal heartbeat. The woman's bag of waters will have to be broken if it hasn't done so on its own, so that the wire can reach the baby's scalp. She may be seen wearing an oxygen mask for oxygen supplementation and typically gives birth on her back, legs wide apart, with the baby sometimes requiring manual support such as forceps or vacuum extraction in order to be born vaginally. If none of this works and the baby is not descending into the pelvis, the woman may need to have a cesarean.

Cesarean birth

When I gave birth in 1980, a cesarean was still viewed as the ultimate intervention performed only in an acute emergency. With improved technology and surgical procedures, that viewpoint has changed, with many women believing a cesarean to be a relatively safe alternative to vaginal birth.

Increasingly, many women today who have had a cesarean are scheduling another one for their next baby without going into labor at all. This is the age of birth by appointment and cesarean on demand. These babies are not born at their true birth times because procedures are used to either speed labor up or slow it down. Women tend to have medically managed births when they are fearful of pain from labor contractions or if they are worried about damaging their pelvic floor muscles.

The fears of both pregnant women and their doctors are contributing to the high cesarean rate today, with doctors believing that if there is any question of risk, they should perform a cesarean. Women are saying the same thing and are increasingly more willing to trust technology than nature, with drugged births being accepted as the norm. Both women and their doctors seem to perceive relatively little risk associated with cesarean surgery.

The increasing number of women who think that a cesarean section (CS) is a safe option for giving birth represents a substantial shift in women's expectations about childbirth. These changes in expectations are centered around two interrelated themes: many women viewing birth as scary and frightening, and a cesarean section now being perceived as an acceptable and safer alternative. Add to this the fact that with a cesarean, birth can have a set date and time, and that many of a woman's friends may have had cesareans and did fine. It is easy to understand how quickly a cesarean has become a popular way of giving birth.

Some women are requesting a cesarean for their first birth with no medical reason, and doctors are complying. According to a study in the *Obstetrical and Gynecological Survey* by Wax, et al, in 2004, primary elective cesareans performed at a patient's request comprised 4 to 18 percent of all cesareans and 14 to 22 percent of elective cesareans in the reported series. The primary reason for cesarean on request was tocophobia, or fear of childbirth, with secondary reasons being decreased risk of pelvic floor damage, fetal injury, maintenance of sexual functioning, and physician and patient convenience.[3] The same article went on to state that evidence favors vaginal delivery as being safer in the long- and short-term for both mother and fetus, and that performing a cesarean section for non-medical reasons is not ethically justified.[4] However, the American College of Obstetrics and Gynecology (ACOG) published the following statement: "If a patient requests cesarean, continues this request after informed counseling, and the physician believes that cesarean will promote the overall health of the patient and fetus more than vaginal delivery, then elective cesarean is ethically justified."[5]

No wonder birthing parents are confused. Since fear of childbirth is cited as a primary reason for interfering with birth times, we have to ask ourselves why women today are so afraid of labor.

Studies have shown that when women are given the opportunity to express their fears before birth, almost two-thirds of them will ultimately choose vaginal delivery and will remain satisfied with their choice.[6,7]

In a 2006 study, forty-nine women who had had a cesarean and preferred to have another cesarean for a subsequent birth were interviewed.[8] These women gave reasons such as the following for having another cesarean:

"They told me that there was no way in the world that my hips were going to work. I just had no choice."

"I knew my doctor would not let me have a normal because he believes in all CS, so I just never expected to have [a normal]."

"No choice…told I would have to have cesareans for any future births."

When studies show that a cesarean section continues to be associated with greater physical and emotional risks to both the mother and baby compared to a vaginal birth,[10,11,12] we have to ask ourselves why anyone would choose the path of more risk when their primary concern is the health of their babies and themselves. This important study concluded that helping women to keep fear of birth in perspective is an important strategy to help decrease the high cesarean rate and to raise the low vaginal birth after cesarean rate. Therefore, a primary aim of any childbirth education class should be to give women and men the opportunity to express birth-related fears so they can be released.

In such a class, expectant parents can learn techniques and current information about birth. This includes pelvic bodywork, good birthing positions, and birth physiology. In response to the reasons given in the study for having cesarean sections, they would learn:

"They told me that there was no way in the world that my hips were going to work. I just had no choice."

Your hips work beautifully and you do have many choices.

"I knew my doctor would not let me have a normal because he believes in all CS, so I just never expected to have [a normal]."

You can change doctors because your doctor is advocating a procedure that may increase risk to you and your baby.

"No choice…told I would have to have cesareans for any future births."

VBAC is very safe for low-risk women with low transverse uterine incisions, and natural birth has less risk to the mother and baby than routine, repeat cesarean.

When women make choices before labor about what type of birth they want, they often hear some form of judgment from other women such as, "You aren't even going to go into labor?" or, "I gave birth to my baby without an epidural!" There is even an expression now, "Too posh to push." Birthing in the spirit means there is no place for guilt, blame, or judgment. Birthing parents need to attend good quality childbirth education classes that can educate them about options and alternatives and that promote both academic and emotional preparation for birth. Parents need to make the best choices they can based on this information and to love themselves regardless of the birth outcome, knowing they have done the best they could. Mutual respect for one another is essential.

With the perceived safety of medical technology, many women now believe that if they don't want to feel contractions in labor, they don't have to, and that they'll still have a baby. In childbirth classes they want to know how early they can have an epidural. Hospital administrators and doctors want to please their "patients" by doing what they request, and have much to gain by patient satisfaction from a marketing standpoint.

The advantages of epidurals are clear: women in labor can be awake, pain-free, and know the anesthesia is relatively safe. But as one childbirth educator said, "I feel like people are going to look back at epidurals, just like we do at "twilight sleep" (Scopolamine anesthesia commonly used fifty years ago) and say, "Why did they want that?" But doctors might say, "This is the real world, and epidurals certainly help women endure labor more comfortably." However, primal health research is beginning to show evidence that these procedures do have adverse effects on body physiology and longer-term effects on the life of the baby that are greater than originally thought.

Place of birth

In today's world, one of the most important decisions a pregnant woman will make is where she wants to give birth. As recently as seventy years ago, most women gave birth at home. Traditionally, this was never a concern because women always gave birth in their homes or villages with a midwife or someone experienced with birth present. Most women today give birth in hospitals, and as this trend has occurred, birth has developed into a technological and medically managed process.

Currently, a woman has the choice to give birth at home, in the hospital, or in a birthing center. She must first ask herself, "Where do I feel safe giving birth?" Sometimes there may not be a birthing center in her community, and if this is the case, a woman's only choice is to give birth at home or in the hospital. A number of women are choosing to stay home and give birth with a midwife in attendance, and others are choosing to have unassisted home births.

Feeling safe in the place of birth

When a pregnant woman gives birth in a place where she doesn't feel safe, her body will instinctively hold back in order to protect her baby. This is the antithesis of the letting go required to give birth.

When a woman is holding back, she is more likely to have a longer labor, which then may require medical procedures to speed it up.

In classes, when I ask women, "Where are you planning to give birth?" they often answer, "Well, we're going to the hospital." I then ask the woman, "Is that where you feel safe?" She responds, "Well, we talked it over, and that is where he [husband or significant other] feels it is safest to give birth in case anything goes wrong."

"Who is giving birth?" I ask.

"I am," she responds.

"Who is it that needs to feel safe?" I ask.

"Well, I guess, me," she replies.

"Yes," I say, "and where do *you* feel safe?"

At this point some know and some aren't sure. We then do a safe birth multi-sensory visualization so they have time to process and determine for themselves where they feel safe. A woman will labor best wherever she feels the safest and most secure. For some that may be the hospital. For others it may be the birthing center or their home. This can only be the decision of the pregnant woman, not her partner, family, or friends. Each woman must go deep inside and determine this truth for herself. Birth is not without risk, but being able to choose the place that feels safe is a way to decrease risk.

I believe that a pregnant woman can have a beautiful birth experience in a hospital, birthing center, or at home. If she believes that she will feel safer being in a place where medical procedures are readily available in the event they are needed, she is more likely to relax in that setting. If a pregnant woman believes that medical procedures performed in the hospital are routine standards of care and not really necessary most of the time, and if she feels safer at home with a midwife, then that is where she will labor the best. I have had a number of clients who really couldn't decide on whether to give birth in the home or the hospital, and they ended up giving birth in their car! The outcomes have been fine in all cases.

The following is information a pregnant woman may find helpful when choosing the place of birth.

Places of birth

The Hospital

Many hospitals have worked hard to make their rooms more homey and inviting with special décor, while still having equipment ready if needed. Women can labor in the rooms and stay there to give birth unless a cesarean is being performed. There are tours provided for pregnant women and their significant others. On these tours it is important to note what you are seeing in addition to what you are hearing. Are women up walking around in labor? Are the rooms with laboring women dimly

lit? Note how you feel in your body while there. Are you feeling comfortable or uncomfortable? Can you picture yourself giving birth there? Finding a place of birth is a little like taking a teenager around looking for colleges. There will usually be one where he just feels like he belongs.

A good childbirth education class will go over questions to ask when on a tour of the hospital. Here are some more questions to consider.

- Is this a teaching hospital? (This means interns will be training there and may be at your birth.)
- Do you have Jacuzzis or pools for labor? If not, do women labor in the showers?
- What positions do most women assume while in labor here?
- What is your policy on fetal monitoring? Are there alternatives?
- Do you have restrictions on who can attend the birth?
- What are your protocols about eating and drinking?
- Do you have birthing balls? Are they used much?
- What is your epidural rate? Your cesarean rate?
- What are the routine practices for the baby right after birth?
- Do you keep babies with their mothers at all times except in emergencies?
- What is your policy on clamping the umbilical cord?
- Upon request, can women and their family have the first hour after birth alone with their new baby?
- Do you encourage breast self-attachment?
- Is there breastfeeding support?
- Do you have certified nurse midwives (CNMs)?

Remember that when giving birth in a hospital, there are standard routines that are followed, and if you want something different for your birth, you will need to plan it ahead of time by asking pertinent questions during prenatal visits and also by going over your birth plan with your practitioner(s).

The Birth Center

A birthing center combines the best of a home and hospital setting and is often a good choice for birthing parents who can't decide between giving birth in the hospital or at home. CNMs at birth centers offer a more relaxed setting and a more home-like atmosphere, and yet a hospital is usually nearby if a transfer is necessary. The midwives are likely to be more patient with the birth process and offer alternatives to medical interventions such as massage, along with encouragement and support. Many have warm pools of water in which to labor. At the same time, they have the

equipment needed to listen to the baby's heartbeat and can sense if further help is needed. Some parents like birth centers, as there is traditionally less intervention in birth.

However, birthing centers are usually affiliated with a hospital and so are bound by rules and regulations. They are strictly regulated, and many will no longer accept women desiring a VBAC. They may have other restrictions, such as not accepting a woman who has gone past her due date by more than two weeks. If that happens, she will need to give birth in the hospital. Also, if there are significant variations from normal birth, the birthing center may be required to transfer a woman to the hospital during her labor.

When interviewing at a birth center, it is important to ask:

- What are your protocols and/or restrictions for birth? Can women birth here if they are two weeks or more past their due date?
- Do you have warm pools in which women can labor?
- Do you accept VBAC clients?
- What are some reasons a woman might be transferred to the hospital?
- Will the same midwife be with a woman from the beginning to the end of her birth?
- What do you do in the event of a slow labor?

Again, sense how it feels just being there, and determine if it is a place where you would feel safe giving birth.

Home Birth

Some women are afraid of hospitals and do not feel they can labor in such a setting. Even if they decide to give birth at home, they should be encouraged to take the hospital tour and have hospital back-up in the event a transport becomes necessary.

The home environment allows a woman to labor in her own familiar setting and generally prevents her from having to travel while working through contractions in the car, which can be very uncomfortable. At home in her own comfortable surroundings, she may be able to relax more, and this will make her labor progress well. Everything is on her own time without pressure of how fast to dilate, and there are no standard procedures to interfere with her labor, such as multiple internal exams. She will not be subjected to electronic fetal monitoring, whose only outcome has been shown to be an increase in cesarean section (but is of benefit in some VBAC studies).[9] She can move freely in familiar surroundings, changing positions, playing her favorite music, and eating and drinking as she wishes. In her own home setting she is exposed only to her own bacteria and there are no restrictions on who can attend her birth. She knows that if a complication arises, she is close enough to reach the hospital for help in plenty of time.

More and more women are choosing to have midwives who are trained in the art of birthing at their births. Midwives are more likely to be patient, offer alternatives, provide comfort measures, and help with positioning. They are also more likely to stay with a woman throughout her labor, whereas in a hospital, nurses will be present and the obstetrician will just come in for routine checks until the time of birth.

There are a number of different types of midwives, all with different qualifications:[10]

1. CPMs, or Certified Professional Midwives, are Direct Entry Midwives who have undergone rigorous training and taken a comprehensive exam. They meet the standards for certification set by the North American Registry of Midwives (NARM). They attend births mostly in the home and other out-of-hospital birth settings. Their legality varies from state to state.

2. CNMs are Certified Nurse Midwives who have a bachelor's degree in nursing or a closely related field and then attended a master's program in nurse-midwifery. They are certified by the American College of Nurse Midwives (ACNM). A Certified Nurse Midwife may risk losing her license by attending home births if they are illegal in her state, but some choose to do so anyway. Although nurse midwifery is legal in every state, strict limitations are imposed by most states in regards to where and under what circumstances they offer their services.

3. CMs, or Certified Midwives, do not need to have a nursing degree. They are certified by the ACNM but are not recognized in all states. Depending on the area, they may practice in hospitals, free-standing birthing centers, or at home.

4. LMs, or licensed midwives, practice in states where midwifery is legal by statute and where they have passed the state licensing procedures. They attend out-of-hospital births.

5. DEMs are Direct Entry Midwives who have little or no formal training but may have enrolled in non-clinical Apprentice Academics programs or clinical programs. They receive on-the-job training by apprenticing with other midwives at homebirths. Contrary to medical opinion, they are usually very skilled in handling emergencies and hospital transport without having to rely on technology. Some may work in free-standing birth centers. The legality of DEMS varies from state to state.

FINDING A MIDWIFE

There are a number of ways to find midwives.

- Contact Midwifery Today via their website, www.midwiferytoday.com. They hold conferences worldwide to increase awareness about the value of having midwives at births.
- Talk to childbirth educators in your area. They usually know practicing midwives in the area.
- Check the Yellow Pages in your telephone book.
- Contact a La Leche League group in your area.

- Contact local health practitioners such as chiropractors or naturopaths and ask if they can give you any referrals.
- Search local websites for practicing midwives in your area.
- Talk to women who have given birth. Word of mouth is usually a very successful way to find a midwife.

SAFETY OF HOME BIRTH FOR LOW-RISK PREGNANT WOMEN

When choosing where to give birth, the safety of the mother and baby is a central concern for all birthing parents. Many birthing parents believe that hospitals are the safest place to give birth because if something goes wrong, medical professionals are there with the equipment to take care of the baby and mother. But others note that while this is true, the medical procedures and obstetrical drugs have their own associated risks and tend to be used routinely instead of when truly needed. Birth in hospitals has become an economic, medical, and industrial enterprise where certain routines are followed that may not be truly necessary for every woman.

The good news for women is that the majority of studies on the safety of home versus hospital birth conclude that home birth is safe for low-risk pregnant women, e.g., pregnant women without complicating factors such as gestational diabetes, high blood pressure, or premature labor. Despite a wealth of evidence that this is the case, a skeptical attitude about home birth persists.

For example, although several Canadian medical societies[11,12] and the American Public Health Association[13] promote the safety of home births for low-risk women, the American College of Obstetricians and Gynecologists continues to strongly oppose it.[14] Their reason is that complications can arise in labor with little to no warning, even in low-risk pregnancies, and the availability of expertise and interventions on an urgent or emergency basis may be life-saving for the mother, the fetus, or the newborn, and may reduce the likelihood of an adverse outcome. Such reasons are not validated by current research on the safety of home birth for low-risk women.

As can be seen in the following studies, pregnant women who are deciding where to give birth should know that there is overwhelming evidence in home birth studies involving low-risk women around the world that continues to support home birth as a safe option.

In 1990, 99 percent of all deliveries in Switzerland took place in a hospital. The Swiss health care system is private for all outpatient care, so each woman may choose where she wants to deliver her baby. As delivery has become safer, more have chosen to move away from interventions and hospitals to more "natural" births. A 1996 study in Switzerland found that women with home births needed significantly less medication and fewer interventions than those who gave birth in hospitals. Researchers found no difference between home- and hospital-delivered babies in birth weight, gestational age, or clinical condition, and concluded that "healthy low-risk women who wish to deliver at home have no increased risk either to themselves or to their babies."[15]

A study in the Netherlands carried out in two periods between 1990 and 1993 analyzed data from midwives and their clients. Their research showed that for women with low-risk pregnancies in the Netherlands, choosing to give birth at home is a safe choice—with an outcome at least as good as that of planned hospital births—and is significantly better for women having subsequent children.[16] This study went on to discuss the fact that levels of anxiety have been found to be good predictors of obstetrical complications. When women are given a choice of where they want to give birth, the levels of anxiety decrease and affect the outcome of maternity care.

The safety of home birth for low-risk pregnant women was brought out again in one of the largest international prospective studies of home birth, conducted by Johnson and Daviss and published February 17, 2007.[17] It examined the safety of planned home births in a cohort study of 5,418 women attended by CNMs in the United States and Canada. The study concluded that there were lower rates of medical intervention in planned home births with CNMs as compared with hospital births, but similar intrapartum and neonatal mortality in planned home births and low-risk hospital births in the United States. A limitation of the study was an inability to develop a workable design from which to collect a national prospective low-risk group of hospital births to compare morbidity and mortality directly. However, one exception was a study by Schlenzka,[18] who was able to make such a comparison. When he compared 3,385 planned home births in California with 806,402 low-risk hospital births, he consistently found a non-significantly lower perinatal mortality in the home birth group.

Johnson and Daviss concluded in an economic analysis that, in the United States, it is just as safe to have an uncomplicated vaginal birth at home with midwives as in the hospital, and that a home birth is much less costly than a hospital birth. Their results were consistent with previous research on the safety of home birth internationally, and also support the American Public Health Association's recommendation to increase access to out-of-hospital maternity care services with direct entry midwives in the United States.[19]

Currently, home birth is legal in some but not all states, leaving some women only the choice of a birth at home without medical backup or midwife, or birthing in a hospital.

THE VALUE OF BIRTH ASSISTANTS, OR DOULAS

Modern-day birth assistants are called doulas, a Greek word for "servant." A doula is hired by birthing parents to give them continuous support during the birth. She usually makes one prenatal visit to go over birthing plans, comfort measures, suggest ideas for optimal birthing positions, and describe what the father can do at the birth. She is not allowed to perform any clinical procedures but knows the art of providing encouragement. For example, she knows how to look into a woman's eyes during a strong contraction and relate a nonverbal message like, "You are doing fine. This is the way it is supposed to be." She can also assist with initial breastfeeding at birth. After birth, she makes one postpartum visit to check on postpartum body changes and breastfeeding. She may also

write an account of the birth, which the parents can keep as a birth treasure for their children to read someday.

In traditional cultures, women have always had the support of other women during birth. I love the tradition in some African cultures where women of the village surround the hut where a woman is in labor and "ride" the contractions with her by making low primal sounds that rise in crescendos and then fade as the contraction ends. In addition, a village midwife attends the woman in labor. If I were in labor again, I think I would find it extremely helpful to have this kind of support.

MAKING DECISIONS IN CHILDBIRTH

We make hundreds of decisions every day, some more complex than others. At any given moment when a decision needs to be made, we wonder if we are making the right choice. I believe most issues that we ponder are basically moral in nature. I always ask myself, "Am I doing the right thing?" "Will the outcome give me peace of mind?" "Am I listening to my own inner voice, or am I doing what others think is right for me?" and "Will this decision make me feel happy and content?" The multitude of questions and decisions surrounding childbirth are vast, and include the following:

Before birth

- Will I decide to continue working or stay home with my baby?
- Should I stay home to give birth or go to the hospital or birthing center?
- Should I choose an obstetrician or midwife?
- What should I eat? How much should I eat?
- What type of childbirth classes should I take?
- Is it safe to exercise in the ninth month?
- My doctor says my baby is breech. He is not comfortable delivering breech babies vaginally and wants to schedule a cesarean. What should I do?
- When is too long to wait for an induction?
- Do I want a medically managed birth or a natural birth?
- Should I hire a doula? What will my husband think?
- After contractions start, when should I go to the hospital? (if planning a hospital birth)

During birth

- Who can I trust? Should I trust others or my own intuition?
- How much of what I have learned will I remember in labor?
- Should I change positions or stay where I am?
- Should I get into the shower or pool?
- Should I go labor on the toilet now?

- What if labor takes a long time?
- What if I can't take the pain?
- What if they don't give me enough time to labor?
- Are there alternatives to electronic fetal monitoring?

After birth

- How will I handle family visits after birth because there is a lot of stress in the family?
- What if having a cesarean makes breastfeeding more difficult, as studies are showing?
- Should I let them give my baby all the vaccinations recommended?
- How long should I breastfeed?
- How will using a breast pump work if I go back to work?
- Should I let my baby use a pacifier?
- Should I pick up my baby every time she cries?

For each question either listed above or on your own list, the question is always, "What is the right thing to do?" Sometimes decisions are like green lights saying "Yes!" and other times they are like red lights meaning "No!" Sometimes decisions are like yellow lights meaning "Be careful," and soul searching is required to know what to do.

In a way, right action can be thought of as "righter action," as it is a continuum of thought influencing experience. For some women, right action can mean rethinking their beliefs by canceling a planned induction or cesarean date and going into labor naturally at the baby's own time. For others, it may be avoiding a cesarean by using an epidural to get through an unusually long labor, and for others it may be having a natural birth at home with a midwife with medical backup. The more women can "birth in the spirit," regardless of what setting or method ends up being necessary in the given circumstances, the more empowered they will feel, as they will have more choice in birth and will feel comfortable with the experience.

Doctors want to satisfy their "patients" and make them feel happy. Women don't want to feel pain. So if everyone is happy, why change anything? But birth offers the experience of a lifetime, and it is an experience given only to women. When we don't feel an experience, learning is lost and birth becomes less than the peak experience in life it was meant to be.

"So what?" some might say. And I say, "Why settle for less? If there is a treasure, why go so far and not reach it?" Knowing the truth that our bodies already know how to give birth, and that they are wise beyond our imagination, helps to build confidence and decrease fear. Focusing on this truth and making it a strong belief is some of the most important mental preparation that women can do for birth.

Women were designed to be able to give birth normally and naturally with only a small number needing medical assistance. In the twenty-first century, technology is advanced enough to be able to

help the small percentage of women that have complications with birth, and should be reserved only for that purpose. But most women can give birth safely without medical intervention. Midwives have always known the art of birthing. The Midwifery Today organization is helping to re-popularize midwifery by holding conferences and educating women around the world about normal, natural birth.

Birth is an exciting and challenging time in a woman's life. Exploring options for birth and becoming educated about what is available can help make birth a positive and fulfilling experience. While doing so, remember to consult your heart to ensure that these decisions are ones right for you.

Birthing in the Spirit

I believe that birth should be an experience that makes you forget your name (and hopefully conception was too!). I have always dreamed of the birth experience filled with love—the deepest, truest love that requires no words; that, when the time of silence passes, all you can say is "WOW!"

—Nikie Caps CCE (BWI)

CHAPTER 6

The Baba Yaga

There are two ways of spreading light: to be the candle
or the mirror that reflects it.

EDITH WHARTON

Birth is an experience that is larger in its scope than words can fully describe. A woman who has given birth can try to describe what contractions feel like to a newly pregnant woman but will find herself at a loss for words, not really being able to describe their intensity. But when describing birth to a woman who *has* experienced labor contractions, there is a knowing and she understands. Birth is a rite of passage. A woman who becomes pregnant and births her baby will never be the same again. In just the span of nine months, she literally "grows up." If she has learned what it means to focus and do the work of labor, trusting her intuition and having faith in her body's ability to give birth, the transition to motherhood will occur more smoothly.

When we are in the world between matter and spirit, we become the medium or conduit between them. The word *medium* comes from the Latin word *medial,* which means "in between." To become familiar with the medial world, one must venture beyond form, beyond body. A woman in labor does this when she goes deep inside into what is sometimes referred to as "the zone" or "another planet" during strong contractions. The experience of labor helps her to reach this primal space. She does this most easily when she feels completely safe. In this way, birth is an integration of the mind, body, and spirit.

Myths and fairy tales are very powerful teaching aids and help us to explore the medial world. Creative stories, songs, and other arts help bring us back to our intuitive side. They can show us what happens when we don't trust our intuition, our inner voice. They help us to think in symbolic language, the language common to all cultures of the world. *The Baba Yaga,* an old story that comes out of Russia, is such a story. There are many versions of the story. Here, I have combined a couple variations of the version referred to as *Vasilisa the Fair* or *Vasilisa the Wise.* This version shows how staying in touch with our intuitive side can help us through any challenges in life.

The woman in the story, Vasilisa, is faced with the task of getting fire (the light of intuition) from the Baba Yaga, who is of the medial world herself. The Baba Yaga is an archetype in that she models qualities that are essential for us to develop to reach our full human potential. Through her experiences with the Baba Yaga, Vasilisa is transformed, becoming more connected to her

intuitive side and gaining clarity and wisdom that brings her home to her true self. Being at home with our true self is intimate, warm, and safe. Our intuitive side is natural, and what is natural is spiritual. When we are separated from our true self, it is as if we are groping in the dark and the light of consciousness is dim. The way back to our home is through symbolic language, which can be considered our mother tongue, the language closest to the heart.

There are many metaphors in this story that symbolically deepen our own understanding of the work of childbirth. The story emphasizes the importance of focus along with character traits such as patience, determination, speaking with love, and following one's intuition that are all needed when giving birth. And now the story . . .

The Baba Yaga

Many years ago, there lived a young girl named Vasilisa. She lived in a small home with her mother and father on the outskirts of a forest. She was a good-natured, beautiful child wearing little red boots, a little black skirt, and a snowy white blouse. Her hair was fixed in long brown braids. Now she stood beside the bed where her dear, sweet mother was dying, her skin transparent almost like waxen roses. Vasilisa, who loved her dear, sweet mother more than anything, was weeping.

Her mother said, "I am so sorry that I have no riches to leave you, no land, and no money; but I do have one thing to give you." She reached down under the covers and pulled out a little tiny kookla doll, dressed just like Vasilisa. "Now when I die, I will not be here to guide you. This is my parting gift to you," she said faintly as she handed her the kookla doll. "Put the little doll in your apron pocket. Whenever you are in need, speak to the doll about it. Just feed her by giving her a little bread and water from time to time and she will help you." Within a short time, her mother breathed her last breath. Vasilisa and her father were inconsolable for a long, long time.

But as the seasons passed, they both healed. Winter passed and springtime came. He decided to marry again. He married a handsome widow with two daughters. But when Vasilisa's father wasn't looking, they behaved and looked like rodents. And these were the family that the young girl named Vasilisa inherited. She felt very happy to have a stepmother and stepsisters, even though they made her do all the work.

"Vasilisa! Comb my hair! Light the fire! Vasilisa! Fetch the firewood! Sweep the yard!" Vasilisa did all she was told to do without complaining, even though she was often hungry and tired. She always said, "Of course, I'd be happy to." And when she completed her tasks at night, often they would find other things for her to do. "Vasilisa, I think I heard a noise. Go and see who it is!" said her stepsister. "Vasilisa! I'm thirsty; go out to the well and get me some water." And Vasilisa would always say, "Of course, I'd be happy to do that."

Gradually something twisted in the stepsisters and stepmother. They became jealous of Vasilisa and her beauty while their own faces were marred by spite. The kinder and sweeter Vasilisa became, the more the stepmother and stepsisters began to despise her.

Finally they could not stand it any longer. "Vasilisa is just putting on an act! Nobody can be so sweet all the time. She's just trying to get something from us. Well, we'll show her!" And soon they made her do things they would never do themselves, like go further and further into the forest. And no matter how much they oppressed her, she became kinder and sweeter to them. Finally, at their wits' end, they conspired together one night, saying, "Let's get rid of her! Let's pretend to put out the fire, and then let's send her into the middle of the woods, deep, deep into the darkest forest, and tell her to get fire from the Baba Yaga who lives in the middle of the forest. And of course Vasilisa will say, 'Of course I will!' and then the Baba Yaga is sure to keep her, and we'll be done with her at last." And they squeaked and squealed and chattered with delight like rodents in the dark while deciding how to carry out their plan.

When Vasilisa came home from gathering wood, she found the house in darkness. And the stepmother said, "Oh, Vasilisa, a terrible thing has happened! We don't know how it happened. Well, the fire went out, and we have no fire to light the house and cook the food! We don't know what to do about it. I can't go out into the forest and find fire because I'm an old woman and it would not be fitting. My daughters cannot go because they are afraid and might get lost."

Vasilisa stepped up to her stepmother and said, "Of course, I would never expect you or my stepsisters to go out into the forest." She put her hand on the arm of the stepmother and said, "Don't worry. Don't worry about anything. I'll take care of it. I'll do it." The stepmother gave Vasilisa a stale loaf and a flask of water and turned her out into the dark forest to seek fire from the Baba Yaga.

Vasilisa put on her cape and disappeared out the door, into the dark of the forest. She felt frightened hearing wolves howling and bears growling in the distance. She was alone in the night of the deep, dark forest and didn't know which way to go. She became tired and instead of walking, was trudging. She stopped at a fork in the road not knowing what to do. Suddenly she remembered the kookla doll in her pocket. She took a little piece of bread and fed it to the doll; and the doll awakened and began jumping up and down in her pocket, and the doll said, "Go this way to the left," or "At the next fork, to the right." And Vasilisa went to the left or the right, and her doll always told her which way to go. And so she followed all the doll's instructions.

Suddenly a man dressed in white on a white horse came galloping through the forest, and not long after it was dawn. A short time later, a man dressed in red on a red horse came cantering by, and soon afterwards the sun rose. Vasilisa walked for many hours. Then suddenly a man dressed in black on a black horse came galloping by, and swiftly it was night.

She journeyed on more days and nights and saw the horsemen each day and each night.

41

Then one day she came to a compound in the heart of the forest. Around it was a fence made of torches. At that moment the horseman dressed in black on his black horse galloped by, and as they leapt the fence they were lost to sight and night came. A moment later all the torches blazed brightly with fire, lighting the compound like day.

Vasilisa was hardly catching her breath at the sight of all this when out of nowhere came a sound like wind roaring through the forest, and a huge, black cauldron came down from the sky. The great trees shook and creaked and their branches cracked. Inside the cauldron was the oldest woman she had ever seen in her whole life. This old woman's nose was so long and curved over, and her chin was so long and curved upward, that they met in the middle. And the long, black, wild, knotty, greasy hair of this woman flew behind her. And her fingernails, Vasilisa could see as she came down closer, were brown and corrugated like the rooftops. The Baba Yaga landed her cauldron, stepped out, and took a look at Vasilisa, saying, "What do you want, girl? What took you so long?"

Her voice trembling, Vasilisa said, "Well, Baba Yaga, I came here...to, to get fire. Our house is cold. My stepmother and stepsisters sent me here to get the fire."

"And what makes you think I'll give you fire? Do you just think I give fire to anyone? Hee, hee, hee. You'll have to work for me!"

"Well, yes, I'd be more than happy to work for you. Wh-wh-what would you like me to do?" Vasilisa replied.

"Well, to begin with, you could wash my clothes. They are over there in a bundle near the wall." Vasilisa went over to the wall and there, sure enough, were Baba Yaga's clothes—a skirt, blouse, and sash. Baba Yaga was so big that it took Vasilisa three days and three nights to drag all her clothes down to the river and then another three days and nights to wash them and lay them out to dry. And it took three days to drag them back to Baba Yaga's hut. And all the time the doll in Vasilisa's pocket said, "This is the right way, the right thing to do. Just keep going."

Now Baba Yaga's hut was up on chicken legs and it walked around in different directions with the rising and setting sun; and so when Baba Yaga was eating, she could always face the sunrise or sunset, depending on which time of the day it was.

And Baba Yaga had required Vasilisa to cook a stew, gather her wood to make a fire, and sweep her yard. After she had eaten, Baba Yaga laid down on her bed, with her foot out one window and her nose out the other, and began to snore—so much so that all the trees of the great forest that were hundreds of years old leaned inward with every inhalation and snapped backward with every exhalation.

When the Baba Yaga awakened, she looked at Vasilisa and said, "You know, you're not half good or half bad, but now I have some very serious work for you. You see that pile of dirt over there?"

"Yes, I do," said Vasilisa.

"Well, look closer. These are poppy seeds, and by morning you have to separate them out from the dirt." And with a flash, the Baba Yaga disappeared in her cauldron into the night.

Vasilisa looked at the poppy seeds and began sorting them out of the dirt, but she could see it was hopeless to finish this by morning. She began to cry, "What can I do? I'll never be able to do this by morning!"

Vasilisa gave the little doll in her pocket some bread and said, "How shall I ever finish this on time before the Baba Yaga comes back?"

The doll said, "Don't worry. I'll do it for you. Go to sleep! Morning is wiser than evening." And while Vasilisa slept, the doll gathered together all the birds of the forest and set them to work sorting out the poppy seeds from the dirt so that by morning the job was done.

Then Baba Yaga came in and said, "Well, I see . . . you completed the task I set for you." The Baba Yaga scratched her mustache, "Well, I'll tell you what. I have another task for you. You're so smart! Over here, you see this room filled with corn? You see the black corns among the gold? The black ones are mildewed, and you must pick out the mildewed corn from the golden corn by tomorrow morning!" And with that, in a flash, the Baba Yaga stepped into her cauldron and drove off into the sky.

Vasilisa started separating out the mildewed corn from the golden corn, and in a short while again saw how hopeless it was to complete the job by morning. She remembered her doll and fed it a little bread and wept, "How shall I ever finish this on time before the Baba Yaga comes back?"

"Don't worry. I'll do it for you. Go to sleep. Morning is wiser than evening," said the little doll. And the doll gathered together all the mice in the forest and set them to work separating the corn. And when Vasilisa woke up in the morning, she was overjoyed to see the job done.

The Baba Yaga strode into the room and said, "Hmmm, what kind of magic is afoot here?"

Vasilisa said, "Well, I don't know. I just found I had abilities . . . I . . . didn't know I had before, and I'm not quite sure, but I have completed the task; and so now will you give me fire?" And then Baba Yaga clapped her hands. Hands! Disembodied hands appeared in the air, picked up the poppy seeds, and began to wring the oil out. She clapped her hands again and another pair of hands appeared on the other side of the room and picked up all the corn, wrung the oil out, and put it in jars and bottles.

And when this was done, the Baba Yaga said to Vasilisa, "Hee, hee, hee, tell me, aren't there some questions you'd like to ask me?"

Vasilisa said, "Actually, I do have some questions. Who was that white man who was on that white horse?"

Baba Yaga answered, "Well, that is my sunrise, and when he strides across the forest the sun comes up." Vasilisa said, "Oh, may I ask another question?"

"Oh yes, please do ask another question," said the Baba Yaga.

Vasilisa said, "Well, who was the red man on the red horse?"

"That is my sunset," said the Baba Yaga. "When he strides across the forest, everything turns to blazing red and the sun sets."

Vasilisa replied, "Well now, that begins to make sense. And who was the black man on the black horse?"

"I'm so glad you asked me one more question," said the Baba Yaga. "The black man on the black horse is my night, and when he strides through the forest, night falls; and you see over there in that great trunk? All of them are in there. They live in my house."

Vasilisa said, "Well, you're clearly a very powerful Baba Yaga, and I think that now would be a good time if you were going to give me some fire . . ."

"You think everything is so easy!" exclaimed the Baba Yaga. "Now surely you have at least one more question!"

Vasilisa thought, I really would like to know about those hands. But as soon as she had that thought, the doll began jumping up and down saying, "No! No! Shhh. No, don't ask! No, shhh; I mean it." And so Vasilisa remained silent.

Baba Yaga urged, "Are you sure you don't want to ask me just one more question?"

"No, I have no more questions," said Vasilisa.

Baba Yaga tried again, "Are you sure you don't see anything unusual in this house you'd like to ask about?"

"I have no more questions," said Vasilisa.

"Well, you're lucky then," said the Baba Yaga, "because if you had asked me one more question, it would all be up for you, for no one who comes here is allowed to ask more than a few questions about the mystery of life and live!"

Vasilisa said, "Well, I'm glad to know that very much. Thank you."

And the Baba Yaga said, "You know, there's something peculiar about you. What is it? How do you know how to sort the seeds from the dirt? How do you know how to sort the mildewed corn from the golden corn? How do you know these things?"

"By the doll in my pocket that my mother gave me as a blessing," answered Vasilisa.

"Blessing?" screamed the Baba Yaga. "We'll have no blessings here! You better be on your way!"

"*The fire!*" *cried out Vasilisa. "Can I have the fire now?"*

With that, the Baba Yaga took a torch from the fence and mounted it on a stick, thrusting it into Vasilisa's hand, saying, "Here, take it! Here's the fire you wanted. You have darn well earned it! Now be on your way!"

Vasilisa started running back through the forest, happy to have gotten the fire. But soon the great torch that had fire blazing from it became heavy and she wanted to put it down. "Don't put me down," it said to her. She held it high, and now the darkest dark forest was lit as bright as day and she could see everything. She could see beasts and she could see the tiniest life. She could see creatures sleeping and mating, eating and killing. She could see everything.

And as she walked through the forest with her great torch of fire, it began to get heavier, and heavier, and heavier, and her arm ached and her shoulder ached. It was really hard to hold onto it. She thought, I could just throw it away, but as soon as she thought that, the torch spoke and said, "Don't throw me away!" And she thought, This is so heavy, and the light is so bright and hurts my eyes. Why did I ever come into this forest, and why am I carrying this light with me that actually hurts as much as it helps? The torch said to her, "Keep hold of me no matter what. Do not throw me away." And Vasilisa, strengthened by all the things she had done with the Baba Yaga to earn the blazing light, held onto the torch.

Meanwhile, back at the house, the stepmother and stepsisters for some reason were never able to kindle a fire. They were cold and hungry, and as a result lived in the darkness. When they looked out the window that night, they saw, off in the distance . . . it looked like a fire, a light of some sort bobbing through the trees. It was a light! Someone who had fire was coming. How wonderful! They all fell through the doorframe at the same time and ran out into the edge of the forest. And out of the forest came Vasilisa with the torch of fire on the stick.

And the stepmother and stepsisters cried out, "Oh, Vasilisa, we are so happy to see you! Oh, come in, come in! It's so good to see you again. Do you know we've been waiting for you and could never start a fire? We've been so cold and so hungry. Here, come in. Have the place of honor. Sit down. Make yourself at home. Here, let me take that torch from you. . . . Oh . . . that . . . torch . . . that fire." And the torch said, only within Vasilisa's hearing, "Don't let anyone else handle me." And Vasilisa said, "No, I'll light the fire." And this she did; and that night, as she was telling them the story of what happened to her, the torch watched the stepmother and stepsisters, and no matter which part of the room they went to, the burning eyes burned into them, and all night long, more and more directly, looking at nothing but the stepmother and stepsisters, until by morning they were burnt to three tiny black cinders.

And Vasilisa kept the torch in a place that only she knows, with the doll and herself, and perhaps they are living . . . still.

Both Vasilisa and women in childbirth are on a journey into the unknown. When we enter the unknown, fears surface and there is mystery and doubt. "What will happen if?" questions flood the mind. We can look at the story to see what Vasilisa does on her journey. She depends heavily on her little kookla doll that her mother gave her before dying. In symbolic language, this is no ordinary gift. It is more valuable than riches or land. Her mother has left her the gift of a doll that represents her intuition, and she is reminded to use it during her journey through the deep, dark, mysterious woods to find the Baba Yaga and get the fire. Her mother left her the gift of knowledge that, when connecting to our intuitive side, can guide us through any journey in life. This gift is within all of us and is often referred to as the "inner voice"; we just have to remember to listen to it, especially when on important journeys in life such as birth.

In their journeys, Vasilisa and pregnant women both encounter forces of the medial world that go beyond our understanding. The Baba Yaga represents Mother Nature herself. How can we really understand her? She keeps the sunrise, sunset, and night in a trunk in her house. She knows how to fly. She wears a skirt, sash, and blouse that take three days each to carry to the river, wash and dry, and carry back. Her home up on sticks turns in the direction of the sunsets and sunrises; and when she snores, the trees bend with each breath. Even more mysterious, she is keeper of the fire, which is symbolic of the light of intuition, giving wisdom and clarity.

In the same way, how can we understand the mystery behind conception, a soul taking form, the sperm knowing where to swim, cells dividing to form organs according to DNA codes, hormones signaling the beginning of labor, and the eventual birth of a baby? We sense this mystery as a force, an energy that is all-knowing and very wise. As a woman watches the baby grow inside of her, she is in wonder and awe of the process and sees it as a mystery of creation, of the spirit.

In the Baba Yaga story and in birth, the journey is taken for a specific reason. Vasilisa is making her journey through the dark woods to find fire. Most women who conceive have a baby or babies at the end of their journey. It is the process of how they both accomplish this that is fascinating. Once she arrives at Baba Yaga's home, Vasilisa experiences another world where horsemen bring in the day and night, where Baba Yaga's home is surrounded by a fence of torches, and the Baba Yaga has her own flying machine. A pregnant woman having her baby enters another world too. At first she hardly believes that there is really a baby growing inside of her. Her first words on seeing an early ultrasound are often, "I can't believe it! It's real!" In subsequent months she sees her body changing shape, with her abdomen growing larger than she's ever seen it before. By the end of pregnancy she is walking in a waddle due to the size of her uterus, having to urinate more often, experiencing changes in sleep patterns, and having mood swings from hormone changes. It is as if she is in a different world, getting ready to become a mother. In labor, if she connects with the spirit within, she experiences a powerful force that she never knew was there and learns even more about herself.

What is gained through the work done on such journeys? Vasilisa's tasks are so difficult that she knows she can't do them within the deadlines given by the Baba Yaga. But she remembers her doll (intuition), who says, "Don't worry, I'll do it for you. Just go to sleep." In symbolic language, the doll is really saying, "Surrender to me completely. You can trust me to get the job done." A woman in labor who surrenders completely to the power within, the mysterious force, the consciousness that knows how to birth her baby, goes into another state beyond mind and body and connects with her spirit. At this moment she lets go completely, which is what is required to give birth. Her intuitive, conscious, knowing side takes over and rallies help from all the hormones to get the job done.

In the end, they have both received what they went for, but because they encountered an experience in the medial world, they are transformed in a very good way. They are not who they used to be, because they have had a powerful experience. They have gone beyond body and mind and connected with a power greater than themselves. In doing so, they have gained great clarity and wisdom. They *know* because they have *experienced*. They have "seeing" eyes that offer more clarity and wisdom. Vasilisa wants to put down her stick with the fire torch because sometimes *knowing* and *seeing* all can feel heavy to the soul. But once we have earned this intuition, it is ours forever and can never go away.

This is the beauty of birth, that we are forever mothers. And all we have to do from time to time is feed our intuition a little bread and a little water (paying attention to it), nourishing it so we can continue letting it do its job in our lives. Becoming a mother is a tremendous responsibility, taking care of a new soul and sacrificing things in our lives for its sake. But to be good parents, we must shoulder this responsibility even if it feels heavy.

Vasilisa needed to stay very focused on completing her tasks in order to get the fire that she had come for. Focus comes from the word *focare*, which means the burning point. The burning point is everything. It is the point at which all rays of light converge onto one area and make fire, creating light out of darkness and warmth out of coldness. Focus holds great power. To hold onto focus is to hold onto the medial world of the spirit. Vasilisa was so intent on this goal that she was bound to succeed.

The ability to focus is essential when working through contractions in labor—feeling their power as they surge like waves, crest, and then come to shore. A woman in labor needs to stay on top of the contractions and work through them as best as she can. If her focus becomes interrupted, she can find herself helpless, scattered, disorganized, and unable to access her resources for coping. If she is not focusing or concentrating on the contraction, her mind wanders from one thing to another. Focus requires hard work and determination even at the point of tremendous fatigue.

In such a story like this, we can look at all the characters as being an aspect of ourselves. There are times when we are cunning and crafty like the stepsisters and stepmother. We are sometimes brave and courageous like Vasilisa. The mystery of the medial world is within us as spirit and when we experience it, we are transformed. The Baba Yaga says, "There will be no blessings in my house!" But she has actually blessed Vasilisa in a very big way by giving her work to earn the fire she came for. Birth is a blessing for all women because it gives us the opportunity to take a journey that offers much learning and insight into ourselves. And we are wiser for it.

Birthing in the Spirit

This transition was infinitely harder than my experience with my first birth. The pain was out of control; it racked my body, and only by moaning as loud as I could was I able to tread water. I wanted nothing more to do with birth, babies, or mothers (and this after answering a call to midwifery, too!). I was completely delirious, yet I knew this was what I (and my baby) needed to go through together. Then finally, the urge to push returned . . . her head was born, and I caressed it, feeling her ears and cheeks; and then I guided her out as she came wonderfully slipping out with no "ring of fire," no tearing, no swelling. And I had the biggest grin on my face. I can only describe her birth as pure ecstasy!

—Vesper Stamper CCE (BWI)

CHAPTER 7

Human Values in Birth

If we are to go forward, we must go back and rediscover
those precious values—that all reality hinges on
moral foundations and that all reality has spiritual control.

MARTIN LUTHER KING JR.

Once upon a time, east of the sun and west of the moon, in a place older than the oldest pine tree but maybe not too long ago, and even just around the corner, there was a wise man in a village. People sought his advice, and he gave them kindness and compassion. One day, he told them he was going to the top of the mountain to talk to God. People were anxious to know what he would say when he returned.

When he came down the next day, they all crowded around him, noting that his face was white and ashen and that he looked terrified. "Zeusa! What happened?" exclaimed the villagers.

Zeusa replied, "The angels told me what they would say to me on my judgment day."

"But Zeusa, you've led such a model life!" they said. "You've spoken from your heart and helped us many times! What could they possibly say to you?"

Zeusa said, "It is not that they will say to me, 'Why didn't you lead my people out of slavery like Moses?' or, 'Why didn't you free the slaves like David?'"

"Well, then," said the villagers, "what will they say?"

Zeusa said, "They will say, 'Zeusa! Why weren't you Zeusa?'"

This very short story is of great significance. Even though the people of the village revered him as a wise man—one that was a model for them all—still, the angels knew he could be an even better person. Zeusa was left to ask himself, "Who am I? What is my truth? How can I live closer to my true nature?"

Many people walk around carrying out their daily activities without pondering the question of their own existence. Perhaps you would like to ask yourself the same question, "Who am I?" Without mentioning your name, your profession, or your gender, what would you say? Give yourself time to process the question and see what ideas come. Do you know who you really are?

When I ask people this question, there is usually silence for a while. Many have never thought about it before. After awhile they begin to say, "I am kind." "I am compassionate." "I am caring." "I help others." "I am love." I acknowledge that this is who we really are and that these are human values already within us. They are our birthright, and that is why they are called human.

Think for a moment, did you ever have to learn how to love? Did you ever read a book to learn how to love? A mother holding her newborn baby at the moment of birth does not have to learn how to love her baby. The love flows naturally and effortlessly from both the mother and baby. Love is already within them, simply waiting to be expressed. The ability to love is within us from the moment of birth.

We are programmed to be happy, kind, compassionate, and loving human beings. One way to know this is to imagine someone walking near you and you see she is crying. You would likely ask, "What is wrong? Can I help you?" On the other hand, if someone is walking down the street smiling, would you ask, "What is wrong?" Of course not. This is because happiness is our natural state of being. We like being happy. We like feeling loved.

There are many values that various sages, prophets, and saints have taught through the ages. For the purposes of this book, the five human values I will discuss are truth, right action, peace, love, and nonviolence. Each primary value has a number of components or aspects. For example, components of truth include honesty, integrity, curiosity, and self-inquiry. Components of right action include determination and perseverance. Components of peace include equanimity and calmness. Components of love include compassion and kindness. Components of nonviolence include respect and feeling a bond with humanity. We naturally practice all of these values in our lives to improve our character, and we also explain the importance of them to our children.

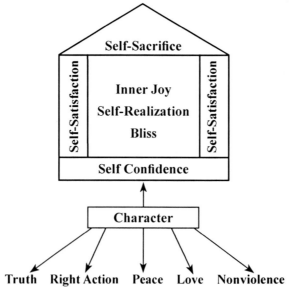

MANIFESTING OUR FULL HUMAN POTENTIAL

The diagram on the previous page demonstrates how the practice of human values leads to the development of our full human potential—the idea that we are much more than we think we are. Putting human values into practice leads to the development of character, which in turn leads to self-confidence, which is the foundation of the building in the diagram. When there is self-confidence, we have self-satisfaction. Self-satisfaction leads to self-sacrifice, and ultimately to realization of our full human potential.

The five human values themselves are expressed in a specific order, and when put into practice, have the end result of bliss. From the diagram it can be seen that the path to inner joy and self-realization of the true self all begins with the practice of truth. It is from truth that the journey to self-realization begins, for truth leads to right action, the experience of peace, the flow of love, and ultimately to nonviolence, both emotionally and physically. When human values are put into practice, they lead to the experience of happiness and bliss. Where there is bliss, there is the experience of the spirit.

I will now explore in more depth the meanings of the values and their application to birth.

HUMAN VALUES

Truth

An infallible truth is one that does not change in the three time frames of the present, past, or future. An example of an infallible truth in birth is that every woman's uterus has the potential to grow a baby. This has always been true and will always be true for all women. What we believe to be true starts with thoughts. Such truths affect our actions and our physiology in the body. For example, imagine yourself sucking on a very juicy lemon just now. Slowly become aware of what is happening in your mouth. Even as I write, I am experiencing more saliva in my mouth, and perhaps you are too. But is there a lemon in your mouth? No. Even a thought of the lemon produces this reaction in your body.

Just as the thought of a lemon affects the body, so do negative thoughts. Inherent in negative thoughts is fear and anxiety, which result in the release of the stress hormone cortisol. This hormone causes the pulse and breathing rates to increase and digestion to slow down. Fear may or may not be helpful, depending on the situation, especially if it concerns our safety. So if we want to have good influences on our bodies, we need to have good thoughts, and then our words and actions will also be good.

Right Action

For there to be right action, truth must first be known. Actions based on truth are right actions. Right action means having consistency in thought, word, and deed. When truth and right action are synchronous with each other, there is integrity, which is a component of truth. Integrity means

that whatever we say is what we do. Therefore, it is essential that we pay more attention to what we say. Doing what we say is one of the first steps we can take if we want to become closer to realizing our full human potential, i.e., knowing our true selves. It means watching thoughts more carefully because once something is said, it carries an energy that results in action.

Right action means that all thoughts are carried out in actions of love, reverence, and gratitude. Because our lives are filled with actions, right action touches every aspect of our daily lives. It requires listening to the inner voice—the voice of the conscience—and acting on it. We trust those who do what they say. The birth team is no exception. An example of right action in birth is a doula who says to her client that she will be with her throughout her labor, helping her to feel safe. The pregnant woman trusts that the doula will carry through with what she says and has full faith in her. When good thoughts are converted into right action, the child, the home, and society will benefit.

Patience, a component of right action, is often lacking in birth today. Both laboring women and the birth team often demonstrate a lack of patience, which results too often in the administration of medical procedures and obstetrical drugs to speed up labor. Routine procedures performed for no medical reason result in medically managed births that prevent pregnant women from feeling their own power. They are like clouds that prevent the "sun," the full power of birth, from shining through.

Pregnant women are opting more and more for inductions and surgical deliveries, and doctors are quick to comply. Medical procedures have become routine, frequently not for medical reasons, but rather, for the mother's and medical team's convenience and/or comfort. When this happens, hormones are prevented from playing their full roles in birth as nature intended. This can be compared to a fruit picked from a vine before it is ripe so it never reaches its full sweetness. In such situations, women working for a natural birth often end up with birth memories being less than what they had hoped for.

Peace

Suppose you say to someone, "Teach me how to have peace." Is it possible? One might gain some insights, but to truly experience peace, we must seek it from within.

When what we say and do are the same, peace is experienced because there is no internal conflict in the message to the body. There cannot be peace when there is tension in the body resulting from saying one thing and doing another. This makes sense because we know that actions that are not right actions eventually, if not immediately, disturb the core of our inner being. Right actions give us a sense of well-being. When we are at peace with ourselves, we feel good and peace begins to radiate from within the body without our even having to think about it.

Meditation brings people a sense of peace, for it helps to quiet the mind. The practice of yoga does the same. We can train ourselves to quiet our minds. As we do so, the peace that was there all along will begin to surface and the benefits will be experienced in powerful ways. The body that feels this

peace will respond physiologically with a lower pulse, less anxiety, slower breathing, and improved digestion. A woman who can feel peace about her labor will approach each contraction with a positive attitude and a feeling of confidence to work with, and not against, it.

Love

When there is peace, love flows naturally just as a spring of water emerging from the earth. There are many different connotations perceived by people when the word *love* is read. Perhaps in our society the most common meaning is that of romantic love or sexual expression. It can also mean desire, such as loving a car, jewelry, or other material objects. Or love can simply mean feelings of high respect for an individual. However, when the word *love* is mentioned in this book as a human value, the word is meant to convey a spiritual love that transcends physical attachment and desires in the material world. Love can be thought of as synonymous with truth and expresses itself as compassion for all living humans and creatures of the world.

The powerful presence and expression of love at birth cannot be underestimated. Its role is to help a woman feel safe. If she is unable to feel safe, all aspects of her labor will be affected, including her ability to let go of tension, her ability to open her body to give birth, and her ability to produce oxytocin, the hormone of love. To do all this, she must feel safe—unconditional love helps her to feel this way.

There is abundant love inside of us just waiting to be expressed. Imagine a house with all the lights turned on inside but all the doors and shutters are closed so it looks completely dark. In our own "body-house," the light of love is also shining brightly, but some shutters may be closed in different areas of the house, which limits the ability of the light and love to shine through.

The more we can put human values into practice in our daily lives, the more brightly we will shine. As a result, we will open ourselves and experience the warmth of the love that is within. This brings us closer to our full human potential. If we keep our shutters closed, our full expression of this love is limited. In other words, we create around ourselves layers upon layers of fear, anger, jealousy, pride, and ego that cover up the light and love that is within all of us. Throughout life we will be happier individuals if we can dissolve these layers one by one to experience our true human potential, our true nature.

Mother Teresa, when serving the sick, was able to see past individual appearances that would turn away most people. By connecting with the common bond of love between them, she derived great happiness from serving others no matter how sick they were or how ostracized they were from society. This selfless love transcends our own personal borders and connects us with the spirit in all.

The practice of human values helps the spirit within us to flow as love. Suppose there are two glasses in front of you. One is sweetened with sugar and one is not. Just looking at them, you cannot tell the difference. It is only when you drink them that you can experience the sweetness in one and not the other. The sugar becomes invisible in the water, and this invisible sugar makes the

water sweet. In the same way, love, which is invisible, makes a person sweet. People can sense this sweetness in the tone of voice, in actions, and through an invisible transfer of energy that feels safe. The implications of this for a woman during her pregnancy, labor, and delivery are profound. As midwife and author Ina May Gaskin says, "Women can 'un-dilate' with one unkind glance."

Any love based on form is attachment love and thus temporary, because what is in form one day will not always have form. It is an infallible truth that what is born must one day die. Yet attachment love is a powerful love. I thought I knew what love was when I was growing up. I loved my parents, our vacations, the new clothes I wore. Then I met my husband and we had a daughter named Heidi. I cried tears of joy the days after she was born, and was in awe and wonder at the miracle of birth. When I became pregnant a second time, I wondered if there would be as much love for the second baby. And there it was as I held my son, Aaron, in my arms. As they have grown older, the love continues to grow.

It is the nature of spiritual love to be beyond form and be ever full. Love flows and flows without end if we keep the door of the heart open. Turning the key of the heart to the right closes it; turning it to the left opens it. Being centered in the heart while carrying out all actions leads to the manifestation of human values and the experience of bliss. Qualities such as anger, envy, jealousy, pride, and ego close the doors and shutters of the brightly lit body-house of love.

The love within us is our most precious possession that must be safeguarded all our lives. It makes sense to hold onto it as a valuable treasure, allowing it to be expressed in all we do and say. Practicing love from the heart in all our actions has transforming power. Just imagine if all people at a birth were able to be guided by their spirit. Birth would be an experience of bliss.

Nonviolence

Where there is love there cannot be violence, and thus there is nonviolence. Nonviolence cannot exist in the presence of love. One who is aware of the fundamental unity or oneness in everyone will not knowingly cause pain or distress to another, for it would be the equivalent of experiencing it in him or herself. Nonviolence expresses itself as love for all beings and all things. It is a consequence of complete unity in thought, word, and deed. Its practice becomes reflected in having patience and tolerance for others.

Words said without love sound cold, dry, and hard, and may contain resentment, fear, and anger. This can result in both physical and emotional abuse. It is not our true nature to behave this way. Words spoken with love have compassion, kindness, and warmth. They make the listener feel safe and open. A woman who hears, "If you don't dilate more in the next two hours, a cesarean may be necessary," will feel threatened. What if she heard instead, "Just keep relaxing into the contractions and they will be more effective. Your body knows how to give birth." These words have softness, warmth, and kindness in them and they are empowering, helping a laboring woman to find her resources for coping with the contractions. Midwives and doulas know how to speak warm words

naturally. Being true to our nature by speaking soothing words and acting with good intentions creates a feeling of peace, which creates a loving and nonviolent energy around us.

INTERCONNECTEDNESS OF THE FIVE VALUES

It is easy to see how the five values are very interconnected. Without one of the primary human values, it is difficult to experience the others. If there is no truth, there cannot be right action. Without right action, there cannot be peace. Without peace, there cannot be love. Without love there is violence. I believe that a breakdown in the practice of human values is one of the reasons that so many women today are going into birth with anxiety, fear, and lack of confidence instead of love, joy, and confidence in themselves when venturing into the unknown of labor.

Character

The natural outcome of the practice of the five primary human values is the development of character. A person with character can be trusted, and people in the community will have respect and feel safe around her. She will often be a leader because she demonstrates other human values such as courage, determination, and integrity. The community will know that she is honest, that she does whatever she says, and that she can be trusted.

Because birth is such a peak experience in a woman's life, it is important that she surrounds herself with people of character. These people will help to empower her when preparing for labor and birth. This is especially important for a woman deciding to have a VBAC. Because it may not have gone the way she had anticipated the first time, she may have doubts about her body being able to work for her. Constant support from like-minded friends who believe in her ability to give birth is crucial.

During labor, it is essential that a woman view contractions as a normal function of her uterus whose purpose is to open her cervix so the baby can be born. If she feels safe, she will be able to let go and work with the strong contractions. She will not be able to do this naturally if she is feeling guarded, tense, or unsafe in any way. Courage and self-confidence are required.

Self-confidence

The outcome of good character is self-confidence. Confidence is essential to perform any duty in our daily lives and is like the foundation of a building. It cannot usually be seen, but forms the basis and structure for the entire building. In the same way, self-confidence supports our ability to carry out any action. Those with self-confidence are more in tune with their inner guidance system.

Self-satisfaction

With confidence, one experiences a feeling of being satisfied, which leads to self-satisfaction. I was once with a woman in labor who had spent a number of prenatal visits convincing her doctor and

giving him research showing that an episiotomy is not necessary in most cases. However, episiotomies were part of his medical training and he had never seen a bulging perineum. In her labor, as she pushed her baby out, his hand would automatically reach for the scissors almost subconsciously, and she would dart a menacing look in his direction, and his hand would back away. Though she had a second-degree tear, at her six-week postnatal visit he agreed that if he had performed an episiotomy, the healing process would have been at least as long or longer. She was confident of her decision not only because she had done research, and knowledge is power, but also because she believed in natural birth. For the rest of her life she will have feelings of self-satisfaction.

Self-sacrifice

Self-sacrifice is a natural outcome of self-satisfaction. The roof in the diagram represents self-sacrifice. Self-sacrifice means doing good deeds for others out of the goodness of the heart without expecting any reward in return. What are some of the sacrifices a woman must make over the course of her pregnancy, labor, and birth, and on into parenting? She loses her pre-pregnant body, with the areola of her breasts becoming brown and stretch marks appearing on her distended abdomen. Towards the end of pregnancy she sacrifices sleep, having to urinate more frequently during the night and having to find comfortable positions in which to sleep. In labor, she sacrifices comfort to work through contractions and birth her baby. Some women who have a cesarean, the ultimate intervention, accept the risk of major surgery for the sake of their baby. Once the baby is born, a woman sacrifices her time and sleep to feed and take care of her baby, and this continues as it grows into a child and young adult. Having the opportunity to make all these sacrifices joyfully brings her closer to the experience of self-realization and bliss.

Self-realization

Self-realization is the experience of knowing one's true self. With self-realization we understand our destiny and have clear vision about our purpose in life. It is also a state of no emotion because when we are in our truth, there is no duality, no opposites such as pain/sorrow. In our truth there is bliss, and bliss just *is*. I believe as humans that we are seeking this state of existence all our lives, because being tossed up and down in the world of emotion only leads to worry and anxiety and general ill health. In a state of self-realization there is also pure love, peace, and contentment. Finding self-realization ultimately depends on the base of self-confidence. We develop self-confidence by improving our character. Character is developed by putting the human values of truth, right action, peace, love, and nonviolence into practice. And it all begins with realizing our truth.

The importance of integrating human values into practice more in our daily lives is that it establishes a habit that will prove helpful in times of great need—birth being one of them. In general, most people have personal goals they want to meet to better themselves in some way. Helping others

is a good way to practice human values, and it makes us feel good. This feeling is not limited to our own culture. During my three-and-a-half-year trip around the world with my husband, Raysh, traveling in forty-eight countries and covering most continents, there were always people who went out of their way to help us, even in our most dire circumstances. It didn't matter which country we were in; the experience of someone helping us was so consistent that I stopped worrying about it when in various predicaments.

I remember a time while traveling in Tierra del Fuego, the southernmost tip of Argentina, when we tried to find transportation after visiting a remote glacier. We were on a dirt road and one car went by in two hours. Even though it was full, it stopped and piled us in with our two large backpacks to help us out. When someone helps us, it makes us want to help others—the "pay it forward" concept.

Pregnancy, labor, birth, and parenting are times of great transition in one's life. Moving into these new roles is much easier when human values are put into practice, bringing us closer to the experience of the spirit. In this journey, character is improved, there is more satisfaction, one experiences an expanded view that allows for self-sacrifice, and the experience of bliss is attained. "Who am I?" is now less of a mysterious question.

Habituation

I am concerned that as a society we are habituating to the existence of birth as being a less euphoric experience than it was meant to be. Habituation occurs when something new starts to feel normal. Medical procedures have become so commonplace in birth that women are forgetting the power and beauty of normal and natural birth. People habituate easily, and habituation can be good and bad. An example of good habituation is when negative qualities such as anger begin to disappear from our lives with the practice of human values. An example of habituation that is not good is having so many women think natural birth includes an epidural.

Birth carries the potential of being a peak experience in a woman's life. Too many women today are settling for less than what birth has to offer due to fear and worry. This results in the release of the hormone adrenaline, which is known to inhibit the birth process by stimulating the neocortex and interfering with the action and release of oxytocin.[1] The practice of human values can help women work through such fears and experience birth as it was meant to be. The question then becomes, "How can fear in the birthplace be minimized to help make birth feel safer?"

Birthing in the Spirit

As soon as I felt the baby leave my body, I turned over and took her into my arms. Oh, what a wonderful moment! There is no moment sweeter in my memories than those first moments after

birth, high on endorphins, and holding a warm, wet baby close to my chest. I was in heaven! Jimmy was supporting me from behind, and my children Lucas and Bethany were beside us, gazing at the baby in amazement. I floated him in the water, and he looked so peaceful and calm—I honestly don't think he knew that he had been born yet!

—JENNIFER CAHILL, CCE (BWI)

HUMAN VALUES IN BIRTH

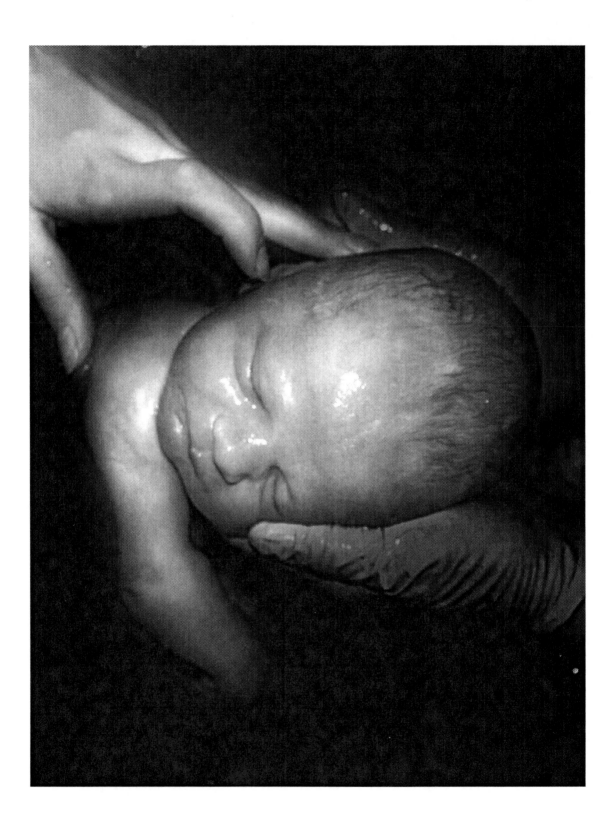

CHAPTER 8

Truth

If it vibrates, it can be tuned. Everything is energy—violins,
people, potato chips, thoughts, feelings, and events.
They all vibrate.

DEENA ZALKIND SPEAR, *EARS OF THE ANGELS*

INFALLIBLE TRUTH

Truth is stronger than any other force, and it is synonymous with the power of love. Infallible truth is that which is true in time periods, i.e the past, present, and future. When it is denied, it remains inside untouched. It cannot change because it is changeless. Whether you believe it or not, it is still within you and will never leave you. This truth within can be considered your guide and closest friend on whom you can always depend.

All matter is in a continuous state of flux and is changing at every given moment. Even scientific laws are not constant and change with new inventions, discoveries, and experiments. An important characteristic of infallible truth is that it can never be affected by decay or change. Apparent truths differ from infallible truths in that they experience change from moment to moment, day to day, and year to year; for what is apparent at one moment is liable to change at another moment. For example, "It is raining," is true for the moment, however long it lasts, but then the sun shines and it is no longer raining. "Sarah is in labor," is true for the time she is having contractions, but then she gives birth and labor ends.

Infallible truths do not change with time. They are not short-term time periods, but rather, truths for all time and they go deep into our inner core with complete acceptance. Some examples of infallible truths are:

1. **We breathe in oxygen and breathe out carbon dioxide.** Furthermore, we depend on trees and plants in nature for oxygen to breathe, and they in turn depend on us for carbon dioxide to make more oxygen. We are interdependent with each other for our survival. This has not and will not change in the three periods of time.

2. **All that is born must one day die.** Energy becomes matter and then matter returns to energy. The soul is born into form, and then when it leaves, the form becomes part of the earth once again.

3. **Women's bodies are designed to give birth.** In humans, only women can give birth. The

female pelvis is wider than the male's, with the coccyx riding even with or above the pubic bones of the pelvis. This provides more space for a baby. Only women have a uterus in which a baby can grow.

4. ***The knowledge about how to give birth is born within every woman.*** Birth is instinctive, and therefore women do not need to be taught how to give birth. They have been giving birth for thousands of years. What women do need in today's world is more confidence, trust, and faith in their body's innate knowledge that already knows how to give birth.

5. ***Being born into the world is being born into duality.*** In life, we would not know day without night. We would not know male without female. We would not know loud unless there was soft. We would not know pleasure unless there was pain. The pairs of opposites are two sides of the same coin and are interconnected. This is duality. There is a saying that pain is the interval between two pleasures. The pleasure of orgasm is followed by the pain of labor (when pregnant), which is followed by a mother's bliss as she first gazes into the eyes of her newborn baby.

6. ***Each woman is unique and gives birth in her own way.*** There is not one right way or method for all women to give birth. Birth is a process and each woman must find her own way through it.

I believe women have lost sight of the truth that their bodies already know how to give birth due to four reasons: the nocebo effect, childbirth education designed to convince women that labor pain is to be avoided, women being led to believe that they need to learn how to give birth, and the mind-set that technology and interventions are the solution to every medical problem.

The nocebo effect

It is the duty of all birth team members to protect the emotional health of a pregnant woman. The nocebo effect does not protect her emotional health. Michel Odent, MD, obstetrician, midwife, author, international lecturer, and founder of the Primal Health Research Center in London, describes the nocebo effect in his book *The Caesarean* as "a negative effect on the emotional state of pregnant women and indirectly of their families. It occurs whenever a health professional does more harm than good by interfering with the imagination, the fantasy life, or the beliefs of a patient or a pregnant woman."[1]

In an effort to provide good prenatal care, doctors are taught—and are doing their duty—to look for anything that might be a potential problem. However, if they verbalize such concerns to a pregnant woman without good evidence that the concern actually exists, the impact can be enormous. In a prenatal visit, being told, "Your pelvis looks small," or "I think you have a big baby in there!" is alarming. Such comments magnify a pregnant woman's own fears of being able to birth the baby, and over the following months of gestation her own doubt increases about her ability to birth

normally. These fears fester like a wound within and lower self-confidence. By the time she goes into labor, she may have already convinced herself that she can't do it (labor) and may have decided to let "them" (the doctors) do it for her.

There are many other examples of the nocebo effect. In labor, if a medical authority says, "You're not making enough progress," what she hears is, "There might be something wrong with my body." This undermines her confidence at a time when she needs to be empowered. "If you don't go into labor a week before your due date, we may need to induce you." "We need to do a cesarean now or your cesarean scar might rupture." "Pushing your baby out can cause damage to your pelvic floor." "We need to put the IV in now in case you hemorrhage." "Your placenta has calcification so we need to do an induction." These words communicated to a pregnant woman induce fear and decrease self-confidence. They are not empowering.

Statements such as these that cause concern, doubt, and fear may be unintentional and unfounded, but a woman may not be able to recover. I once saw a friend who looked dejected. She had just found out in a prenatal visit that her glucose tolerance test (GTT) was positive. "There is no history of diabetes in my family. I have had a healthy pregnancy. I can't believe this is happening to me, and now I am afraid there is something wrong." A subsequent, longer GTT came back negative, but still she was afraid something else would go wrong.

Childbirth education classes

I believe that a childbirth class that teaches women how to avoid feeling labor contractions is doing a disservice to pregnant women. Any attempts to avoid feeling impacts our ability to learn more about ourselves. The emphasis in classes needs to be one of empowerment—filling participants with the amazing wonders of the human body, its wisdom, and ability to bring forth life. Classes need to build confidence about ways in which to work with the body in labor, rather than to describe what drug or medical procedure can be given when the contractions become stronger and tighter. However, a balanced approach is important, and this includes providing information on when the procedures or drugs may be helpful. If women hear, repetitively, that labor contractions are good and that they are normal, they may be less fearful of them and enter labor with more confidence.

Birth is instinctive and doesn't need to be taught

People often ask me, "If birth is instinctive and women don't need to be taught how to give birth, then what are you teaching in your childbirth classes?" In Birth Works® International classes we help women to have more *trust and faith* in their bodies that already know how to give birth. This is a completely different approach from traditional childbirth classes that are typically designed to tell pregnant women what to do and when to do it in labor. Women in prehistoric and ancient times all gave birth and nobody taught them how to do it. It is not different for women today, nor will it be any different in the future.

In fact, the more we teach women about how to give birth, the more complex it becomes and the further women grow away from their instincts. I believe that one of the biggest mistakes we've made in modern times is convincing women that they need to learn how to give birth. How can that which is instinctive be learned? Instead, what women need is childbirth preparation that helps to instill more trust and faith in their body knowledge that already knows how to give birth.

The fact that women have strayed too far from their own truth that they know how to give birth is reflected in the 30.2 percent cesarean rate of all births in 2005.[5] This rate is out of balance from what nature intended. Because women are losing sight of this truth, birth for many women in America and increasingly around the world has become a medically managed event requiring numerous obstetrical drugs and medical procedures for the baby to be born.

Odent says, "The less a woman knows about the right way to give birth, the easier it will be for her." In other words, the more the neocortex, or thinking brain, is stimulated in labor, the harder it will be for her to access the "primal" brain that already knows how to give birth. Odent reminds us that animals give birth instinctively and that humans are also mammals; therefore, pregnant women need to remember their mammalian aspect when giving birth so they can do the same.

Just imagine what it would be like if doctors, midwives, nurses, childbirth educators, doulas, family members, and friends all reminded a pregnant woman that her body already knows how to give birth and that all she needs to do is have more trust and faith in her body knowledge. This is such an easy thing to do, especially in childbirth education classes, and the impact would be enormous. If a pregnant woman heard this confidence coming from everyone around her throughout her pregnancy, she would go into labor with more confidence and a mind-set ready to work with her body instead of against it. There would be less fear and less need for medical procedures and obstetrical drugs. There would be more patience on the part of everyone and improved communication among all. The end result would be birth experiences that would be beautiful memories for a lifetime.

In classes, women need to hear that labors progress in their own unique ways, sometimes going a few hours without further dilation but then becoming completely dilated in an hour, or with initial contractions starting very strongly instead of gradually. They need to hear that upright positions are the most advantageous for helping the baby to move down into the pelvis. They need to hear that if they position their pelvis forward, the baby can pass in front of the pelvic floor musculature. They need to hear that IVs can be inserted at the moment if needed and don't have to be inserted routinely. They need to hear that most placentas have some calcification towards term and that this is not a concern.

The dilemma comes when women hear, for example, that medical research shows that wearing an electronic fetal monitor increases their chance of having a cesarean section, yet when they go to the hospital, this is how fetal heart tones and the progress of labor are monitored. The only options available now are using a doptone that utilizes short bursts of ultrasound, or accepting intermittent electronic fetal monitoring—neither of which she may want for her baby. Few if any nurses are trained in the use of a fetascope, though more midwives may have retained this skill.

The age of technology

The technological age is not an easy time for women to be giving birth. Though medical technology has improved safety for at-risk mothers and babies in some circumstances, its routine use on low-risk women has increased and is unwarranted. Medical procedures may seem to have made birth easier because a woman can now plan the time of her birth and not have to feel labor pain if she doesn't want to, but primal health research is continuing to show us that an electronic environment is not good for the baby unless needed for true medical reasons. Women who are informed about the risks and benefits of such medical procedures are thrown into dilemmas of whether or not to accept them during pregnancy and birth. It has led some women to choose to stay home to give birth so they won't have to deal with such pressures.

Odent predicts that we will gradually move out of the current "electronic age" into a "post electronic age" as more research shows the emotional and physical adverse effects on the mother and baby. The mind-set that technology is the answer to every medical problem is well established in society today. If a woman doesn't begin labor by her due date, an induction is performed. If she is taking too long to dilate, she is given Pitocin and/or her bag of waters may be ruptured. These procedures have become so commonplace that many women think this is the natural way to give birth.

When numb and connected to tubes and machines in labor, it is difficult for any woman to tap into her instincts. More mystery surrounds birth today, with the focus of birth having changed from home to the hospital. Women are left mostly unfamiliar with the sights and sounds of birth before having their own baby. What is unknown and unfamiliar is often fearful.

Now let us look at some characteristics of truth to more fully understand its deeper meanings and associations with birth. The characteristics I will describe, but which truth is not limited to, are the three time periods (past, present, future), honesty, integrity, curiosity, self-inquiry, and vibration.

SIX CHARACTERISTICS OF TRUTH

1. Exists in the three time periods of the past, present and future

The past

Of the three time periods, which one do you think holds the most power? Imagine yourself immersed in the past. What are the thoughts and experiences that immediately come to mind? Perhaps a fun vacation, birthing your children, an embarrassing moment, or a failure? No matter what these thoughts are, there is one thing they have in common: first they become memory, and then, over a period of time, they fade into imagination. This is the nature of the period of time called the past. The more significant the event, the longer it will be remembered. Elderly women often remember the smallest details about their births.

The future

Now place your awareness in the period of time called the future. What thoughts, dreams, and aspirations are coming to your mind now? Of course, there is no experience yet except as imagined in the mind, but there are many thoughts. Such thoughts of the future usually contain emotions of uncertainty, doubt, excitement, optimism, anxiety, or worry: What will happen if I switch doctors? What will my husband say if I tell him I want to give birth at home? What will it be like to be a mother? Can I trust my midwife? Should I quit my job after I have the baby? How will I be able to breastfeed while at work? Such thoughts consume more energy than we realize. Though birthing parents do need to make some plans for the future, worrying about it too much expends energy and results in fatigue.

Plans for the baby include who to invite to the birth and whether or not to hire a doula or birth companion. There also needs to be money budgeted for baby supplies and arranging a space for the baby at home, complete with furniture such as a crib and changing table. If the mother plans to work and wants to breastfeed, she needs to make plans to purchase a breastfeeding pump. Making such plans for the future will help the transition of having a new baby flow more smoothly.

The present

The period of time called the present can be considered a gift because it is a *present*. It is in the present moment that the most power and energy exist. The present is fresh, new, inspirational, full of learning, and creative. How can we stay in the present to maximize our power and energy? One way is to look at life in a new way—living life as a series of moments. When life is perceived as a series of moments, each moment is in the present. This concept has tremendous value when applied to pregnancy and birth.

When a pregnant woman has morning sickness in early pregnancy, or finds it hard to sleep in certain positions in later pregnancy, she can choose to stay in the present moment and be glad her body is working to grow a baby. Staying in the present moment in labor means not worrying about how many contractions have already occurred and how many more might be ahead as the cervix continues to dilate. Staying in the present moment after birth means accepting joyfully the work of feeding and taking care of the baby, and making the sacrifices in life that are necessary to do so.

2. *Has components of honesty and integrity*

Components of truth include those of honesty and integrity. When put into practice, they instill faith and trust. You may even be thinking of such people in your life. I talk to many women who, in birth, have a guarded trust in their doctors. A lack of trust means there is the beginning of a breakdown in communication, for there will not be faith. Chances for a good birth experience are then at risk. Some women don't even trust their midwives or themselves. Honesty and right action are closely linked together, and without honesty there cannot be right action. Women need to find caregivers who believe in the normal and natural process of birth and work to build a relationship of trust that will serve them both well at the time of birth.

Integrity means having unity in thought, word, and deed. This means that what we say and do must be the same. In Birth Works® classes and workshops I often have people do the following exercise:

UNITY IN THOUGHT, WORD, AND DEED EXERCISE

Just now, raise your right hand up high over your head while saying, "I'm raising my right hand up high over my head." Now do it again and say it with even more conviction. Do it a third time with much confidence. Now say, "I'm raising my right hand up high over my head," with much conviction, but don't do it. Become aware of what is happening in your right arm. You may notice it feeling limp, confused, tingling, and wanting to move. You have told your body that you are raising your right hand up high over your head but are not allowing it to do so. Your body is Truth, and when there is no integrity—when what you say and do are not the same—an inertia and conflict will be the result. This is what you are feeling in your arm. So now, release the arm and raise it up high over your head.

This is the same inertia and conflict the body experiences any time we say one thing but do another. For example, after I gave birth to my daughter, the team of three doctors said they would support me in a VBAC for my next birth, but when I approached them, none came through for me. I quickly lost trust and faith in them. Another example is a woman who says to her child, "I promise I'll read you a story tonight," but then her mother calls on the phone, the conversation becomes long and involved, and in the meantime her child falls asleep. The woman has said one thing, but has not followed through on what she said. This sets up conflict in the body. Fortunately, children are understanding, and if this mother explains the next morning what happened and reads her the story that day, the child will be happy. Children are good at living in the present moment.

3. Has the component of curiosity

Curiosity is what motivates us to seek the truth of anything. It has led us to find out more about how the body works and functions. When pregnant, a woman is curious as to how she will feel as her abdomen grows and her body changes shape. In labor, she will be curious to experiment with different positions to see which ones feel more comfortable. At the moment of birth, she is incredibly curious to see what her baby looks like.

Curiosity has also led to the development of technology and drugs to help a woman "suffer" less in labor. This has all been done with good intentions, and many women are grateful. However, this has led to a biomedical model of care that suggests that it is by breaking things down into smaller and smaller parts that we can better understand the whole. Thus drugs and medical procedures have

been developed and refined with the goal of decreasing or eliminating pain in labor. In contrast, a systems philosophy represents a concept in which the whole is seen to be greater than the sum of its parts.

The systems approach believes that we cannot fully understand the interaction of the parts without awareness of the whole. In a systems way of thinking we might ask ourselves, "When pain is eliminated from labor, how does this affect hormonal production, and what longer-term effects might it have on caring for the baby in the primal period? A balance of both the biomedical and systems approaches are needed in birth.

4. Has a component called self-inquiry

Another component of truth is that of self-inquiry, which means seeking a deeper understanding into our own reality. Living in the world not knowing who we are is like wandering aimlessly through life without direction or guidance. When one inquires within, "Who am I?" and seeks the answer, it will serve as a guide that will give sustenance and inner guidance and direction throughout life for both birth and parenting.

5. Has vibration that resonates

Vibration is inherent in the bonds of all molecules and is responsible for anything that moves. Vibration is even present in that which appears unmoving. For example, vibration in molecules can be observed when magnifying a small section of a chair. Even in the chair, which appears solid to the naked eye, atoms are moving in response to vibration.

All sound is composed of vibration, and the louder the sound, the greater the vibration. The low, deep sounds a woman makes during contractions can help move the baby down into her pelvis. Vibration moves cells and substances through the body and distributes food to the organs and cells. The entire body works through the means of vibration, including the sperm swimming to unite with the ovum or egg. Thus the entire process of conception occurs due to vibration.

We can gain a clue into the mystery of conception from a spiritual teacher named Sathya Sai Baba, who explained how the principle of vibration causes a soul to enter the womb of a pregnant woman:

> *Till the child in the womb is four months and nine days old, the fetus is just a round mass of jelly. Then a force of vibration enters the embryo. Wherefrom does that vibration come? It is the life principle. From that moment on, the child in the womb starts moving. Simultaneously, this life principle enters the fetus. The combination of the two in the body is one of the secret doctrines of Vedanta. This process is treated as a human phenomenon. It is not something human. It is a divine manifestation.²*

When there is an idea that resonates within us, its vibrations are synchronous with each other. This was my experience when I first read about the idea of a soul entering the body through vibration. It also occurred to me that the first time women feel purposeful movement in their womb is at about sixteen weeks of gestation. Could it be that the purposeful movement only happens when the soul enters to take form? Sixteen weeks' gestation is the beginning of the second trimester; and it is a time of sudden change for the fetus, as it begins to experience rapid growth—doubling in length and quadrupling its weight from one to four ounces. Instead of staying curled up, its body begins to elongate. To hold its head up, the neck and back muscles develop, along with bones of the spine, rib cage, and shoulders. [3]

Every child (even twins) has a different personality from others. A mother can be heard saying, "They both grew in me under the same conditions, but I don't know how they can be so different!" I'm treating identical twins in physical therapy now. They are adorable redheads, and the only way I can tell them apart is by a freckle in the middle of one twin's forehead. One twin is clearly the tease, and the other is more serious. How is it that such different personalities can grow within the same woman? Though environment plays a role in terms of experiences, and genetics plays a role in regards to physical characteristics, within each of us is a "being-ness"—our soul—and though the form changes from youth to old age, the soul never changes.

So if you are pregnant and your dates are good, and if the idea of the soul entering the body of a pregnant woman at four months and nine days resonates within you, let that day be a very special one for you—keeping yourself happy and relaxed—for cosmically it may be of tremendous significance.

6. Naturalness

The idea that all women are born with the knowledge about how to give birth feels like a very natural idea. That which is natural is spiritual. Birth is a normal, natural, and spiritual event. Just the fact that a new soul is being born into the world makes it a spiritual event to be celebrated; I like to call it a spiritual birthday!

When I gave birth to my son in 1980, there was a high cesarean rate and low VBAC rate similar to today. After my daughter's birth by cesarean in 1978, I was looking for a doctor to support me in a VBAC for my second birth. I was living in Boston at the time, and Christianne Northrup, MD, had just graduated from her residency. She was the only doctor in the Boston area that I knew who would accept me as a VBAC client. Later, she published the popular book *Women's Bodies, Women's Wisdom*, and a quarterly newsletter entitled *Health Wisdom for Women*. In her newsletter she acknowledged the fact that the knowledge or wisdom about how to give birth is within every woman. She also wrote about why she believes in and recommends natural childbirth for women:

"Deep inside each of us is the wisdom we need to give birth. We are born with these instincts; they are part of our collective psyche. For ages, women have given birth with relatively few problems. Yet in recent times, we stopped believing in our own body's intelligence and turned to so-called pregnancy experts who rely on tests, machines, and surgical implements. As a result, modern obstetric practice is more invasive and more likely to lead to complications that will affect the health of the mother and her child, and even their relationship. Frankly, nothing is more important for a mother and baby than an optimal start in life."[4]

Dr. Northrup addresses the idea that when modern obstetrical practice is more invasive, it is more likely to lead to complications that will affect the health of the mother and her child and even their relationship. When something is invasive, it is no longer natural. Parenting consumes much energy and begins outside the body the moment the baby is born. It is easier for a woman if she is not recovering from medical interventions and/or surgery.

COMMUNICATING TRUTHS OF BIRTH

Words and tone of voice

In childbirth classes, the words chosen, the message given, and the tone of voice in which it is communicated all matter a great deal. Consider the two following scenarios where a childbirth education instructor is teaching a class.

Imagine birthing parents sitting in a childbirth class, and their instructor saying with sincerity and much warmth and caring: "You already know how to give birth. That is not something I need to teach you. This knowledge was born inside of you. Your body is amazing and is very wise. What I can do is help you to have more trust and faith in this body knowledge and encourage you to believe more in yourself. Then all you need to do in labor is 'let go' and follow your body, seeing it as your guide." The pregnant woman may then think to herself, *Oh, I already know how to give birth. My body is so wise. All I need to do is learn how to tune into myself so my body can do its work in labor and I'll follow its guidance.* This is empowering and builds confidence.

Compare this to an instructor who says to class participants, "Birth is one of the hardest things you will ever do in your life and all women need support in labor. In this modern day and age, there is no reason why women need to suffer in birth. I am going to teach you exactly what you need to do when the contractions become too strong and painful. Just tell the nurse/doctor when you need some help, and they can give you an epidural to take the pain away. And then when you are fully dilated, you'll be rested and they can stop the epidural so you can push your baby out." The message this pregnant woman receives in her psyche may sound like, *This sounds scary; but I don't have to feel the pain, so maybe I can get through it. I will need help. The contractions in labor will reach a point*

when I won't be able to handle them. But I don't have to suffer. I can have an epidural to take all the pain away and still push my baby out. That sounds good to me!

The seeds of doubt have been planted and lead to an increased chance of intervention in labor. This is not empowering. The woman feels low confidence in her body's natural ability to give birth, and believes she will need the help of medical procedures to birth her baby. Remember that all medical interventions have their own risks, and that during labor, one must constantly assess whether the risks of the interventions are greater than if they were not used. The presence of fear clouds truth and makes it harder for women to access their intuitive, instinctive side that already knows how to give birth.

Every birth is unique

Another truth is that since every woman is unique, she has and always will give birth in her own individual way. The idea of each woman finding her own unique way to give birth and not being dependent on a "method" needs to be taught in childbirth classes. When she is in her instinctive or primal brain, she will move her body as it prompts her to. To do this, she needs privacy, love, and a feeling of being safe.

In childbirth classes, we need to teach that there is not one right way to give birth. Relying on a "method" means that the woman will have to think about what to do. This stimulates her neocortex, with the effect of inhibiting labor. When she can gain access to her instinctive side by quieting her mind and going deep inside, the labor will progress the way it is supposed to for that particular baby. It is then that the woman can connect with her spirit to guide her through birth.

Women's bodies know how to birth

When women forget the truth that their bodies already know how to give birth, they become dependent on others to do it for them. Medical procedures may become necessary to help them through labor, and these all have risk-benefit ratios. Forgetting this truth leads to others delivering the woman's baby or babies, versus her feeling empowered and being in control of the experience herself. As a result, over the last few decades we have gradually strayed away from the normal and natural process of birth that nature has refined over thousands of years.

In this modern day there is still much we have to learn about the human body and how it functions. Any time we interfere with a natural process, I believe that we will sacrifice something. The problem is that we aren't quite sure what these consequences are at this time. For example, a random, controlled, and blind study explored the effects of the analgesic fentanyl on breastfeeding, and showed that women who received 150 ug fentanyl had a significantly lower breast-feeding success rate at six weeks postpartum as compared with women receiving less or no fentanyl.[5]

I believe that today we are straying too far from truth in birth, and that we are experiencing the consequences of general confusion, dissatisfaction, suffering, and disrespect. In other words, there

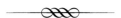
is a breakdown of human values, which means we are losing touch with the spirituality of birth. Rays of light and love emanate from us day and night. The happiness, bliss, and love that a new mother feels for her baby come from inside her. In the same way, the knowledge about how to give birth is already inside every woman. When thoughts are based on truth, they will be in tune with the belief that babies know how to be born and that women can have trust and faith in their bodies to do the job of birthing.

Though birth gives us an opportunity to experience happiness and even bliss for a short time, wouldn't it be nice to feel that way more often in life? The challenge is how to continue manifesting this delight on a more regular basis. A deeper understanding of our truth lies in going even more deeply into the body, understanding the role of the neocortex and the physiology of birth.

Birthing in the Spirit

My births were very spiritual and personal in nature. During my labors I felt an intense connection with the generations of women in my family before me. I opened myself to their knowledge and guidance—I felt their love, pride, and wisdom.

I also reached out to connect on a psychic level with all the women in the world who were laboring and birthing at the same time as myself. For those women who needed more strength, I shared some of my own.... Almost four years after the birth of my first baby, I met a remarkable woman and immediately connected and felt a bond with her. After talking for a while, we realized that both of our firstborn children were born on the same day... and at that moment she said to me, "You 'touched me' during my birth, didn't you!?"... Yes, I did!

—RACHEL SILBER CCE (BWI)

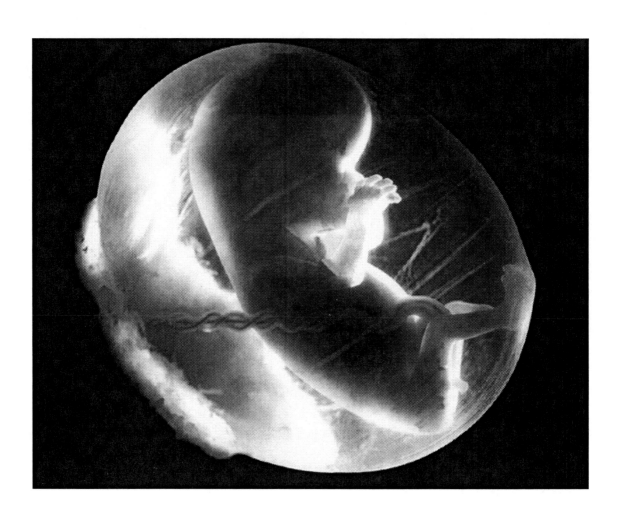

CHAPTER 9

Fetal Development and the Formative Years

Experience is the chief architect of the brain.
DR. BRUCE PERRY OF BAYLOR COLLEGE
OF MEDICINE IN HOUSTON, TX

DEVELOPMENT OF THE FETUS

It all begins with the love of two sexually mature bodies in intimate contact. A mature, healthy man produces about 300 million sperm cells a day, and the ejaculation force is strong enough to propel them halfway toward their goal with enough trail mix of rare, super-sweet sugar to fuel them the rest of the way.[1] As soon as one sperm penetrates the woman's egg in the fallopian tube (conception), the egg stiffens to repel all other sperm, and the fertilized egg becomes a zygote. The zygote contains all of the genetic information (DNA) necessary to become a child. Half of the genetic information comes from the mother's egg, and half from the father's sperm.

The zygote spends the next few days traveling down the fallopian tube and divides to form a ball of cells. Further cell division creates an inner group of cells with an outer shell. At this stage the zygote is called a "blastocyst." The inner group of cells will become the embryo, while the outer group of cells will become the membranes that nourish and protect it. Now molecules, cells, and organs "talk" to each other through feedback loops. The blastocyst measures less than one hundredth of an inch across—barely a visible dot.[2] It reaches the uterus at roughly the fifth day after conception. At this point in the mother's menstrual cycle, the endometrium, the lining of the uterus, has grown and is ready to support a fetus. The blastocyst adheres tightly to the endometrium and immediately implants into it on about day six after conception by boring itself into the maternal blood vessels of the uterine lining and rupturing them. The hemorrhaging uterine tissues respond by releasing a starch that becomes what is now called the embryo's first meal. At once the embryo gorges itself and

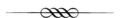

starts to grow at astonishing speed—doubling daily in size. Before the expectant mother knows she is pregnant, the basic relationship between mother and child is established."[3]

The cells of the embryo now multiply and begin to take on specific functions. This process is called "differentiation," which produces the varied cell types that make up a human being (such as blood cells, kidney cells, and nerve cells). In the first four weeks of gestation, the fetal cells have already folded in on themselves to begin development of a fluid-filled cylinder known as the neural tube, and the heart has begun its lifelong and tireless heartbeat. As the nerve circuitry is developing, the more repetitive the sensory input, the stronger the pathways of the nervous system.

During this time of rapid growth, the baby's main external features begin to form. It is during this critical period of differentiation (most of the first trimester) that the growing baby is most susceptible to damage from:

- Alcohol, certain prescription and recreational drugs, and other substances that can cause birth defects
- Infection (such as rubella or cytomegalovirus [CMV], a common virus that can be harmful to babies born to women who have a first-time CMV infection during pregnancy)
- Radiation from x-rays or radiation therapy
- Nutritional deficiencies

Just as the roots of a plant or tree grow into the ground, and just as blood vessels grow into the rich vascular tissue of the uterine lining to attach an embryo, so a web of wire-like fibers known as axons grow and transmit signals to dendrites, the tree-like extensions of a neuron, which receive them. Synapses form where the axon of one neuron beams signals to the dendrites of another. A creepy, crawly sprout, looking similar to an amoeba and called a "growth cone," comes equipped with the molecular equivalent of sonar and radar and it searches the surroundings for certain proteins. When axons make their first connections, the nerves begin to fire. The developing nervous system forms the equivalent of truck lines between the right neighborhoods in the right cities. Now it has to sort out which ones belong where.

Development of the baby's brain is a miracle in itself. At six weeks the brain already contains most of the nerve cells it will ever have, but the system of wiring them together in a meaningful way has not yet occurred. The brain has laid out the circuits it will need for such processes as vision, language, and so on. Vast sensory input will take this rough blueprint and gradually refine it.

By the seventh week, nerve cells in the brain have begun to touch via projecting molecules. Some start to form primitive pathways. The rate of production is stunning: 100,000 new cells a minute. At birth, the brain will consist of about 10 million densely entwined nerve cells—some 100 billion cellular units in all. It has been estimated that all two billion of the specific nerve cells that make any individual educable are located in the outer covering of the brain, its cortex, and that these two billion cells could be stored in a thimble.[4] There are also about one trillion glial cells, named after the Greek word for "glue," that form a honeycombed shape around neurons to protect and nourish them.

In the first year of the baby's life, its brain will produce trillions more connections than it will ever use, and gradually the brain will eliminate those connections or synapses that are seldom or never used. Neurons responsible for vision disappear within nine days after birth if not used. If a child is born with a cataract, it needs to be removed immediately because if the clouded lens remains, the brain's visual centers will not receive the sensory stimulus of light hitting the retina of the eye, which helps it to maintain its connection. The expression "If you don't use it, you lose it" seems to be especially true in fetal and newborn brain development.

As the fetus moves toward the second trimester, there is an explosion of activity and growth as all the organ systems and limbs develop further. It is a miracle to behold what started out as an egg with dividing cells turning into a human being. An overview of the progression of these changes can be seen in Diagram 8 (see Appendix).

INFLUENCE OF SENSORY STIMULATION ON FETAL
AND INFANT BRAIN DEVELOPMENT

The first experiences in life are the most powerful and have long-lasting effects on brain development. The brain is the organ of behavior, feelings and emotions, intelligence, and creativity. Advances in science have determined that sensory stimulation is necessary for normal brain development. A fetus begins having experiences while in the womb through hearing its mother's voice, tasting its own sweet amniotic fluid, sucking its thumb, and having hiccups! It feels the woman's stress and her joy, and these sensory experiences are encoded in the developing brain, laying down patterns for peace or violence. Such sensory stimulation can be viewed as "nutrients" for the brain. The experiences based on sensory input lead to the development of beliefs that determine if the world is a safe or unsafe place. Fetuses at seven months' gestation are believed to have the ability for such thoughts, and beliefs and behaviors of a child into early childhood and adulthood are influenced by these early experiences.

A child's full potential is dependent on good brain structure. Good brain structure is the result not only of good nutrition but also of basic trust, physical affection, and intimacy with the mother and father. These are the foundations upon which our individual human potential is based. The imprinting of experiences on the brain instinctively teaches it to either trust or to guard and become defensive as a survival mechanism. At the slightest threat, a child's heart begins to race, stress hormones surge, and his brain anxiously tracks the nonverbal cues that might signal the next attack. Such early experiences form a kind of template around which later development is organized. Emotional deprivation early in life has been found to have a similar effect.[5]

As synaptic connections that are useful become reinforced with experiences during the postpartum period and on into childhood, the child becomes a product of his or her environment. The brain develops in sequence, with more primitive structures stabilizing their connections first. When sensory stimulation that is so necessary for brain development is negative or lacking, there is

an actual physiological response where brain cells either do not develop or develop with malformed cells, and brain abnormalities can result.[6] For example, brain wave patterns of infants with depressed mothers were studied,[7] and their brains showed markedly reduced activity in the left frontal lobe, a center of the brain associated with joy and happiness. The children were followed, and at the age of three continued to show abnormally low readings. However, not all children with depressed mothers showed low readings, and further study found that it was the emotional tone of the exchanges between the mother and child that mattered. Mothers who were irritable, impatient, or disengaged had babies with sad brains, whereas mothers who were able to rise above their depression while interacting with their infants in playful games had infants with happier brains.

WINDOWS OF OPPORTUNITY IN THE BRAIN

It seems the brain becomes less malleable as it grows older, with the child being less able to rebound from early life trauma. This has led scientists to believe that there are certain sensitive and critical periods, or "windows," when the brain requires certain types of input to create or stabilize certain long-lasting structures. "There is a time scale to brain development, and the most important year is the first," notes Frank Newman, president of the Education Commission of the States.[7] He goes on to say that by the age of three, a child who has been neglected or abused for years may be unable to fully recover. This concept of "windows of opportunity" is seen in zebra finches, where the window for acquiring the appropriate song opens twenty-five to thirty days after hatching and shuts down some fifty days later. Odent holds the same theory, believing there are periods of sensitive growth in fetal organs, which is why he is writing and educating consumers and caregivers in birth about the importance of the primal period.

A window of opportunity for learning is seen in the ability to learn a second language, which seems to be highest between birth and age six. After that, it can be learned, but perhaps not as easily. Yale University neuroscientist Dr. Pasko Rakic says that the overproduction of synaptic connections seen early in life increases the ranges of possibilities in the brain; but later, as the brain perceives certain connections unnecessary, it loses them, and this leads to patterns in the brain.[8]

It has been found that by the age of ten, humans reach a peak between synapse creation and atrophy. After ten years of age or so, the brain preserves those connections or synapses that it perceives to be important in that person's life. By age eighteen, pathways that have been nurtured are ready to blossom. Though pathways for learning continue to develop over one's lifetime, the ease of mastering new skills or recovering from setbacks will not be the same.

Sensory stimulation is so essential to the developing brain that children who are not stimulated and rarely touched develop brains that are 20 to 30 percent smaller than what is considered normal for their age.[9] In experiments with rats at the University of Illinois at Urbana-Champaign, those given the opportunity to play with toys were found to have 25 percent more synapses per neuron than those that didn't.[10] Parents should be educated about the importance of interacting joyfully

with their babies both before and after they are born, and this should be a part of good childbirth education.

Imagine the explosion of sensory stimulation a baby receives when it first opens its eyes after birth. It uses all its senses of seeing, hearing, smelling, touching, and tasting. A newborn held in its mother's arms is able to see eight to twelve inches clearly, just the right distance to see its mother's smiling face. It now associates her smiling face with her loving words, uses smell to find her breast, and regulates its temperature when lying on her soft skin. This sensory stimulation sets in motion more neuronal circuits that make connections in the developing brain. This is a very special time for the infant's sensitive brain structure, and we must all work to make it a gentle, loving, and positive experience.

An important way to help the baby at the moment of birth is to delay the cutting of its umbilical cord.[11] When the baby takes its first breath, the pulmonary musculature must be supported with an infusion of blood. Waiting about six minutes until the cord stops pulsing ensures additional blood supply to the baby, increasing oxygen through higher hemoglobin-carrying potential, and providing blood rich in nutrients such as iron, which is crucial for neurological development and vitamins. The cord blood also has stem cells that maintain health by fighting off free-radical formation that can lead to growth of tumors.

Instinctively, as soon as their babies are born, parents begin to talk a language they never studied, that of "Parentese." They put their faces closer to their infants and "sing" their words in short utterances that have exaggerated, vowel-rich sounds. "Ahhh, pretty ba…by…big eyes. I love you, yes I do. You are so smart! Strong too…squeezing my fingers, soooo strong. Long fingers! And someday you'll say your ABCs—A, B, C, D, E, F, G. Gooo, gooo, goooo, the world is waiting for you.… Bababababa, lalalala, I love you, yes I do!" The heart rate of the infant increases in response to this stimulation, and this is regardless of the language or gibberish that is spoken.

Speaking Parentese seems to increase the speed at which the infants connect words to objects. For example, Stanford psychologist Anne Fernald found that twelve-month-olds directed their eyes to the correct picture more frequently when spoken to in this way than when the instruction was delivered in normal English.[12]

By the age of two, a child's brain contains twice as many synapses and consumes twice as much energy compared to an adult brain. The microscopic connections between nerve fibers reach their highest average densities (15,000 synapses per neuron) by the age of two and remain at that level until the age of ten.

Primal Health Research and the primal period

Michel Odent, MD, founded the Primal Health Research Center in London to study the long-term consequences of early exposures and experiences during the primal period (conception through the first year of life). He believes that our health is shaped in the womb and during infancy and that the effects carry over to our adult life. Therefore, we must be especially careful how we treat the fetus

during pregnancy and neonates at birth. Visit www.birthworks.org for a link to Odent's databank with more than 600 studies worldwide, including abstracts and summaries of articles on primal health research.

The primal period represents one of the most impressionable time periods of our lives because the earlier the experience the more impact it has on our emotional and physical development. Odent is concerned about factors affecting babies during pregnancy, how babies are being born, and what effects these may have in their lives as adults. He believes that disturbances from severe bouts of stress, depression, malnutrition, or infection during the time of sensitive growth periods in fetal organ development affect the health of the baby on into adulthood. His research is showing that such diseases seem to span all fields of medicine.

Primal Health Research is studying everything from autism to dyslexia and obesity to criminal behaviors. Of interest to me is the fact that a number of these studies are showing correlations with birth regarding three major issues of great concern prevalent in our society today: drug addiction, violence, and obesity. These and other studies are showing us that it is crucial how we treat babies during the primal period.

The growing concern of how babies are treated in the primal period and the connection to health in later life as an adult is brought out in such studies as one carried out on 300,000 men born during the famine in Ireland from 1944 to 1945. This study established a correlation between the risk of obesity in adulthood and starvation in fetal life and the neonatal period. The incidence of obesity was greater if deprivation occurred in the first half of gestational life. It was reasoned that early on, the fetus learned to store food as a means of survival, and that this carried over into adult life.[13]

Another study is one conducted by Jacobson and Nyberg involving drug addiction in 200 opiate addicts born in Stockholm from 1945 to 1966. In this study it was found that mothers who received analgesic pain-relieving drugs during labor had children statistically at risk of becoming drug addicted in adolescence.[14]

Other questions such as, "What will the future be for a generation of children born under the influence of an epidural?" do not yet have answers, but evidence is mounting that there are adverse effects on the mother-baby relationship, and that these are greater than originally thought.

During the primal period, pregnant women need to eat healthy foods low in sugars and saturated fats, and avoid trans fats. They need to keep stress levels low, exercise, and sleep well. In addition, Odent advocates two practices for pregnant women: eating fish from the cold seas to give the fetal brain preformed, long chain omega-3 polyunsaturated (DHA) fatty acids necessary for its survival;[15] and keeping a pregnant woman happy so she will produce hormones such as oxytocin, known as the hormone of love. Thus he advocates that women should be taking good care of themselves both emotionally and physically long before they become pregnant.

Still another way to ensure a healthy baby is to find ways to keep the mother and baby in close contact with each other during the hours after birth, even if there are complications. The two are

already very connected, and a mother's touch and love can profoundly affect her baby during this sensitive time.

Mirror neurons

The mysteries of the brain continue to be unraveled in such discoveries of what are called "mirror neurons." Just as circuits of neurons are believed to store memories in the brain, so it is believed that mirror neurons encode templates of actions that are observed by the person.[16] An example of mirror neurons at work is when a newborn looks intently into the face of its mother and studies her tongue moving in and out of her mouth. Soon, the newborn will also do the same. Thus, the action of one person activates the motor pathways in another person's brain. That person then understands viscerally what the first is doing because of the mirror mechanism that allows him to experience it in his own mind. I believe our mirror neurons are active all our lives.

Mirror neurons seem to be lacking or ineffective in children with autism, as a classic behavior is their inability to imitate the behaviors of other children and having decreased eye gaze. From direct observation and twenty years of experience working in pediatrics with handicapped children, I know that I am treating a higher number of children with sensory issues and also those in the autistic or Pervasive Developmental Disorder (PDD) spectrum than ever before. Forty years ago it was estimated that the true incidence of autism was 4 in 10,000, but today it is 30 to 60 per 10,000. Environmental factors cannot be ruled out, and it is possible the increase is from a broader diagnostic concept of autism,[17] but I believe there is more at stake and have a hunch that exposing the delicate fetal brain to drugs and an electronic environment at birth is a factor that needs to be explored.

Reaction, reflection, resounding

When we experience fear, it is projected onto us from the external world, which in turn projects it internally onto our cells. Reversing this process, we can see that whatever we project from ourselves is projected out into the external world. When someone says something positive, a positive resounding reaction is reflected back. When there is a negative comment, there is a negative resounding that is reflected back to that individual. All is reflection, reaction, and resounding. When we are afraid, we shut down with a powerful protection response. As long as the mind is afraid, we will experience fear in the external world. Herein lies the value of working to see good in the world, for then it is good that will be reflected back to us.

In the primal period and formative years, the brain is highly malleable and still developing. Its biography actually becomes its biology, meaning that what it receives via sensory input is directly impacting its body physiology. In practical terms, these principles translate into the importance of treating infants in the primal period with love, compassion, and kindness. For adults, it means never indulging in talk that hurts others, because ultimately it is reflected back and hurts us.

TREATING INFANTS WITH RESPECT

The eyes of a newborn are wondrous and mysterious. It is as if they "talk" with their eyes. David Chamberlain, PhD, writes, "Observations indicate that babies demonstrate human traits, learn from both traumatic and pleasurable experience, may communicate telepathically, and possess spiritual powers unrelated to their age."[18] Research continues to reveal that a fetus is able to use its senses well, reacts to its environment in the womb, expresses its feelings, and is aware of both love and danger. It is able to do all of this by way of its hormones. Birthing parents and health professionals need to be aware of how sensitive the newborn is to all of its first experiences, and to treat the newborn with love and respect. When its first sight of the world outside the womb is one of quiet, dim lights, and handling is minimized, the baby will move into a quiet but alert state of consciousness, taking in all the sensory experiences. Its first experience will be that of warmth, kindness, love, and safety.

Because it is so important to keep a positive and loving environment for babies and young children, we must all work hard to watch our words and stay heart-centered, for this has a direct impact on fetal brain development. We must work to find ways not to separate babies from their mothers at birth unless absolutely necessary. We must provide better childbirth education to birthing parents so they understand the possible effects of obstetrical drugs and medical procedures on the fetus and work instead to provide safer alternatives. We must provide an atmosphere that feels safe and is full of love, for love is what really matters in fetal and newborn brain development and on into the formative years.

Birthing in the Spirit

At one point I remember saying to my sister, "I just gotta get it out!" and that's when your head was born. She helped your shoulders emerge, and then the rest of your body was born into your Daddy's waiting arms. It's so hard to describe the physical sensation of the moment when your baby makes an exit from your body. It's like a cork popping or a dam bursting. It's so intense, and for a second you feel as if you're falling. I remember yelling out, "Oh, God!" as you went shooting out of my body, and the intensity was actually startling as you catapulted into the world. I was so glad, for you and Daddy, that his loving hands were the ones to catch you and bring you up out of the water into the morning air. It was 8:58 when you took your first breath. At this point your brother had taken off his clothes and was in the Jacuzzi with us. There we were, a new family of four. It was lovely.

—HEATHER STEWART

The Physiology of Birth

The greatest challenge with this birth was in keeping
my new brain out of the way of my old brain.
The physical part took care of itself.

CALLIE FOULK, CCE IN TRAINING WITH BWI

Within the human body are mysteries we cannot begin to comprehend, and its intricacies are beyond our imagination. Take, for example, the ion channels that exist in every cell of the human body. These proteins are necessary for establishing the resting membrane potential and allow for a diversity of cellular functions with a remarkable specificity. For example, a unique set of amino acid residues lying within the sodium and potassium channel pores create an energetic environment that only allows an ion with a specific set of properties to pass through. The body continually relies on such extraordinary specificity for its normal function. Within a woman's body is all the information that knows how to conceive, grow, and birth a baby. It does this instinctively through such physiology as the ion channels, and what is instinctive does not have to be taught.

We are learning that birth hormones play both mechanical and behavioral roles. For example, the body's natural opiates, endorphins, help a woman in labor to cope with contractions and also dilate a baby's eyes—both mechanical roles—but they also help to establish bonding and attachment between the mother and baby—a behavioral role. Understanding more about body physiology that is responsible for all these actions becomes more and more fascinating as new research continues to uncover the mysteries of the human body.

Research in birth physiology is already having a deep impact on the way women are giving birth, regardless of whether it is in a hospital, at home, or in a birthing center. For example, as we learn more about the role of the neocortex, we understand the importance of decreasing its stimulation while a woman is in labor by dimming lights and providing pools of warm water in which to labor. I believe that as birth practitioners and birthing parents gain a better understanding of the physiology of birth and pregnancy through primal health research, birthing practices will change dramatically.

In this chapter I will discuss the key roles that various hormones in a woman's body play during

pregnancy and birth. The hormones of oxytocin, prolactin, prostaglandins, endorphins, and adrenaline all work together with many other hormones to make birth possible. I like to call them "the birth hormones," although they play other roles outside of birth as well. I will also describe how stimulation of the neocortex inhibits labor and what it means physiologically to feel safe. Included also are sections on epidural and spinal anesthesia, synthetic oxytocin called Pitocin, and the blood-oxygen dissociation curve and its relationship with oxygen supplementation.

OXYTOCIN

The hormone oxytocin has always been important in birth but is growing in importance in the eyes of researchers as its behavioral and physical properties are better understood. It plays a large role not only in the baby's development but also in our very existence throughout our lives. Dr. Kerstin Uvnas Moberg in her book *The Oxytocin Factor*, writes, "Oxytocin is with us throughout our lives. When you were born, oxytocin helped expel you from your mother's womb and then made it possible for her to nurse you. As a small child, you enjoyed your mother's and father's loving touch because it released oxytocin in your body. As an adult, you experience the effects of oxytocin when you enjoy good food, or a massage, or an intimate interlude with your romantic partner. Oxytocin is active in all these situations, and more."[1] She goes on to say that oxytocin is part of a coordinated, modulating system that works through the bloodstream and through many nerve branches that link to important control areas of the brain. It influences and is influenced by other classic neurotransmitters such as serotonin, dopamine, and noradrenaline.[2]

Oxytocin is secreted by the posterior pituitary gland of the hypothalamus. It circulates through two separate pathways—the bloodstream and the nervous system. It is one of the hormones responsible for our ability to experience calmness and relaxation in the body. Without its presence, we would be in a constant state of anxiety and stress. Its levels are higher in nursing women, and it is well known that breastfeeding is most successful when a mother is calm and relaxed.

Oxytocin is normally produced in a pulsatile way by the posterior pituitary gland in response to stimulation; for example, by the baby's hands on its mother's breast when suckling. These oxytocin pulses help stimulate the ejection of milk and also dilate blood vessels in the mother's chest, providing warmth for the baby. However, women who have given birth by cesarean average fewer oxytocin pulses when breastfeeding in the first two to three days after birth as compared to non-cesarean mothers. It is well known that cesarean mothers tend to have more difficulty breastfeeding, and it is believed that this is due in part to a reduction in oxytocin levels.[3]

One of oxytocin's behavioral properties is that of love. Oxytocin is called the hormone of love because it is present wherever there are experiences of intimacy, such as in birth, breastfeeding, sexual relations, and even gathering around a family meal. The connection between oxytocin and the feelings of love has been shown in many studies. When virgin female rats were treated in advance with the hormone estrogen and then injected with oxytocin, they began to exhibit maternal

behavior.[4] Increased interest in oxytocin led to the publishing of a 500-page book in 1992 on the behavioral effects of oxytocin by the New York Academy of Sciences.[5]

Both the baby and the mother produce increasing amounts of oxytocin from the moment of conception. At the time of birth, oxytocin levels are at their peak if there have been no medical interventions, and birth becomes a moment where mother love is literally meeting baby love. Moberg emphasizes that the peak levels of oxytocin are even higher in the hour after birth than when in labor.[6] This is an important reason to keep mothers and babies together immediately after birth, as it is a peak time for breastfeeding, bonding, and attachment.

Oxytocin stimulates the production of prolactin, a hormone produced by the frontal lobe of the hypothalamus and whose role is to increase milk production. As such, it is called the "mothering" hormone. It reduces sexual desire and the ability to conceive, which is why many breastfeeding women have less interest in engaging in sexual activity, much to the dismay of their husbands or significant others.

As a mother holds her baby close to her, together they experience intimacy with skin-to-skin contact. Since oxytocin and prolactin are present in breast milk, the baby is actually drinking "love." Have you ever observed a baby's face who has fallen asleep after breastfeeding? She has literally been drinking "love," and this can be seen as an expression of bliss. Birth and breastfeeding are truly expressions of love.

There is still another amazing wonder of the human body and the interaction between a mother breastfeeding her baby. I used to wonder how my babies could get enough nutrition from my breast milk. My daughter outright refused any solid foods until she was over twelve months old, yet she was growing fine. Now, many years later, I understand how it happened. Nature has devised an amazing system to ensure maximum nutrition from a mother's breast milk. When an infant suckles, the mother's breast fills its mouth and the pressure of the nipple on the inside of the infant's mouth causes an outpouring of nineteen different gastrointestinal hormones in both the mother and the infant, including cholecystokinin and gastrin, which stimulate growth of the baby's and mother's intestinal villi, increasing the surface area and absorption of nutrients with each feeding.[7] We can only imagine what other physiological processes may be happening about which we are as yet unaware.

Oxytocin's mechanical roles include helping sperm to move towards the woman's egg and helping the embryo move down the fallopian tubes. The fetus begins producing oxytocin in the first weeks of its development—which is essential, since oxytocin also stimulates the pituitary's release of growth hormone—and adrenocorticotropic hormone (ACTH), which directs the production of the stress hormone cortisol by the adrenal gland. When a nursing baby sucks its mother's breast, the amount of oxytocin released in the mother is about the same as during orgasm.[8]

In his book *The Scientification of Love*, Odent discusses the presence of receptors for oxytocin on the uterus, which also seem to play a role in birth.[9] An increased sensitivity to oxytocin is required to initiate birth, and this sensitivity is regulated by binding sites on the uterus. In this way, the mother

and the placenta work together to start labor. But more than oxytocin is required. The uterine muscles need to be stretched taut when the baby reaches a certain size. These stretch receptors also send signals for labor to begin. I imagine that oxytocin must play such a large role in fetal development, and on into our adult lives, because it is the hormone of love and our natural essence is that of love.

PROSTAGLANDINS

Enzymatic proteins also play a role in birth by dissolving the collagen fibers of the cervix, helping them to stretch and open for birth. Chemicals called prostaglandins are produced in part by the placenta. They help to soften the cervix in a process called effacement. The pressure of the baby's head on the cervix stimulates the increased release of the prostaglandins and—*Voila!*—labor begins.[10]

Some women are completely effaced before labor contractions begin, and others, like myself, worked through the night to achieve complete effacement. This interconnecting sequence of events is like a dance between the mother and baby, working closely together for the baby to be born. Signals from the pulling of muscles and pressure on tissue are like switches for hormonal releases that know exactly what to do for labor to begin.

Oxytocin is more easily released when there is a feeling of safety and love since it is the hormone that calms us. Thus, words spoken softly, sweetly, and with love have direct physiological effects on the body. On an energetic level, feeling safe helps us to feel relaxed, and this is crucial for a woman in labor. Midwife Ina May Gaskin says, "I have never noticed anyone's cervix remain tight and unyielding while speaking loving and positive words."[11] She goes on to say that sphincters of the body that need to open for birth, and which are under the body's involuntary control, are influenced and affected by emotions and function best in an atmosphere that is calm and relaxed.[12] Walking in nature or taking a warm bath do wonders for increasing the release of oxytocin.

ENDORPHINS

During labor, the body produces its own pain relief by secreting endorphins, which are the body's natural opiates. Endorphins are morphine-like substances that help a woman in labor cope with strong contractions. Just as the drug morphine has characteristics of producing dependency and attachment and can become addictive, so the body's natural endorphins create powerful feelings of bonding and attachment between the mother and baby. This is enhanced by endorphins' behavioral role of dilating the baby's eyes so it can see its mother more clearly right after birth.

Thus birth hormones play a key role in bonding and attachment, and in nurturing and fostering feelings of love between the mother and baby. The process provides the foundation for a relationship that will last throughout their lifetimes. Interfering with the natural process that is the foundation

for a mother's relationship with her infant and child is perilous and should only be disturbed if there are clear and immediate benefits for the mother and infant.

I am concerned about the fact that, according to the *Listening to Mothers II* survey[13], 76 percent of 1,573 women polled in 2005 had an epidural or spinal anesthesia. This means that they were numb below the waist and couldn't feel contractions or anything happening below the waist. When we lose feeling, we also lose learning and interfere with a sacred process that has been part of the experience of mothers for thousands of years.

ADRENALINE

Adrenaline is known as the main stress hormone and has beneficial and detrimental effects depending on the situation. It can effectively help prepare a person for an exam or race, or help a person run to safety—situations for which it was intended to serve; but its presence in early labor—a situation for which it wasn't intended—interferes with a woman's ability to establish labor. Odent states, "Any situation likely to trigger a release of hormones of the adrenaline family also tends to stimulate the neocortex and to inhibit the birth process as a result. This means that a laboring woman first needs to feel secure."[14] The most important consideration for the birth team in labor is, "How can we help the laboring woman to feel safe and calm so that her production of adrenaline in early labor remains low?"

Odent goes on to describe a paradoxical effect of adrenaline, in that there is a rush of it in the minutes preceding birth.[15] This also makes sense; the body needs to expend a large amount of energy to actually birth the baby, and adrenaline helps this process. A woman in labor can know that her body is producing more adrenaline at the very end of labor by its symptoms of making her feel thirsty for water and wanting to clutch something with her hands. A woman who is feeling her labor can feel excited when she has the symptoms of the adrenaline rush, because it means it is nearly time for her baby to be born.

EPIDURAL AND SPINAL ANESTHESIA

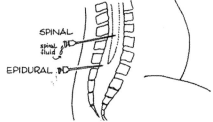

EPIDURAL AND SPINAL ANESTHESIA

The epidural space lies inside the spinal canal and just outside the dural sac that contains the cerebrospinal fluid and the spinal cord. An epidural is administered in either a side-lying or sitting hunched position, with a hollow needle inserted into the lumbar area of the woman's spine. A catheter of plastic tubing is threaded through the needle. The needle is removed and the tubing is taped in place. A combination of anesthetic and narcotic pain relievers is administered through the catheter. The woman is given an IV of normal saline solution to maintain pressure in her peripheral vessels, and Pitocin is often, but not always, administered to keep her uterus contracting.

Once a woman has received an epidural, she can no longer walk, and thus she is confined to a hospital bed. "Walking" epidurals that combine lower doses of narcotic analgesics with an anesthetic, but without complete sensory or motor blocks, have not proven to be practical for walking because of safety issues and are slowly going out of use. It is the amount of anesthetic, not the narcotic analgesic, that affects a woman's ability to walk.

With an IV, fluids and also anything she is drinking now fill her bladder. The anal sphincter becomes flaccid, losing its muscle tone during epidural anesthesia, and the mother's ability to perceive bladder fullness is likely to be decreased, making it necessary for her to be monitored or catheterized. If she is not moving around and emptying her bladder frequently enough, the full bladder (which sits on top of the uterus) can actually impede descent of the baby.

If a woman is having a contraction during insertion of the needle, or if the needle inadvertently goes too deep, it punctures the dural sac and a spinal anesthesia results instead of an epidural. The anesthetic now mixes with the freely flowing cerebrospinal fluid (CSF), which moves up around the brain and down around the spinal cord. It is not uncommon for this to happen, and if the anesthetic reaches the respiratory centers, the woman will need to be intubated and placed on a respirator until the anesthesia wears off.

Any time the dural sac is punctured, there is a risk of developing what is called a spinal headache. These headaches are typically severe, and incapacitate a woman to the point where she cannot tolerate a standing position and is confined to a back-lying position for days after the birth. During this time, her ability to care for her newborn baby is very limited. The incidence of a spinal headache is directly related to the size of the needle used. Larger needles leave bigger holes, creating greater pressure changes in the CSF, which are believed to cause the headaches. A smaller needle has less risk but is harder to push through all the body tissues to reach the dura. A blood patch can be performed to literally "patch" the hole, but it does not always work the first time.

An epidural is not always successful on the first try and repeated attempts may be necessary, which further interfere with the woman's labor. When it does take effect, the numbing can often be patchy so that she feels contractions on one side of her body but not the other. A woman said, "I thought if I had the epidural I wouldn't feel anything!" when she was continuing to feel contractions on one side of her body. Women usually feel cold and clammy with the epidural and complain of their inability to move their legs.

It is not uncommon for the mother to develop a fever when she has an epidural, and that means a full hospital work-up of tests and procedures for the baby at the time of birth to make sure there is no infection present. This means there will likely be separation of the mother and baby at birth. Other complications of an epidural or spinal include 20 percent of women experiencing long-term backache and intravenous line points of insertion being painful for several days after they are removed. Because hormones are affected by anesthesia, an epidural or spinal also affects the process of breastfeeding.

If the epidural interferes too much with normal descent of the baby, a cesarean may become

necessary. After a cesarean, women receive pain medications that alter their state of consciousness. Infection of the incision is common. They will have postsurgical abdominal distension and gas that can feel very uncomfortable, and there will be incision pain—which is increased by coughing, laughing, and holding their newborn baby—usually requiring narcotic pain medications. Women who think they are avoiding pain from birth by getting an epidural or having a cesarean need to be informed about what the full recovery period entails.

Epidural theory

It is important to realize that the body is a live, thinking, conscious organism. For example, there is a blood brain "barrier"—more like a sieve—that is composed of tightly packed cells in the blood vessels of the brain that prevents some substances from leaking into the brain tissue. This is the body's way of protecting the brain from dangerous toxins. The theory is that when an epidural is administered, there is a sequence of physiological events that interfere with normal hormone behaviors. With epidural anesthesia, Pitocin is usually given to the mother to keep the uterus contracting. Thus the body senses it doesn't need to produce as much oxytocin, and so less is released by the posterior pituitary gland in the hypothalamus of the brain. In addition, because the lower half of the body is numb, the body doesn't feel a need to produce endorphins. We now have a situation where there is a decrease in both oxytocin and endorphins, which, according to their behavioral properties, may affect the degree to which the mother is able to love and bond with her baby at birth and also the clarity of the baby's vision.

A balanced perspective is important, and there are positive uses for an epidural or spinal anesthesia. An epidural is useful for the purpose of pain relief in labor for a woman who cannot relax or who is exhausted from a very long labor. It provides continual anesthesia, and the catheter can be withdrawn at the end of labor so a woman has sensation and can actively birth her baby. Both epidurals and spinals help a woman to be awake during a cesarean so she can see her baby in the first moments of birth.

We live in a day and age when medical procedures can make some births safer. However, because we don't yet have a complete understanding of the human body and its physiology, it makes sense to allow the body to labor and birth without interventions unless medically necessary.

PITOCIN

Synthetic oxytocin is called Pitocin. Oxytocin has the behavioral property of love, whereas Pitocin does not, even though it has the same molecular formula. When an epidural anesthesia is administered, Pitocin is often administered intravenously to further stimulate uterine contractions.

Normally, the uterine muscle has its own cycle of contracting and relaxing, squeezing blood away from the uterus during a contraction and then replenishing itself with blood and nutrients during relaxation. When Pitocin is administered, it no longer allows the normal rest time in between

contractions, so the uterus can't fully replenish its blood supply between contractions. If the strength of Pitocin is too great, the uterus can be affected to the point where there may be such a short time of rest in between contractions that the uterus finds itself contracting in quick succession, never being able to fully rest and empty and replenish its blood supply. This leads to a condition called uterine inertia, where the muscle stays in a perpetual contraction, not being able to fully contract or relax.

Most women who have had Pitocin administered during labor will talk about the "Pit contractions" as being one of the most difficult experiences of their births. It is often administered in labor without a woman's knowledge. This is illegal, as informed consent is legally required before the administration of medication or to perform medical procedures in non-emergency situations.

My friend Carol, who recently had a baby, said this: "I was about six centimeters dilated when the doctor gave me Pitocin without telling me. All of a sudden the contractions became very strong and I couldn't rest in between. They took hold and overpowered my body. I knew this wasn't natural but there was nothing I could do. I started to pass out. My birth ended up in a cesarean, not the way I had intended it to be."

Muscle Fatigue Exercise

There is an exercise I do in classes to demonstrate the concept of uterine inertia. Holding a woman's elbow with one hand, and her hand in my other hand, I tell her to bend her arm, bringing her hand up to touch her. As she does so, I apply resistance in the other direction. I maintain this resistance for an extended period of time until she finds herself weakening, unable to sustain the contraction. Such is the case with the uterine muscle that is not given enough chance to rest in between contractions due to the administration of Pitocin. Over a period of time, it simply loses its ability to contract, and medical intervention becomes necessary.

Oxygen masks and the blood-oxygen dissociation curve

What do we think when we see someone wearing an oxygen mask? Probably that it is an emergency and they are having trouble breathing, or are very ill. Here it is important to understand the principles of hemoglobin—which carries oxygen in the blood—and the blood-oxygen dissociation curve.

Our normal partial pressure of oxygen is at least 97mmHg. This means the hemoglobin, which carries oxygen to the body, is completely saturated. A good way to understand this concept is to imagine holding an eight-ounce glass of water, mixing a tablespoon of sugar into it. The sugar will dissolve into the water so you can't see it. Now what if you add another tablespoon, and then another, and another? At some point, no more sugar will be able to be dissolved into the water, and some sugar will settle to the bottom of the glass. The water has become supersaturated and simply cannot hold more sugar.

This is the same principle as the blood-oxygen dissociation curve. Diagram 9 of the blood-oxygen dissociation curve shows us that the partial pressure of oxygen has to go down to 60mmHg for there to be any significant change in the oxygen received by the body.[16] Most women in labor are healthy and have a normal PO2. A person with a PO2 of 60mmHg is likely to be in an intensive care unit. With a normal PO2, hemoglobin cannot carry any more oxygen, so it is pointless for a woman to wear an oxygen mask in labor if she has a normal PO2.

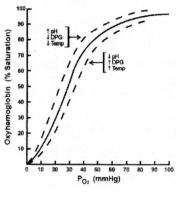

THE BLOOD-OXYGEN
DISSOCIATION CURVE

However, Marshal Klaus, MD, states: "If the baby is truly in distress, there is a chance of less than 1 percent of some oxygen getting to it through a complex interconnecting system of arterioles, capillaries, and arteries in the rich, fertile uterus and placenta."[17] Most of the time that I have seen women in labor wearing an oxygen mask, they have been healthy with normal PO2s, and their babies were fine. Midwives have asked me why the fetal heart tones begin to pick up after putting an oxygen mask on a woman. I ask them what the woman in labor was doing just before they gave her the oxygen mask. They realize they changed her position and most likely that took pressure off the fetus, affecting its fetal heart tones. Physiology simply does not allow more oxygen to reach the baby (except as described by Klaus) if the mother's hemoglobin is completely saturated.

NEOCORTEX

Animals like to give birth in small, dark corners where there is intimacy. It is well known that women giving birth naturally like to go into labor more at night than during the day, as dim lights or candlelight and darkness encourage intimacy. The knowledge about how to give birth is in the primal brain; and intimacy, privacy, and quiet are the environmental modifications that facilitate access to this "old" part of the brain. In such conditions, the neocortex or "new" brain is quiet, making access to the primal brain easier. Oxytocin levels are higher too.

The neocortex is the outermost layer of the new brain from an evolutionary point of view. It is associated with learning that which is new, and also with rational, analytical thoughts. It is active when stimulated with questions, music, rational language, and new skills. This is in contrast to the old or primal brain, which governs instincts. The neocortex is so well developed in humans that it tends to overcontrol and even repress activity of the primal brain. Maybe this is why it is difficult for women in labor to move beyond their thinking brain into the primal space. The neocortex is not as developed in animals, which is why they are able to give birth more instinctively.

The neocortex plays an important role in labor. The basic principle is that when the neocortex is stimulated, it becomes an inhibitor, a brake for labor.[18] When the neocortex is stimulated, a woman in labor has more difficulty going deep inside herself to access her primitive brain that already knows how to give birth. We need to think more about how to not stimulate a laboring woman's

neocortex so that she can find her way into her instinctive brain. The first question the birth team must ask themselves is, "How can we help to keep the woman's neocortex quiet in labor?"

What stimulates the neocortex? Odent believes the primary consideration for any birth practitioner should be finding ways *not to disturb* the labor of a pregnant woman. Ways to stimulate the neocortex and thus disturb progress of a woman in labor are having bright lights, a lack of privacy, and talking too much, asking rational, analytical questions.[19,20] Learning how these affect a woman's physiology and her ability to birth are important for anyone attending women in labor, and for birthing parents themselves. This information should be a part of every childbirth education class.

(1) Dim the lights!

An EEG (electroencephalogram) shows that bright lights stimulate the neocortex. In a birthing room, therefore, the lights should be dim. In daily life, the presence or absence of light is an important stimulus for waking and sleeping. In Alaska and other locations near the Artic Circle, people stay up late as the sky remains light. On a visit there, I saw children playing at a playground even though it was midnight; but the sky was light, stimulating them to stay awake. The Alaskans told me they look forward to winter, when the days are shorter and it gets dark earlier, so they can get some sleep!

Many people find it hard to go to sleep with light on in the room and resort to wearing eye blinders. Animals are affected by light too. Cows are known to head home during a total eclipse of the sun, even though it is the middle of the day. Keeping lights dim helps to quiet the neocortex. This helps a woman in labor to go to an inner world as if *beyond mind* to access the primitive and instinctive knowledge that already knows how to give birth.

Most animals like to give birth in small, dark places where there are no bright lights. Humans are no different. It is well known that maternity floors in hospitals used to be busier in the night than the day, when more women were birthing normally. The era of inductions and planned cesarean sections has changed this.

(2) Privacy

Privacy means not feeling observed. Privacy is a strategy to keep the neocortex quiet so labor can progress well. What does it look like when a woman does not have privacy? She is surrounded by people who are looking at her while she is having contractions, and she is aware of the fact that they are looking at her. Midwives know that the more people who are with a woman in labor, the longer the labor tends to be.

An invasion of privacy can be felt in prenatal visits.

> *"I was sent to a little cubicle where I was told to take off all my clothes and put on a hospital gown. I could hear what the doctor was saying to the woman in the next room. I could hear him putting on his gloves, and could hear her gasp as he stuck them into her vagina and then*

withdrew them. I felt clammy. Now it was my turn. I was told to lie down, and then I saw intern doctors gathering around the table. I didn't know they would be there, and nobody asked my permission. Too shocked, I didn't say anything. My legs were wide apart and they were staring into my perineum."

Another woman described this invasion of privacy during her labor:

"The doctor was teaching interns, and they came with him into the room during my labor. He performed vaginal exams to see how dilated my cervix was. My contractions were pretty intense. The lights were bright, and I was trying to be a good patient and so didn't complain, but it hurt. But I felt helpless and so even joked about it. After my birth, my thoughts kept coming back to the feeling of invasion of his hands inside me. I thought, How could I have let him do that to me with the interns watching?"

There are a number of other ways that women can lose a sense of privacy at their births. Video cameras recording the birth can result in a woman feeling conscious of how she looks or what she sounds like. She is working hard and perhaps wants to take her clothes off, but is aware that the camera is "watching" her. The electronic fetal monitor also draws attention away from the laboring woman, as it beeps and constantly reminds her that her every contraction is being recorded and watched. Privacy is an invitation for relaxation—the optimal performance of the hormones of loving and caring—and a feeling of safety. It is an open door for accessing the spirit.

Animals give birth instinctively, without even thinking about which position to assume. Nobody makes an animal lie on its back to give birth! They like to give birth in privacy and in small, dark places, especially at night. Small, dimly lit corners or spaces help create a feeling of intimacy. My sister has a horse ranch in California. A mare was to give birth. They were watching her closely through the night, but she managed to give birth just in the short time they were not there. Cats will find dark corners for privacy.

Humans like intimate, small spaces too. Take, for example, the story of a woman who covered her large living room floor to protect the carpet when giving birth, but where did she end up giving birth? Right in the far, back corner where the floor wasn't covered!

(3) Avoid analytical questions

Another way to stimulate the neocortex is to ask analytical or rational questions. In birth today, we are very good at stimulating the neocortex of a woman in labor by asking questions like, "What is your Social Security number?" or "When do you want to get into the shower?" "Do you feel a contraction starting now?" In the midst of contractions, women are often asked, "Would you please sign this consent form for your epidural?" Those on the birth team may be talking with each other

about what they did last night, their plans for the day, foods they ate, friends they have in common while walking with a woman who is working through contractions. This is very distracting for any woman while working through contractions. Doulas with good intentions, or family and friends at the birth, may ask too many times, "Is this contraction stronger than the others?" "Do you want to stay in this position, or change?"

Looking at the clock, a laboring woman measures her dilation of the cervix by the hour. To prevent neocortical stimulation and give a sense of timelessness, a cloth can be placed over the clock to avoid linear thinking. Neocortical stimulation must be avoided as much as possible for a woman in labor to be able to focus inward and make contact with her primitive brain.

THE IMPORTANCE OF SILENCE

Silence is golden; it is precious. Much energy is expended when talking too much. The art of silence means choosing words wisely and saying only that which is truly necessary. In labor, this can empower women and help to decrease neocortical stimulation. There are five rules that can serve as a guide. Before speaking, it is good to ask yourself, "Of what I am about to say:

Is it true?

Is it kind?

Is it necessary?

Will it harm anyone?

Will it improve upon the silence?"

A member of the birth team may have something to say that is true and kind, but it might not be absolutely necessary when considering the concept of keeping the neocortex of a laboring woman as quiet as possible. Birth team members need to resist the temptation to talk more than they need to. The more quiet and steady the mind, the better a laboring woman can hear her inner voice guiding her from within. If her doctor, doula, midwife, or partner/husband can do the same, all in the birth team will connect on an energetic level that requires few spoken words.

VOCALIZATION (SOUND)

Though it is good to limit normal conversation, making sounds with labor contractions is a natural feeling that gives them a "voice" of expression. Words such as "Ahhhhhh," "Ommmm," or "Maammmaaaa," are commonly heard.

In labor, relaxation does not mean silence. It is good for a woman in labor to make sounds through the contractions. The more she can make sounds with her contractions, the better she will be able to relax in between them. I have women practice hearing themselves in childbirth classes by placing their hands on their chest and saying "Ahhhhhhhhhh" as they exhale. They can feel the vibration of

their sound moving with their air and practice breathing these vibrations all the way *down* into their pelvises. This can help them feel familiar with vocalizing contractions during labor. Making low, deep, sustained sounds is called toning. Toning means making open, sustained sounds that emerge from deep within the body and fill it with vibration.

Vocalizing in labor can become stronger in a crescendo as the contractions peak, and then softer in a decrescendo as the contractions fade. Toning words that have vowel-consonant combinations, such as down, out, come, open, or "aum," are very powerful. Group toning or vocalization is often carried out in traditional societies by women of the village as a way to give strength to the woman in labor as she rides the contractions up and down like waves. I have seen a woman's husband or significant other tone with her through contractions and it is beautiful.

Eyes

Other environmental stimuli include visual and/or tactile input from those accompanying the woman. When labor contractions are long and strong, simply looking into the eyes of her doula or her loved one is all that is needed. Eyes can communicate nonverbally and powerfully. They can *say*, "I love you," "You are beautiful," "You can do it," "You are strong," or "Everything is fine." Eye gaze can help a woman in labor focus and not lose concentration during the peak of a difficult contraction. Words of love have a calming effect physiologically because they stimulate the production of oxytocin.

Combining eye gazing with breathing is very effective. A significant other, doula, midwife, or friend who models long, slow deep breaths can lower the breathing rate of a laboring woman who is fearful of the next contraction, helping her to relax. We learned how to mirror or imitate facial expressions as a baby and haven't forgotten how to do this as adults. As the woman sees a long, slow, deep breath, she will instinctively try to do the same.

Hands

Touch is another excellent form of nonverbal communication. Your hands are very special. Here is a beautiful exercise you can do just now.

Hand Exercises

1. ***Hand stories:*** Open your hands up in front of you with the palms up. What do you see? What stories do your hands tell? See if you can remember the things that your hands have done. Have they loved? Have they hated? Have they helped others? Have they hurt others? What would you like to tell your hands? How can they serve a woman in labor? When you are ready, take a moment to reflect on all these things. Hands only carry out what you tell them to do. Work to ensure that they do only good things.

2. ***Energy field:*** You can feel the energy field that is around your body by holding your hands upright about one inch apart from each other. Closing your eyes helps to eliminate visual distraction so you can feel it better. Keep your hands in that position for several minutes and see if you start to feel a tingling sensation. This is energy radiating out from your hands. Now bend your fingers as if they are holding an imaginary ball. You will feel a "thickening" feeling between your hands. Open your hands a little more and then bring them back closer together. In this way you can feel your "ball" of energy getting larger and smaller. If you hold them there long enough, you may even be able to feel your hands pass through each other to the other side. Your hands are full of energy, and that energy is love when your awareness is in your heart. Take a moment to reflect on your amazing hands. Remember each day to treat them with respect so they can always be kind.

Hands are important because they touch. Touch is one of the most powerful sources of input to the calm and connection system within us all. When awareness is in the heart, touch expresses love. This is a principle behind Reiki, a special type of massage. When people are massaged, they begin to develop trust in the person massaging them. They start to talk about how they are feeling, how their life is going, and problems they are having. If a woman in labor feels like being massaged, it can enhance her trust in that person, and help her to feel more safe and relaxed in stressful situations.

Concentration and learning are improved when there is a peaceful environment and nurturing relationships. During labor, many women feel good when receiving deep massage on their lower back, shoulders, and especially their feet. Slow, light touching over the abdomen often feels good. When strong and hard contractions are coming in quick succession towards the end of labor, holding the woman firmly can help her to feel safe. Other women may not want to be touched, and those attending them at birth need to respect their wishes. A woman who initially does not want to feel touched in labor, perhaps due to sexual trauma, may begin accepting massage first to the feet. She may accept it on other parts of her body as well when it feels safe.

Premature babies who are allowed to have extensive skin contact with their mothers thrive better. They need to be held, snuggled, feel their mother's warmth, and be stroked gently on their skin. Because their lives may be in jeopardy, their mothers are praying for their well-being. A prayer from a mother's heart is extremely powerful. The love of a mother for her child is unlike that of any other.

Hands should be warm and relaxed while touching. Massage oils, especially if scented, are not necessary for women in labor and are not advisable because they can confuse the newborn baby's delicate sense of smell for its mother on first contact.

Keeping these key concepts in mind, intention and awareness at birth has a new focus. With an understanding of the key role the neocortex plays in birth, birthing parents and the birth team would do well to plan ahead, even educating those who will be at the birth about the importance of such things as dim lights, ensuring privacy, and putting into practice the art of silence.

It is also helpful that the room in which a woman gives birth has a familiar feeling. Our own bedrooms are typically not spotless and clean. They usually have a few clothes lying around, articles or books resting on a chair or shelf, and pictures that feel pleasing to look at. If a woman decides to birth in a birthing center or hospital, it is helpful to take such items with her that will make the room feel more familiar, such as a picture, her nightgown, and even her own sheets.

FINDING A SAFE BIRTH PLACE

A woman will labor the best wherever she feels the safest and most secure. Feeling safe helps us to relax. When we are relaxed, we tap into our calm and connection system and oxytocin levels are higher. The question for a pregnant woman then becomes, "Where do I feel safe?" or "What makes me feel safe?" A safe birth multi-sensory visualization helps to give her insights into places where she feels safe, and she can then determine if that is a place where she would like to birth a baby. Sometimes women discover that the place they feel safe is not the place where they were planning to give birth, and they decide to make changes in their birth plans. It is a woman's decision, and she must determine this for herself. Wherever she feels safe is where her hormones will best be able to do the work they know how to do.

Another good use of the safe birth visualization is to help birthing women feel safe in the birthing room of a hospital or Alternative Birthing Center (ABC) if that is where they have decided to go. Doing a short, safe birth visualization in their minds while on a tour serves the purpose of connecting energetically to the place in which they will be birthing. Many women report feeling a sense of belonging when they actually go there in labor.

The beauty of the safe birth visualization is that once a safe place has been determined, it can be accessed at any time, as in Janet's story:

"I planned to have a home VBAC, but since my blood pressure began to rise, my midwife decided we should go to the hospital. Once there, the nurses began attaching an electronic fetal monitor to me, which I didn't want. My husband didn't say anything; we were so caught up in the transition from home to hospital and the safety of our baby. It was only when my midwife mentioned, "I thought you didn't want the fetal monitor," that we realized what was happening and requested that it be removed after one initial reading. Now, there was a lot of activity as they set up the IV; taking my blood pressure, bringing equipment into the room. I thought I was going to lose my ability to focus on the contractions, as there was too much chaos around me. Then I remembered how calming the safe birth visualization was that we did in Birth Works® classes. So I closed my eyes and went to my safe place. It didn't matter that I was in the hospital. I could bring my safe place to me anytime I wanted to. I went deep inside and labored while in my safe place, and regained the focus I needed to work with my labor. I had a successful VBAC and a beautiful daughter."

An interesting addendum to this birth is that during the childbirth classes, Janet's husband only attended the first of the ten-class series. In that one class, all he wanted to know were the statistics of any studies on VBAC that I could show him. Patiently, I went over them one by one after the class. These studies showed the safety of VBAC as opposed to planned repeat cesareans. Months after the class, I received a call with a male voice on the phone. He said, "I don't know if you remember me. I was the one who came to only one class and asked for all the statistics. Well, I just want you to know what a difference these classes have made in our lives and in our relationship, and I just want to thank you."

Helping a woman to feel safe in labor impacts her entire birth, especially on a physiological basis. Safety leads to relaxation, lower pulse rate, greater ability to open her mind and body for birth, less fear, and more effective dilation of the cervix.

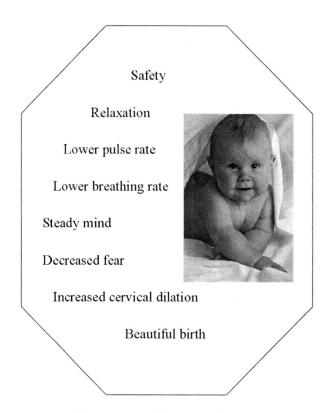

Safety

Relaxation

Lower pulse rate

Lower breathing rate

Steady mind

Decreased fear

Increased cervical dilation

Beautiful birth

PHYSIOLOGICAL EFFECTS OF SAFETY

A SAFE BIRTH VISUALIZATION

Here is a safe birth visualization you may find useful in your own births.

When you are ready, allow yourself to take a moment just to sit back…and close…your eyes, breathing out any thoughts and worries of the day, just allowing your mind to begin to relax. The slower your breath…the more relaxed your body can be. See if you can imagine a chalkboard with all the words of your mind on it. Slowly…erase them so the mind can become quiet to just be. Feel your mind becoming…more quiet with each breath, letting your body go…just a little more. How good it feels to "let…go." We all deserve a time to rest…during the day. Just now, allow the mind to drift like clouds in the sky…letting daydreams be in your awareness. I wonder if somethingcomes to mind…a place where you feel safe and secure, where you can let go completely. See if you can allow your thoughts now to drift back in time, like turning back the pages of the book of your life.…Full of memories…allowing the mind to be playful, exploring very early memories…going back, maybe even memories before you knew words. Now I wonder if a place comes to your awareness where you feel very safe. Perhaps a vacation place, recent or long ago from your childhood. Wherever it is, feel free to go there now…taking your time.…And as you do so, be curious to see if your breathing is slowing down. People relax when they are in safe places. Allow yourself to take in the sights, sounds, and smells of this place.…Feel free to adjust anything that needs adjusting. When everything is exactly the way you want it to be, determine if there is anyone else you wish to be with you in this safe place…anyone who helps make you feel safe and secure so you can just let…go…while in your safe place. Sense who is appearing, if anyone…again, taking your time. Now, see if this is a place where you would feel safe birthing a child into the world. If so, imagine in your mind's eye, doing so just now, feeling contractions, however long they need to be. Allow yourself to move into any positions that feel good, letting go to birth in whatever time is needed, with only those around you who help you to feel safe and secure…breathing into…the experience as long as you need to. It feels good to be in a safe place, and this is a place where you can go, anytime you need to.

Birthing in the Spirit

I had a homebirth with my only child. My waters broke early on the day I went into labor. When labor started, I easily slipped into my own world and wasn't always aware of what was going on in the house. I was only dimly aware that people were nearby, but was much more aware of the rhythmic sensations in my body. That all changed briefly, however, when my husband and the midwife began to talk about who should pick up my friend. They mentioned the time, how long it would take to get to the airport and back, and how far along I was. They were talking

very quietly to the side, but just their talking about numbers and time frames broke into the place where I had been. My labor slowed down and I was very distracted by their talk. The whole thing must have lasted about thirty seconds but seemed a lot longer; and once the decision had been made, I quickly resumed labor and went into "my place" again. Looking back now at that event, I marvel at how strong and forceful are the hormones that set up the dance of labor and delivery, and yet how fragile they are—being so easily disrupted by just the mention of numbers and times.

—LEE WALD CCE (BWI)

CHAPTER 11

UNDERSTANDING THE SELF:
The Five Human Sheaths

Most people are about as happy as they make up their minds to be.

ABRAHAM LINCOLN

To access the instinctive, primal, "old" brain that already knows how to give birth, a woman must go deep within herself. To do this, it is helpful for her to become more familiar with what is inside her body. A human being is more than just a body—we have a mind, a heart, and a number of other dimensions or aspects of our being. I will describe these as "sheaths," and they are, from the outermost to the innermost, the food (physical body) sheath, the vital air sheath, the mind (mental) sheath, the intelligence sheath, and the bliss sheath. As we journey from the outermost food sheath, going deeply inward to the innermost bliss sheath, it becomes more mysterious but also more wondrous. Each sheath plays an important part in the process of childbirth.

It is for this reason that I have written a chapter on the topic of deepening our understanding of ourselves through learning about the five human sheaths.[1] The more we are in awe and wonder at the miracle of our own body, the more likely we are to surrender to its wisdom. Becoming familiar with that which is within us is of immense value, especially for a woman in labor; for that which is familiar to us feels safer, and she will feel more comfortable going within herself to connect with her spirit to give birth. Preparation for birthing in the spirit needs to start long before conception or labor by becoming familiar with ourselves and the human sheaths.

Did you know that the body has about ten gallons of water, one gallon of lime, enough calcium carbonate for 9,000 pencils, enough phosphorous to make 11,000 matches, and enough iron to

make a nail two inches long? These are all components of the body, but scientists don't know how to make a human body out of artificial means regardless of technological advances. How these all work and function in the body remains mostly a mystery.

There are three aspects to the sheaths of the body: gross, subtle, and causal. Progressing inward, each subsequent sheath becomes subtler than the preceding one. The outermost sheath is "gross," the next three are "subtle," and the innermost sheath is "causal." To understand these concepts, there is an analogy with waking and sleeping. When awake, we are aware of the "gross" body, meaning our physical form. While in the dream state, we are not aware of the physical form, but we use the three "subtle" sheaths of vital airs, mind, and intelligence. In the deep sleep state, the mind disappears and we experience the "causal" bliss state, going on to awaken very refreshed and blissful. This is why the dreamless state is the most restful state, because neither the body nor the mind are active.

To truly know ourselves, the journey of life is to travel from the outermost food sheath, which is the body, to the innermost and most subtle sheath, that of bliss. The food/physical and vital air sheaths are the outermost sheaths and enable us to follow material pursuits and pleasures. Thus they are the ones with which we are the most familiar, and are responsible for our actions. These first two sheaths require a physical body, and when the body passes, it again becomes part of the earth. The other three sheaths—mind, intellect, and bliss—continue to exist even without the physical body because they are not dependent on form for their existence.

FOOD SHEATH (PHYSICAL BODY)

We are most familiar with our outermost food sheath, the physical body, because it can be seen; but it is just a small part of who we really are. The physical body is composed of muscles, bones, organs, lymph, nerves, more than 7,000 miles of blood vessels, and more cells than there are stars in the Milky Way. These all have form and so can be seen, even if only through a microscope.

The food sheath is the outermost sheath and is composed of the food that we eat. Literally, the body is composed of food from the earth. A baby grows in the womb of its mother and develops its food sheath from the food she eats. After birth, the baby's body continues to grow and is sustained by food from the earth. Plants of the earth can only grow with sunshine, water, and soil, so these are present in the food we eat. We cannot grow a plant in the palm of our hand, even if we give it water and sun. The soil is necessary for it to grow. So the cycle is from the soil, to food, to man. As we eat, so we become. The closer food is eaten to its source in the food chain, the more life force it will contain. The life force gives us energy to do our work of the day, and also for women to birth a baby.

The food sheath is perishable, and upon our passing, decomposes—returning to the earth. While alive, we need to keep this food sheath, our physical body, in good health by eating foods that bring us vitality and strength. Good examples of these foods are beans, nuts, and plants that grow out of the soil and directly receive the sun's rays.

VITAL AIR SHEATH

The next innermost sheath is the vital air sheath, which is the first of the three subtle bodies of which we are composed. It gives energy to the body, senses, and mind and thus acts as a link between the body (gross) and mind (subtle). The physical body cannot survive without the vital air sheath. Vibrations from the vital air sheath are what keep the body alive and pervade the entire physical body, providing a motivating force. Without breath, there cannot be life.

Chi (pronounced "*qi*") is a fundamental concept in Chinese culture. It is described as spiritual energy, life force, energy flow, or simply breath. The Chinese believe that the body has natural patterns of *chi* that circulate in channels called meridians and that if these are blocked for some reason, disease is the result. The concept of a life- energy inherent in all living beings appears in many cultures and religious traditions. The Japanese refer to life force as "*ki*" and tap into its power in martial arts, as do the Koreans and Chinese. In India it is called "*prana*" and to Wilhelm Reich, father of orgone, *chi* or life force energy.

Reich believed that traumatic experiences block the natural flow of life-energy in the body, leading to physical and mental disease. The spiritual teacher Sathya Sai Baba says that an individual's life force resides like a lightning flash in the womb of a blue cloud between the ninth and twelfth rings of the spinal column.[2] I wonder what that means for a woman receiving an epidural or spinal? One thing is sure: when there is no life force, there is no life, so it must be present to enable us to live.

If we were to ask the human brain if it would rather be functioning in a random, disorganized state or a harmonious fashion, it would surely choose the latter. When the mind is at peace, the vibrations are steady and bring peace to the body. When the mind is in turmoil, the vibrations increase, causing discontent and worry along with higher pulse rates and heartbeats. How can anyone help someone to relax if they themselves are anxious?

To help someone relax, we ourselves must be relaxed. This is a phenomenon called entrainment. Entrainment occurs when vibrations are synchronous, in harmony, with each other. We can observe this by observing the effects of entrainment in certain behaviors. For example, fireflies that settle on a bush will, after awhile, all start blinking on and off in unison with each other. This is called rhythm entrainment.[3] Women in a dorm will all start menstruating around the same time.

The desire for harmony and resonance can be observed when two violins are tuned. When the string of one violin is plucked, the same string on the other violin lying on the table starts to hum on its own. There is a sympathetic resonance between the two![4] In the same way, a woman in labor will feel the energy around her and become one with it.

Imagine a doula or midwife at a birth. If either of them is anxious and worried, the woman in labor will sense this and also become anxious and worried because she is very vulnerable to the energy around her. If a childbirth educator believes that all women know how to give birth, he or she will convey this to the class participants. Because they feel her energy when they are in close proximity with each other, they start to absorb it into their own psyches. As we think, so we become. This is a

good reason for pregnant women and their significant others to choose childbirth education classes that teach these concepts.

Feeling at peace relaxes the entire body and preserves energy. A body at peace generally has four to six breaths a minute. Some yogis are able to slow their breath down to as low as one to two breaths a minute. Here is a little experiment.

CONNECTION OF THOUGHTS AND PULSE EXERCISE

Take your own pulse rate and record the number. A normal pulse at rest is anywhere from 60 to 100 beats per minute depending on the age and what kind of shape the person is in. Now focus your awareness on a time you can remember when you were very worried and anxious about something. Play it out in your mind, remembering as much detail as possible. Now take your pulse again. See if it is higher than your normal pulse. If so, you will realize how much extra work your body is doing at that moment just by thinking about that time.

Now take a deep breath and steady your mind. Even after about five deep breaths, you will feel a difference in your body. You may also experience a deeper sense of clarity and a lower pulse. This exercise is even more striking if you know what your resting pulse is over a fifteen-second period and then remember to check your pulse at a time when you are truly feeling stressed.

The phenomenon of "white coat hypertension" is well known in medical circles. This occurs when one's blood pressure taken in a doctor's office is higher than when it is taken in the familiar setting of home. Just as breathing responds to the state of the mind, so does blood pressure. A woman in labor who is able to breathe slowly and deeply, even through very strong contractions—welcoming each one and surrendering to each one—will have more effective dilation of her cervix since tension and anxiety are not hindering the process.

MIND (MENTAL) SHEATH

The next innermost sheath is that of the mind (mental) sheath. We talk freely about having a mind, but aren't sure exactly what it is because it has no definite shape or form. We associate thoughts with the mind and the mind with the brain. We know there is electrical activity in the brain, and chemicals that send messages to neurons through synapses, but still the mind remains largely a mystery. The mind has no boundaries. We can close our eyes and imagine ourselves halfway around the world while sitting in our own bedrooms! Some think the mind is in the brain, while others view the whole body as a thinking mind. Still, we know that a mind out of control has no peace and everything is in pieces. It is the steady mind that has peace and equanimity.

The mind serves as our instrument through which we contact nature and gather information about things. It controls and directs the senses. How we use our minds determines the state of our emotional and physical health. This is why so many people pray for peace of mind. In pregnancy,

due to hormonal changes, women are more prone to mood changes of weeping, laughing, worrying, depression, or elation. Men need to be prepared that their wives will experience these emotions and understand the root cause, not taking it personally. During these times, if men can remember to breathe slowly and deeply and keep steady minds, they will be a source of comfort and love to their wives or partners.

In the same way that water has no shape of its own and assumes the shape of the container in which it is kept, so the mind takes the "shape," being easily stirred up by the external or internal environment in which it operates, making impressions on the inner senses. The way to cure this agitation is positive thinking. Engaging in positive thoughts and action is the way to a calm and peaceful mind. A woman who has practiced steadying the mind will find pregnancy, labor, and delivery a smoother process with less worry and greater clarity of vision.

INTELLIGENCE SHEATH

The intelligence sheath is subtler than the mind sheath. This very subtle sheath is the state that can be reached when we feel at one with all humankind. In other words, this sheath is universal and is able to perceive the unity in diversity, or the one as many. For example, human beings come in different sizes, shapes, colors, and races, and speak different languages, but they all experience emotions such as happiness, sadness, joy, and sorrow. All religions of the world teach us to treat others as we would wish to be treated ourselves. This means never doing or saying something to another that you wouldn't do or say to yourself.

Similarly, all women are different in their personalities, belief systems, and are from various cultural backgrounds, but all carry the potential to give birth. This is the sheath that helps a laboring woman to connect with all other women who have given birth before her. During labor she can derive great strength from the thought, *If all women before me have given birth, I can do it too.* Such a connection can give her courage to continue working through contractions, especially when they become long and difficult.

No matter how many times a woman gives birth, each birth experience will be unique. Each baby that is born is being born for the first time and will never be born again. Therefore, it is not helpful for a woman to compare her birth with that of others, or even for her own children. Looking for unity in diversity means acknowledging the different ways in which women around the world give birth, but sensing a common bond with all women who feel joy when seeing their baby for the first time—and also relief that labor is over.

BLISS SHEATH

Once the intelligence sheath is reached, the bliss sheath will be automatic. The bliss sheath is the causal aspect of the body because it goes beyond form. Even as you are reading this book right now,

I'm sure you can remember a moment of bliss in your life. It is a moment of pure love. When there is an experience of bliss, time stands still. The moment goes beyond form, and so awareness of form at that moment is gone.

At the moment of bliss, there is sheer joy that goes beyond what we have ever known. It feels so wonderful that we want it to last forever. The peak of orgasm, a mother looking into a baby's eyes for the first time, viewing a sunrise or spectacular scene in nature, or having an out-of-body experience are all examples of times when the bliss sheath is accessed. I was visiting the Grand Canyon and we hiked into the canyon from the north side. As we approached, the sun was setting, but there was a rain cloud over part of the canyon, and a full rainbow with all its colors could be seen. Everyone present was focused on the sheer beauty that filled us with awe and wonder and took us beyond form in those moments, directly to our bliss sheath. A woman who looks into her baby's eyes for the first time sheds tears of joy, forgetting all the work and fatigue of labor. She is beyond form at that moment and in her bliss sheath.

MIND, BODY, SPIRIT

It is the mystery of our existence to learn how to live simultaneously in the three realms of body (gross), mind (mental), and spirit (causal). We are so dependent on our senses to collect information, and satisfied with the more temporary pleasurable experiences of the world, that vast regions of our inner consciousness remain ignored.

Being in a form ourselves, it is important to realize that the human sheaths are all very active in every aspect of our lives and that the spirit is an indweller of the body that gives life force to all. So long as we continue to seek joy only in the external and objective pleasures, we will be unable to reach our innermost sheaths where the treasure of bliss lies waiting. It is a treasure worth working for. It is my belief that when the mind, body, and spirit are in balance, not only will we be happier and more content human beings, grateful for our very existence, but also that birth will become a more sacred and powerful experience.

Birthing in the Spirit

Last night I had a dream. I dreamed I was pregnant... again. That is not so unusual except for the fact that I am nearly fifty years old and had my tubes tied fifteen years ago. I have had five children, all born by cesarean. That is the reason I became a midwife, doula trainer, and childbirth educator; I felt my experience in birth was not good and the spirit of my births was stolen from me. I felt a mission and commitment to help other women to find their individual birth strength through support and information. I awoke feeling the same thing I have felt when

a child ent ... *and dancing. At this point*
in my life ... *. However, I appreciate the*
spirit of l

RD CCE (BWI), CD (DONA)

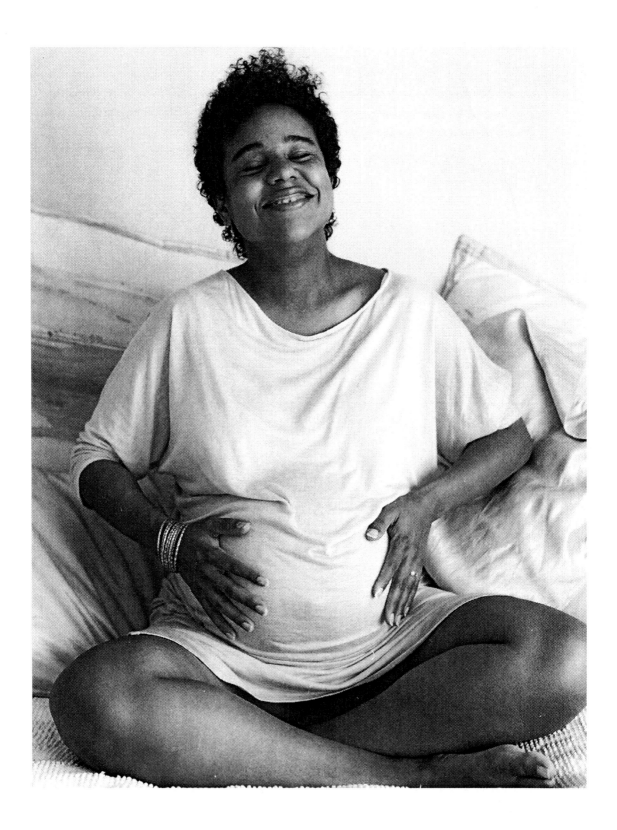

CHAPTER 12

THE POWER WITHIN:
Positive Thinking

Our deepest fear is not that we are inadequate.
Our deepest fear is that we are powerful beyond measure.
It is our Light, not our Darkness, that most frightens us.

NELSON MANDELA QUOTING MARIANNE WILLIAMSON
(*A RETURN TO LOVE: REFLECTIONS ON THE PRINCIPLES OF A COURSE IN MIRACLES*)
IN HIS 1994 INAUGURAL ADDRESS

Everything that exists in the universe is composed of atoms with subparticles of protons, electrons, and neutrons that travel at lightning speeds around each other with tremendous energy. In fact, the universe is one giant field of pulsating energy. Nature is full of this energy. Flowers spring from plants, trees burst forth with leaves, birds fly and build nests to birth their young, and squirrels jump from tree to tree and up and down tree trunks. The sun pours continual energy out into our Milky Way galaxy and thus on the earth. Rivers flow relentlessly to the ocean. All around us there is an abundance of energy. This energy has within it atomic power that is immensely powerful. There is no place that it is not, and it is freely moving.

The human body is no exception and has the potential for manifesting this same energy. Subatomic particles that make up our body are really vibrations of the larger pulsating field of energy. A human embryo initially looks like a sprouting kidney bean, as seen in *From Conception to Birth* by Alexander Tsiaras; and by the time it is born, energy has transformed it into what we recognize as a human being.[1]

THE POWER WITHIN

Experience is life's best teacher, which is why we learn by doing. Women giving birth are very lucky. They are...*very*...lucky! The human body is full of atomic power in every cell, but there are few times in life that we are able to experience the magnitude of this power. Labor and birth is one such experience.

There is atomic power in every contraction. Women have been given the gift of being able to feel a fraction of the atomic energy within them in the form of powerful contractions. A woman who experiences such contractions will tell you, "It was as if my body took over—there was no going back and no fighting it. I had to surrender to it." We are more powerful than our greatest imagination. Remembering this, a woman can work with her body through any contraction.

The purpose of this chapter is to inspire pregnant women about the tremendous value and learning that comes with feeling strong contractions in labor. In today's world many women are fearful of labor contractions and resort to obstetrical drugs and medical procedures so they don't have to feel them. But in so doing, they lose the opportunity of experiencing their own power within. Feeling this power is what makes a woman say, "If I can do this, I can do anything!" Feeling the power within is empowering and lays the foundation for the work of parenting.

Food of the earth is infused with the pulsating field of energy. As the physical body is composed of food from the earth, it has this same energy within it. A pregnant woman brings this energy to her fetus, thereby developing its physical form via a beautiful, intertwining system of two arteries and one vein in the umbilical cord. Nature even provided for two vessels in which to bring food to the baby, and one vessel for elimination, to ensure that the baby receives plenty of nourishment.

As a baby grows in a pregnant woman, the flow of energy helps internal organs to adjust and make room for the growing baby. The power from this energy allows a few simple dividing cells to develop into sophisticated organs for sight, hearing, smelling, digestion, and elimination, along with arms, legs, and a central nervous system. It does all of this without the woman even having to think about it and without having to be told what to do. This flow of energy is instinctive and its actions do not need to be learned.

When labor advances, women who feel this amazing power within are initially fearful of it—they are afraid to "feel" themselves. With the encouragement from a positive birth team, a woman will have the courage to feel a part of herself she never felt before. When the atmosphere remains safe, she is free to let go and can more easily surrender to the power of birth. Most women in labor come to the point where they think, *I don't think I can do this anymore,* but those with a desire to birth naturally say, "But I must and I can!" It is a moment of complete surrender to the power from within, and trust and faith in the process of birth.

Women who can relate to contractions as manifestations of the power of the universe are filled with wonder at their own human body. A woman said, "At the height of a very strong contraction, I felt the heavens open, pouring light and love on me." Another said, "Time stood still as this amazing power took over my body. I was in wonder and awe of it and knew I had to relax into the contraction to help my body do its work. It was a moment of peace and total surrender that filled me with a sense that God was taking care of me and that all was well." In the film *Birth Day* by Sage Femme, Inc., Naoli Vinaver Lopez—the midwife giving birth—describes this power by saying, "It felt like the sunshine was bursting out of my belly."[2]

At such moments in labor, the mind can utilize the presence of the power within to a woman's

advantage. A doula can constantly reframe the contraction in a positive way and help the laboring woman to keep her focus on the positive. For example, she can say, "The stronger the contractions, the sooner your baby will be born!" The laboring woman wants her baby to be born, and if stronger contractions will help her to do this, she may face them with more courage and determination. Instead of running away from the contractions, she may be encouraged to welcome them as a means to an end.

At this moment of complete surrender, she can focus on relaxing into the contraction, breathing slowly and deeply, opening her hands, and visualizing the power of the contraction of her uterine muscles doing their job to open the cervix. She can visualize the baby riding the wave of each contraction to the top, sensing the moment when it just won't get any tighter, and feeling it wash down to the shore—fading and fading and fading—as she rests and her body rests, while deep out in the inner ocean another "wave" begins to form.

The uterus is a muscle and it is always contracting. It is contracting when a woman is awake and when she is asleep. What makes the uterus continue to contract day and night? It is the power within that does this without her conscious awareness or effort. It is governed by the autonomic nervous system, which also keeps the heart beating and the lungs breathing so we can survive while sleeping. A non-pregnant uterus is about the size of your fist, and so a woman won't feel it contracting. However, towards the end of the gestational period, a pregnant woman will feel the normal uterine contractions as Braxton-Hicks contractions. These are not labor contractions, as they do not change in strength or length. Labor contractions do change in strength and length, and also pull the abdomen down and towards the left.

Much focus and concentration is required to stay on top of labor contractions, especially as they become longer and stronger; but in between contractions, there is time to rest. The rest periods always come in natural births and give time to prepare for the next contraction. I remember looking forward to them and would remind myself at the height of a contraction that the rest period would be coming soon. During periods of rest I would eat or drink juice and water, adjust my position, and ask for anything I needed.

Positive thinking

Positive thoughts strengthen our immune system and negative thoughts weaken it. Learning to see the good in every situation is a way to feel strengthened. Living in a world of duality, both the good and the bad, the positive and the negative will co-exist. We need to learn the power inherent in positive thinking and choose to see the good. Choosing to see the good connects us more deeply to the power within.

The law of action and reaction dictates that whatever behavior we project onto another person is reflected back onto us, be it positive or negative. If our behavior is positive, neurochemicals that reflect the positive are produced in the body. If our behavior is negative, neurochemicals that reflect

the negative are produced in the body. A woman in labor who knew how to think positively said, "I promptly threw up when I got out of the tub, but I didn't mind and was actually excited because I had learned that is a sign of full dilation." Another woman said, "Joy? When everything about this was fraught with fear? How in the world would joy be the outcome of all this? And yet I held onto that promise and believed God for it."

Birthing in the spirit means learning how to see the good in everything that comes our way. This philosophy is crucial for women during pregnancy, labor, and birth. It is crucial for the birth team attending the woman in labor as well. Strong contractions are good because it is this power within that brings a baby into the world. Weak and comfortable contractions are not what birth a baby.

Regardless of the birth outcome or type of delivery, the woman and her birth team need to look for the good that comes out of such a profound experience. This is a philosophy that believes that in every experience there is something to learn, and our job is to find it. As human beings we entertain negative thoughts so easily, so automatically. Learning to see the good brings balance and better health to all those who are involved. The world gives us many opportunities to see negativity, but we can choose not to entertain the negative thoughts and just let them pass like clouds on a windy day; instead, working to see the good in each situation. Being able to entertain only positive thoughts transforms us by helping us escape from self-limiting and fear-based attitudes into attitudes of wholeness.

Seeing the good in all brings an attitude of positive anticipation to any woman going into labor. Perceiving the contractions as waves helps a woman to connect with the power in the ocean. Tremendous power is within the ocean, and that same salt water composes more than 80 percent of our bodies. When in labor, connecting with the amniotic "ocean" inside helps the woman to feel the same potential power within as surges of creation that culminate in the birth of the baby. Connecting to the idea that we are full of millions of atoms—meaning that atomic power is within us—connects us to the spirit inside us all that has infinite power.

SEEING THE GOOD EXERCISE

Here is an exercise to start the practice of seeing only that which is good. Close your eyes and think of something that happened to you, perhaps birth-related, that you perceive as being negative. Open your eyes and draw this on a piece of paper. Now underneath your picture, list all the good things you can think of that came out of that experience. When you can't think of more, close your eyes and go deeply inside. Calm your mind. See if more good things about this experience come to your awareness. Add them to the list. Breathe slowly and deeply as you look at your list.

Women can access the power within to assist them with the birth process simply by thinking good thoughts. Ultimately, the power within is the power of love, which is contradictory to the feeling of fear. Feeling love and thinking positively will automatically dispel fear and facilitate labor.

When contractions become very strong, the woman in labor may not want to change positions because it is uncomfortable. But, thinking good thoughts, she can say to herself, "The more I move, the more I am helping my baby to move and be born." If she has labored for many hours, and in spite of moving into different positions is not making progress in labor, she cay say, "I've done the very best I can do and need help."

Most women are surprised at the magnitude of the love they feel towards their newborn babies either in the moments after birth or during the first days at home. I remember lying on my mattress on the floor in my bedroom and gazing at my daughter lying there, just a week old. An incredible urge came over me to want to squeeze her, an urge so strong that I was afraid that if I did, I would hurt her. The power of my love for her in that moment was magnetic and I simply laid my hands on her, gave a gentle hug, and poured the overwhelming love into her through my hands.

Feeling the power within is enhanced by positive thinking. We have everything to gain by beginning the practice of thinking good thoughts. It affects our moods, our health, our sleep, and our friendships, as well as increasing self-confidence. It takes time because we are so conditioned to thinking negatively. Awareness helps us to be more conscious about what we are saying, and then we can use the power within as willpower to start changing the negative to the positive.

Never underestimate the power of positive thinking fueled by the power within. With this, anything is possible.

Birthing in the Spirit

It's just like when God enters you. You shake because the power is so enormous.... That's usually when the woman says, "I can't do it." Then you know the baby is going to come. As soon as the woman lets go of her control, God comes in; the Power and the Spirit comes in birth. So when I was able to do that with my children—with the second one I did much better—I felt the power of God.... I think as midwives we're honored with that opportunity to be present when that happens.

—MIDWIFE FROM THE ONEIDA NATION IN WISCONSIN
AS QUOTED IN SHEILA KITZINGER'S BOOK *REDISCOVERING BIRTH*

Intuition

Intuition is the clear conception of the whole at once.

JOHN KASPAR (SWISS THEOLOGIAN, 1741-1801)

I reached down and rubbed my abdomen with my hands. The fundus, the top of my uterus, was reaching up high into my ribs at thirty-six weeks of gestation and I was now walking with more of a waddling, side-to-side gait. My legs simply didn't want to go straight forward anymore. I was amazed by the fact that a human being was growing inside of me, and pressed on my abdomen to figure out what part of her I was feeling. I could feel two big parts and thought one must be the head and one the bottom. The part on which I was rubbing felt hard. I thought about the responsibilities that becoming a mother would bring, but I was ready. It was exciting to know that in just four weeks I would really be a mother.

But an uneasy feeling started coming over me as I rubbed the hard part. Something didn't feel right. I didn't know what it was, but I pressed more deeply, feeling the border of the hardness, again trying to figure it out. The upper part of my abdomen was definitely feeling harder and the lower part was feeling softer. I kept feeling them, and the uneasy feeling became more intense. I thought to myself, *A bottom is supposed to be soft. The head is supposed to be hard.*

I felt my abdomen again, totally engrossed now in trying to figure out what was happening. Everything in my previous prenatal visit was normal. The doctor hadn't mentioned anything about the baby not being in the right position, head down. Surely he would have told me if something was wrong. He did say something about the baby being engaged in the pelvis, which was a good sign. But he didn't say anything else.

I pushed a little deeper into my skin. Yes, the hard part *was* on top and the soft part *was* on the bottom. It was becoming clearer to me that my baby was not in the right position for birth, even though the doctor seemed to think everything was okay. I had a hunch that my baby was in a breech position with her head up.

Fear started to overcome me. I had to do something about this. I called my doctor and went in for a visit, and knew before I went what he was going to say. Then I saw the look in his eyes that confirmed my fear even before he spoke the words, "Yes, your baby is in a breech position and we might have to do a cesarean. You will need to plan this for two weeks before your due date."

My intuition immediately flashed a big "No" in response to his statement. I believed completely in the normal process of birth. Nobody in my family had had cesareans. I had learned in childbirth

class how to do the pelvic slant exercise to help the baby turn. I would do that. So for the next two weeks, I laid upside down on my couch for a period of time each day, hoping that this exercise would help the baby turn. It was not very comfortable. Still, she did not turn.

Now it was two weeks before my due date, and it was January in Boston and very cold. The doctors were putting pressure on me to plan a cesarean, but I believed too strongly that anything can happen in labor and that she would probably turn on her own during the contractions. My due date came, along with the biggest snowstorm in the history of Boston. The entire city shut down for three days. Nothing could move.

My hospital was a twenty-five-minute drive from my apartment. We walked on paths over the tops of cars. Everything was quiet, including my body. No contractions. If they did begin, I would have to walk three blocks to a local hospital where I didn't know anyone and where I wouldn't stand a chance for a normal birth with a breech baby.

Slowly, the city of Boston began to move again, and by then I was two weeks past my due date and still no contractions. It was white and beautiful outside. I was very nervous on the inside but excited about having a baby soon and becoming a mother. The heartbeat was fine, so we just waited. Finally, at three weeks past my due date, I started to feel contractions. This was the moment I had been waiting for. I knew my body was ready now, and I believed completely that it knew how to birth this baby.

When the contractions progressed to being three minutes apart, I went to the hospital and got settled. They wanted to insert an IV, but I said that it would interfere with my ability to labor and that it wouldn't be necessary. If it really did become necessary, I knew they would be able to put one in. They brought the electronic fetal monitor. It was used one time to listen to the baby's heartbeat and then they used a doptone at my request.

Nine hours went by, with the contractions getting stronger and more powerful. I kept changing positions, walked, sat on the toilet, and then walked more. Then something I didn't anticipate happened: I began to feel an urge to push. An internal exam revealed that I was only six centimeters dilated. I visualized the baby's head coming through a cervix six centimeters dilated and knew my predicament. They did an x-ray to confirm her positioning, and there she was—doing a split with one foot over her shoulder, and one down in my pelvis. Her little foot was slipping down into my vagina, causing the urge to push. She was in a single-footling breech position.

The urge to push was the most intense thing I had ever experienced. How amazing that my body had such power inside of it. There was no stopping it, as hard as I tried. It felt like the surge of an elevator lift. Any attempts to stop the pushing feelings were futile. I had to make a decision. At that time, nobody around me had confidence to assist me in a vaginal single-footling breech birth. I also didn't know if it was safe, as I was only six centimeters dilated. *What if her head got stuck?* More powerful pushes came that overwhelmed me. I looked up and said, "Do the cesarean."

I believed I had done all I could do. I believed that she had a chance to turn in labor, but either she chose not to or couldn't. Her safety was the most important thing to me at that moment. They

placed an IV in my arm and administered a spinal anesthetic in the operating room. With a history of cystitis, I asked them not to insert a urinary catheter. They agreed, saying that my bladder wasn't full because I had not had an IV. They wanted to put up a barrier between my face and my belly. I told them it was important for me to see her being born and would they please take it down, which they did. Yet I was surprised that my abdomen was still so big that I couldn't see anyway. However, to my amazement, the doctors were wearing glasses that were like mirrors, so I could see everything. I could feel tugging and pulling and some pressure and saw them pull her out of me.

And there she was in my arms, which they had agreed not to tie down. I held her while they stitched me up and was totally consumed with her beauty. So small. So amazing. I was a mother, and I cried tears of joy. I was able to nurse her in the recovery room and hold her close to me. A fierce urge to protect her came over me. It was a primal urge I didn't know could be so strong.

The cesarean birth was a good experience and I have positive memories of it because I was the one who made all the decisions. Choice is important. I felt respected, and experienced the power of my body in labor. If they had sectioned me before labor began, I would never have known if my baby would have turned by herself. I loved feeling the labor contractions; not that they were easy, but I felt like I did the work to bring her into the world. I do not have to spend the rest of my life wondering what would have happened if I had not experienced labor. Therefore, I have peace about her birth and my experience because I took each moment in the present and made decisions based on what my intuition told me.

At the time of my daughter's birth, the doctors had told me I could have a vaginal birth after cesarean for my next birth. When I became pregnant, two of these doctors would not support me. The third said he would, but I heard through my friend—his perinatal nurse—that he said in doing so he might have a "coronary" (heart attack). In spite of what the doctors said, I trusted my intuition and knew I felt completely safe having a VBAC the next time. *Each birth is unique,* I told myself.

Even though most women with one cesarean were having planned repeat cesareans, I had no intention of doing that. My intuition was strong towards having a normal and natural birth. I had no thoughts about taking any drugs for pain relief. I wanted to feel birth and do my own work of bringing my baby into the world.

It was two years later. I walked the halls of the hospital all night and moved in various positions throughout the day. I drank juice for energy. I just "knew" I was going to have a natural birth. I wish I had known to be on my hands and knees, but because I was on my back, I ended up pushing very hard to the point where I was sore for several days. My son Aaron's birth was completely natural. When he came out, I marveled that my female body could grow a male. My only regret was being examined for the cesarean scar from my daughter's birth, which was very painful and, I felt, totally unnecessary. But it was a beautiful birth and I felt proud of myself.

In my births, at each step of the way there were important decisions to make. I felt close to my intuition and listened to its guidance. I felt confident in my choices and knew that I was making the right choices at the right time for both my daughter and my son. These birth experiences have

been a highlight of my life and are responsible for my leap into a career as a childbirth educator and birth doula, and for my founding of Birth Works® International. The commonality in my births was a strong belief in my innate ability to give birth, and in the normal, natural process of birth. Even though the methods of birthing my daughter and son were different, the outcome was the same: I felt empowered and birthed two beautiful babies, and I have peace about both experiences.

WHAT IS INTUITION?

Intuition is as an immediate insight or understanding. It is a sudden, direct knowing that can be so compelling that we can't help but follow it. I believe that most of us live closer to our intuitive side than we think, and that the discriminatory aspect of our intellect sheath is more active than we realize.

We have all had experiences of intuition in our lives because we are intuitive beings. However, learning to hear and trust the inner voice of intuition takes practice. A woman once sent back an evaluation form from her Birth Works® classes. To the question "What is something you learned that you didn't know before?" she answered, "I realized I was beginning to forget to listen to my inner voice." Tuning into the consciousness is what helps us to remember, and this is an inward journey.

Children are very intuitive. If you are a parent, you already know that you can't hide anything from your children. They are so perceptive, and so good at reading body energy, that no matter what you say, they know the truth. For example, perhaps a woman is having an argument with her husband. The mother puts her child to bed and the child asks, "Mommy, is everything alright?" "Yes," responds the woman, "everything is alright." But the child senses that things are not quite right. She hears tension in her mother's voice. She sees a troubled expression in her mother's eyes, even though she may be able to smile. She feels the feelings of her mother, and the mother cannot hide them, try as she may.

There are various terms used to describe intuition. These include a "gut feeling," the "inner voice," a "creative impulse," the "voice of consciousness," instinct, or simply a "hunch." Other characteristics of intuition are spontaneity, truth, surprise, and insight. Some call it "the voice of the soul." Many people close to their intuition can sense some things before they happen. A woman may be standing in front of her caregiver at a prenatal visit and suddenly realize that something doesn't feel right and that she should change to another caregiver. Midwives sense a baby's spirit and talk to it when it is born and often sense if something is wrong. Or, despite apparent problems, a midwife may know that everything will be okay.

Intuition is at work when a pregnant woman walks into a birthing center or hospital and just "knows" that it is the place she wants to give birth. She has an intuitive sense that it is the right place for her. Others may feel this way about their own home or a birthing center.

Malcolm Gladwell based his book *Blink* on the premise that decisions made very quickly can be just as good as those made cautiously and deliberately, and that snap judgments and first impressions

can be educated and controlled.[1] He likens intuition to a giant computer that quickly and quietly processes a lot of the data we need in order to keep functioning as human beings, and calls "thin-slicing" the "ability of our unconscious to find patterns in situations and behavior based on very narrow slices of experience."[2]

BLOCKS TO RECEIVING INTUITION

It is often said that first impressions are correct ones, but then almost instantly the rational mind enters and begins to cloud intuition. When the mind takes a "backseat," intuition can be heard more clearly. As psychologist Timothy D. Wilson writes in his book *Strangers to Ourselves,* "The mind operates most efficiently by relegating a good deal of high-level, sophisticated thinking to the unconscious, just as a modern jetliner is able to fly on automatic pilot with little or no input from the human, 'conscious' pilot. The adaptive unconscious does an excellent job of sizing up the world, warning people of danger, setting goals, and initiating action in a sophisticated and efficient manner."[3]

The mind can block intuition when it is consumed with the negative qualities of jealousy, anger, greed, pride, desire, fear, and attachment, which cloud intuition, making it appear vague and distant with the result that it can't be heard as clearly. It is in such times that instinct or intuition seems to betray us.

Consider a woman who did not have a good experience with a doctor at her first birth, yet goes back to him or her again for her second birth. Intuitively she may sense that it is not a good idea to go back to the same doctor, but her rational mind takes over and decides that what is familiar is easier than that which is not familiar. This block to intuition is based on fear and on attachment to that which is familiar. If she could truly act on her intuition, she might have a very different birth experience.

I have been at births where women intuitively knew they wanted to stay upright to birth their babies, but the doctors told them they needed to lie down. Thus they allowed medical authority to overrule their desire; the mind prevailed over intuition.

Another example is when a woman's intuition may be saying, "Don't wear the fetal monitor," but the medical team says, "Wear the fetal monitor so we can tell if something is wrong with the baby." The woman hears the words, "If something is wrong." The fear of something going wrong with her baby overpowers her intuition that says, "Don't wear the monitor."

Sometimes a woman's intuition overrules her own anticipated plans for birth. A woman who had planned to have an underwater birth may suddenly "feel" an urge to get out, and minutes later will find herself giving birth. She just knows it is the right thing to do and acts on it.

Intuition is good at sensing danger, which results in a fight or flight response, and this is an important way the body leads us to safety. It also signals a woman to ask for help when she intuitively feels something is wrong in labor. When we are truly in tune with our intuition, I believe we will

never regret following what it says. Anytime we don't listen to our intuition, we experience a degree of conflict that results in tension and increased energy expenditure.

Have you ever had the thought, *I wish I had done that*? A woman's intuition may initially be saying no to medical procedures being offered without medical reason, but if she perceives that her baby is in danger, she should trust her intuition and seek help. She may feel that even with encouragement from a doula, she cannot do more, and her intuition may be saying yes to medical procedures and obstetrical drugs to help birth her baby. But if she finds herself in a state of conflict, surrounded by fear and controversy, she will doubt herself and become confused too. How can she open herself to give birth in that emotional state? One woman said, "The Pit contractions were making me pass out. I couldn't do any more." At that moment, it was a right decision for her.

I believe that when such hunches are clear, they are guides from the consciousness that need to be followed. Such a "knowing" goes beyond right or wrong; it just is. Intuition is always a moment ahead of our conscious awareness and may often take us by surprise. Childbirth classes need to be places where birthing women and their partners or significant others can express and hear their own fears, thereby releasing them. This will allow intuition to be a stronger, guiding force during pregnancy, labor, and birth. Group support in childbirth classes is invaluable in accomplishing this because birthing parents will realize they are not alone in their fears, and this is a comforting feeling.

Is it intuition or mind?

Characteristics of intuition

How can we tell whether what we are sensing is coming from intuition or from the mind? Here are five characteristics of intuition that I believe serve as ways to identify its presence.

1. *Intuition is in the present moment.* Have you ever been with someone you felt very close to even though you have just met each other? What is it that makes you feel closer to one person than another? On the first night of one of my Birth Works® childbirth education classes, I met the participants for the first time as they walked in the door. They entered my sunroom and sat in chairs I'd arranged in a circle. About fourteen people were in the room, but when I saw Linda for the first time, an immediate thought flashed through my consciousness. I felt drawn to her and remembered thinking, *We will be close friends for a long time.* Indeed, now eighteen years later, we are best friends and have shared many wonderful experiences together with our families.

2. *Intuition presents itself as a "flash."* When intuition presents itself as a lightning "flash," it takes me by complete surprise. It is almost as if my whole body is nothing but light just for a split second. It feels like an instant message from the spirit, and is so powerful I know I will have to follow through on it.

    This sudden insight has little to no thought preceding it. One such example that comes to

mind was one time when I was standing on the doorstep with my friend Linda, who had stopped by to visit. All of a sudden I felt a lightning flash and immediately heard myself blurt out, without any pre-consideration, "We need to take our mothers out for dinner!" The thought seemingly came out of nowhere, but as soon as I said it, it felt so right. We planned it for the next week and had a wonderful time. Both of our mothers were about the same age, in their early eighties, and it was an evening to be remembered. A week later, Linda's mother was diagnosed with pancreatic cancer and she died shortly afterwards. That was her last dinner out with friends.

3. **Intuition as resonance.** Another way is to have a feeling of resonance with the idea. Resonance occurs when wavelengths are vibrating together at the same frequency. It is a moment of clarity where there is pure vision without any sense of conflict. The woman who suddenly realizes she should change doctors knows at that split moment that it is what she should do. The feeling of resonance is similar to a feeling of being *home* with ourselves. It feels safe. It feels comfortable. It helps us to relax. Using intuition at every moment throughout the birthing process can help a woman to have the most optimal birth experience as well as finding greater peace within herself.

4. **Intuition is heart-centered.** A fourth way is to feel it as an impression that is heart-centered, without sense of ego or selfishness. I believe that the heart is the voice of the conscience that resides in the heart, and that it will never lead us astray. Listening to the "voice" of the heart takes trust and faith and is based on the idea that our higher self knows more than our conscious self.

   There is a valuable and useful technique that can help you to remember to be more heart-centered and that can also help when making decisions. It is called *The Three H's of Head, Heart, Hands.*

The three h's of head, heart, hands

When a thought enters your conscious awareness, learn to take it directly to your heart, which can be considered a consultant. The heart is full of love, kindness, compassion, and all that is good. Listen to what your heart says. It may feel like an impression, an urge, a hunch, or a feeling. Wait until you have a sense of what your heart is saying, and only then allow the thought to go to your hands for action.

Believe that whatever comes from the heart can be trusted. Listening to your heart requires training and much practice because we are so used to bypassing the heart and taking thoughts directly from the subconscious mind to our hands. Doing so subjects us to patterns of behavior that have been carried down through family systems through generations, all stored in the subconscious mind from experiences in the world. The process is so automatic that it usually happens without our conscious awareness. Thoughts that bypass the heart end up in actions that may lack full compassion and love.

5. *Intuition as a metamessage.* A fifth way to know that it is your intuition that you are hearing is to sense the metamessage. A metamessage refers to how a message is interpreted between the sender and the receiver. It is that which is communicated or "said" nonverbally, without words, and it is strongly intuitive.

To the heart....

Take thoughts from the head.....

And only then to the hands.

HEAD, HEART, HANDS

Reading body energy is a form of the metamessage. We know the mood of someone just by the look on her face. A woman meeting her doula for the first time may be talking about what she wants to do in labor or doctor visits, but intuitively she is asking herself, *Can I trust her? Do I feel safe with her? Does she make me feel relaxed? Does she talk too much? Can I depend on her?* At the same time the doula is asking herself such questions as, *Does she exhibit confidence? Does she have faith in herself and her ability to give birth?* Another example is a pregnant woman at a doctor's visit who is thinking, *Will I be able to open myself up to him? Can I trust her to do what she says? Is he patient with my questions?*

Characteristics of the mind

The mind doesn't function in the same way as intuition. It is the nature of the mind to doubt, argue, rationalize, or impose a bias or judgment. The mind is crafty, working to find a way around doing something or to get the best deal. The mind can be directed toward planning fun family times, big events, or inquiring into the nature of its own self. The mind can also be viewed as a means to reaching self-realization and experiencing the soul. However, more often than not, the mind influences intuition, often talking us out of what our intuition is saying, and such an influence is very powerful.

The woman who realizes she needs to change doctors may have that as an intuitive thought, but then her rational mind says, "But my friends liked him," or "I'd have to interview more doctors," or "Maybe it will end up okay after all," and she literally allows her rational mind to preside. The mind is more likely to influence intuition through what I call the negative qualities of jealousy, anger, greed, pride, desire, and attachment. There is a constrictive quality to such negative qualities, whereas impressions or intuitions from the heart are selfless and expansive in nature and more concerned for the greater good of all.

I find that I have different intensities of intuition. When my intuition is weak, I can be convinced in another direction through rationalizations. This is when I let my mind predominate. When my intuition is very strong, I have to follow through on it, for to go against it is to go against the very

core of my being. I remember such instances the rest of my life. An example for me is a workshop I feel I need to attend. There may be many obstacles into arranging to attend the workshop, but if I really feel I am supposed to be there, the obstacles all seem to drop off and I am freed up to go. Wanting to experience labor is another example. I have never regretted such decisions.

INTUITION IN BIRTH

A woman who has knowledge about birth *and* who is in touch with her intuitive side (education and educare) will go into labor with a sense of confidence. This combination will allow her to discern when something looks good but isn't good. She will be able to size up initial impressions and make decisions based on her knowledge and intuition. She will be open to each new moment and be able to work with what it has to bring. Because a characteristic of intuition is that it is in the present moment, what we hear our inner voice saying can change from moment to moment. For example, prenatally a woman's intuition might have been that it would feel good to be massaged during labor, but when in labor she may find that she doesn't want to be touched.

The intuition of a woman in labor is powerful. A woman who goes into labor believing that her body already knows how to give birth will be open to the signals her body gives her and will be able to act on them. She will be able to visualize and feel movements of the baby. As Gaskin says, "The big secret is that women can better accomplish what they want if they imagine or 'picture' it in their minds that a vagina takes the size of what it contains, whether a penis or a baby."[4] Body signals include how and when to move into different positions, when to sit on the toilet, when to drink, and when to go into or out of the shower or pool of warm water. She will have full trust and faith in her body. Even when unforeseen circumstances in labor occur, she will be able to meet them with clarity of vision and an ability to make decisions right for herself.

With the birth environment becoming so technical today, it is especially important that women hold onto their intuition and follow it as their guide. Although most women are choosing to give birth in a hospital, there are an increasing number of women who value the wisdom of nature and their own natural bodies over science and technology. They believe in medical procedures when they are truly warranted for medical reasons, but they want to feel their bodies working through labor, experiencing its rhythms, sexuality, fluidity, ecstasy, and healthy pain or pressure of contractions. Many of these women are giving birth in the familiarity of their own homes or in birthing centers with midwives. Acting on our intuition takes courage and strength and much faith to trust a direction that may feel unsure.

A doula needs to be close to her intuition because her job is to say words at specific times that help to empower and encourage a woman to keep working through the contractions. Doulas are trained in the power of positive thinking, and say, "This is a good time to move into another position so your baby can move down into the pelvis more," or "Let horse lips [sound made by blowing air through relaxed lips] help you relax through this next contraction," or "Your body has its own

time clock and knows exactly when your baby will be born." These statements build confidence and empower women to work with their bodies. Communication that is open, honest, and heart-centered is vital.

Midwives also have a strong intuitive connection with the women they assist in labor. It is as if their spirits are one, providing information and reassurance in key moments. They draw on their experiences with many women at birth, and those who have given birth from ancient times and will in the future. The following quotations from the book *Intuition* reflect the strong intuitive side of midwives.

"Assisting women at birth—that's all it is, is intuition. I listen to the baby's heartbeat, because, you know, I listen to the baby's heartbeat, but I don't really care about it because I have this inner knowing that everything's fine."
"Do you know when everything isn't fine?"
"Sure, you know, there's an energy there."
"Has there ever been a time when the stethoscope told you one thing but your intuition another?"
"No, if I detect a problem with the baby's heartbeat, there have already been signs that I'm suspecting there may be a problem. The heartbeat almost never tells me anything, except it looks nice on a piece of paper to document it. I do that for the lawyers."[5]

"I think that every time a midwife goes to the edge, it is the intuition that everything is all right that takes her there. I had to keep examining with this woman whether or not it was all right for us to continue, and every single time was an internal process about—we have these signs, and this is not "the rules," but I knew the baby's all right, and I know that the mother is all right, so we can go on from this point."[6]

"I never made a decision based on anything that was written on the chart—blood pressure, urinalysis, information about rate of dilation and progression of labor,...because every time I checked with the woman in labor, she would tell me that she was fine and that she knew the baby was fine; and every time I looked at her and every time I looked inside myself, and every time I saw that, whatever it is, the place where the baby was, the baby was safe....Inside my head I saw the baby safe—and this is my own metaphor, I realize, but I saw the baby surrounded by sparkling light, kind of like glittery flecks of amniotic fluid. My inner vision of the baby corresponded with that of the mother."[7]

The relationship of midwives and doulas with women at birth is a good example of the reaction, reflection, and resounding that represents all our interactions with each other. As one midwife described the intuitive experience she has with her birthing mothers: "Mothers and midwives mirror one another. I know that I get all of my courage from the mother. And I bounce it back to her, and she gets her

courage from me.... It's a dance—the woman has to trust her midwife, and the midwife has to trust her woman for that bouncing back."[8]

LOSING INTUITION

What happens when we don't listen to our intuition? It means focusing externally rather than internally, or letting fear be a cloud blocking intuition. It is as if we are wandering through the world lost, trying to find our way through life without guidance. In birth, it is as if the woman in labor is running from the contractions and unable to work with them, unable to find or feel the spirit guiding her through them.

The external world will grab us here and there, tossing us up and down. We will be susceptible to all attractions and dive into them without boundaries or limits. Have you ever heard the expression, "He is a lost soul?" or "She doesn't know what she is doing"? Such people are out of touch with their own self and tend to rely on everyone and everything for answers, not being able to find their own way through the predicament. A woman in labor who loses her focus and who allows fear to cloud her intuition becomes dependent on others instead of being held in awe of her own power. When we don't listen to our intuition we may make choices that are not in our best interest, for they are what someone else said to do instead of what we know is right for us.

Women live with their birth experiences the rest of their lives. Intuition plays a key role in birth and helps a woman to have a good birth experience regardless of the outcome. Intuition is our instinctive side and should be considered our best friend. A good friend will support you through good times and difficult times, whether you are rich or poor. A friend will be with you whenever you are in need. Remember Vasilisa and her kookla doll in the Baba Yaga story? She consulted it throughout her journey to get the fire. Intuition is like this. If we remember to consult it, it will never let us down. Because intuition is based on truth, when followed it will always be the right decision at that moment in time.

Birthing in the Spirit

I am a midwife, and I attend births at home. Not coincidentally, I am also a student of spirituality and comparative mysticism.... When I drive to a birth, it is my habit to open to the universe and to look for the quiet center within. I ask for the humility to act from that center and to let it manifest in all that I am about to say or not say, do or not do.

—LUCIA RONCALLI, MIDWIFE

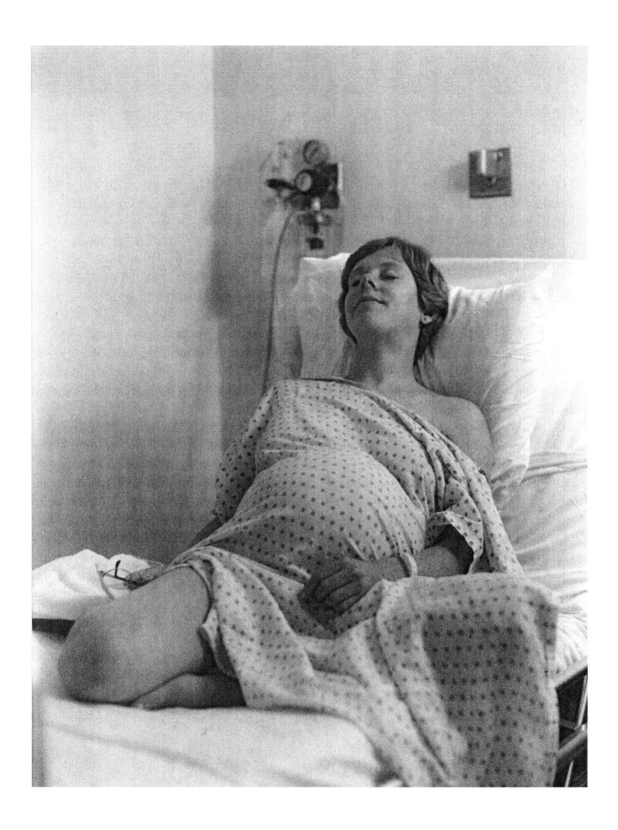

CHAPTER 14

Dharma, the Mind, and Beliefs

Very often, in order to bring about stillness we have to be tirelessly active in the outer world. You might suppose this would agitate the mind. It will not, if it is the dharma.

TENANT OF BUDDHISM

DHARMA

We live our lives based on what we believe. What we believe is based on our perception of our dharma. *Dharma* is a Sanskrit word that refers to the inborn nature specific to a given entity. The inborn nature of something is its truth and also its spiritual practice. When we base our actions on truth, they are right actions and are in tune with our dharma. What is dharmic is so true that it is not likely to be questioned. For example, the dharma of wood is to burn. Wood loves to burn. The dharma of a fruit tree is to yield fruit. More specifically, an apple tree's dharma is to produce apples. Try as it may, it cannot produce pears. The dharma of a cow is to produce milk. The dharma of the earth is to grow plants and trees for our survival.

One dharma of women is having the potential to conceive, grow a baby, and give birth. This ability is instinctive and therefore does not need to be taught. Women's bodies are designed to give birth and are therefore programmed anatomically and physiologically to be able to bring a soul into the world. Men cannot give birth and thus giving birth is not their dharma.

What is the dharma for men? In terms of relationships and birth, I believe it is to protect and provide for their women who are bringing a child into the world. This is a natural ability in most men that I know. They are very good at protection. It is not something they need to learn, as it is instinctive for them. This is also the role I believe they should have at birth, and in talking with many men across the country over the last 20 years, it seems to be a role in which they feel very comfortable.

Just as a tree sends roots down deep into the soil for nourishment, so I believe we use the concept of mind and life experiences to help form beliefs that go deep into our psyche to understand our dharma. The Dalai Lama describes dharma as the underlying current and reality of our existence. He says, "…The practice of Dharma, real spiritual practice, is in some sense like a voltage stabilizer. The function of the stabilizer is to prevent irregular power surges and instead give you a stable and

constant source of power."[1] Our dharma is not something that any of us can escape. We are destined, at some point in our lives, to realize it and be true to it. We have many dharmas depending on our work in society.

This stabilizing influence of dharma can be likened to the water flowing in a creek. Walking upstream, we meet the resistance of the water. This takes great effort and is tiring. Walking downstream with the flow of water is much easier. All obstacles seem to give way. Following our dharma is like this because when we base actions on our truth, we are "in tune" with ourselves and our own destiny. Doing what we say, being who we are meant to be, and doing what we are meant to do result in a feeling of harmony in the mind, body, and spirit.

Just as it is a woman's dharma to have the potential to give birth, so is it the dharma of all human beings to realize that their essence is that of love. Fighting, cursing, saying unkind things to another, or harming one another are all discordant with our intuitive sense of what is right. We know this to be true because doing or saying something unkind to others, or receiving it from them, doesn't feel good and we develop defensive reactions for protective purposes. When kind words are spoken that are heart-centered, there is unconditional love and we feel safe. It also has the effect of bringing out the good in others, along with a desire to help those in need.

People who do not feel loved lose a sense of purpose for living. The love within us wants to be expressed and we feel best when we express it. Human life would be meaningless without the expression of love. Pregnant women who are surrounded in pregnancy and birth by those aware of their dharma of love, and who manifest it in their actions, experience pure joy. For birth to be anything less than an experience of pure joy is a sadness for any woman.

STEADYING THE MIND

The mind is so vast and infinite that we cannot fathom its extent. It has no boundaries and is very active in daydreams and night dreams, traveling any distance in the blink of an eye. With just a thought, it can be halfway around the world in an instant. Though what we call the mind is in the body, it is not limited to the body because it is not dependent on form and its characteristic is that of expansion.

I perceive the mind as being wonderfully mysterious. No one has yet been able to unravel the mystery of the mind. In fact, how do we know that it exists? We can't see it, touch it, or dissect it because it has no form; and yet we make references to its existence all the time in such expressions as "I don't know what my mind was thinking!" "You need to be more mindful." "My mind is whirling!" "My mind is spent!" "My mind is racing!" or "I have such a monkey mind." It is interesting to note that in such expressions, the mind appears on the verge of being out of control. A mind that has no control is like a "mad" monkey. It wants this, it wants that, and it always wants more. It says, "I want, I want, I want," and grows in strength every time it yields to desires. This keeps us from having peace. But as much as the mind is viewed as being a bundle of thoughts full of desires, I also believe

that when it is "tamed," focused, and directed, it leads us to know more about ourselves and who we are.

The most plausible theory I have heard about the concept of mind is the acknowledgment that there actually is no mind. One idea is that just as the moon has no light of its own, and what we see is only the reflected light of the sun, so what we believe to be the mind is just the reflected light of the consciousness shining on the heart. Thus, in reality there is only heart. I like this idea because it takes me back to the idea that our nature, our dharma, is none other than love. If we were true to this, true to our dharma, we would behave only in ways that reflect our consciousness.

I like to think of the mind as a bundle of impulses that need to be controlled, directed, or focused in whatever direction we choose. If the mind is left uncontrolled, it becomes the master and we are subject to its every whim. This is the way many people function in the world and it leads to discontent, the seeking of fleeting pleasures, and ultimately, to sorrow. Making the heart your master and the mind your servant is a way to begin controlling the mind and achieving peace.

If you have ever tried to meditate, you know how difficult it is to control thoughts of the mind. As soon as we try to focus on one thing, many other thoughts manage to flood the mind. Repeating mantras—short incantations or prayers—is a good way to steady the mind. A woman in labor can make up her own mantras, repeating them over and over again especially during strong contractions. Examples are "Down, baby down," or "O...pen, o...pen." The expression used is not as important as the constant repetition of words, which have the hypnotic effect of calming the mind; however, mantras that are affirming in nature are even more powerful. A mantra gives focus, which is necessary to ride contractions like waves of the ocean, one at a time. Mantras work because out of sheer repetition, constant thinking about a thought helps it to become imprinted on the consciousness. Focus in labor is essential and is the secret to working through contractions. A woman who feels out of control has a mind that is whirling. A woman with a steady mind has focus.

There are many other advantages to having a steady mind. A mind that lacks focus results in excessive talking, which leads to a greater consumption of energy and increased fatigue. Did you ever feel tired when listening to someone who is talking too much? Many people are not accustomed to silence, but a quiet mind helps a woman in labor to access her inner guidance system more effectively. If a birth team member finds herself talking excessively, she can imagine her mind as a tape measure that snaps back when the button is pushed. Her awareness is the button. This is a visual that works. There is also slower breathing and a greater feeling of peace with a steady mind.

The importance of beliefs in birth

Is knowledge anything other than belief?
Can anything be proven beyond belief?
Is science more than consensual belief?
Is faith more than belief in the unprovable?

129

Beliefs are our codified perceptions of the world,
And the world we know is created by them.
Beliefs are shared and thus become the beliefs of others.
Beliefs are the structural pillars of consciousness.
What is the nature of conscious awareness beyond belief?

HILTON L. ANDERSON

Beliefs are a collection of thoughts that are composed of short impulses of energy transmitted by neurochemicals. Beliefs govern our actions and the choices we make in life and are based on life experiences. They provide safety and protection in a mysterious world. How we look at life is reflected in our words and beliefs. When women are empowered during the prenatal period, they are more likely to enter labor ready and willing to work through strong contractions to birth their babies.

I like to think of the body as a computer, programmed with the software of our thoughts. Thoughts get imprinted on the mind and are immediately accompanied by neurotransmitter and hormone changes in our brains and bodies. This can be likened to a camera. Just as a camera takes a picture in whatever direction it is turned, so the mind reflects the nature of things to which we are attracted. These thoughts are the "software" being installed into the computer body. Eventually these thoughts form our beliefs. When we have a change of thought about something, there is also a change in how we feel about it. This connection between our thoughts and the physiological response of the body happens instantly, before we are hardly aware of the thought. It matters what we choose to "see" with the mind. Therefore, we literally become what we contemplate. As we think, so we become.

If a woman looks at life as a "glass half-empty," she may attract experiences of scarcity or of never being good enough to succeed. This includes not believing she can birth her baby. However, a birth team that is effective in encouraging and empowering her through labor can help her to succeed and offer the opportunity to change her belief, especially if they can help her visualize it in her mind. A woman who looks at life as a "glass half-full" will always see the possibility of potential and have confidence to carry it out. If we allow ourselves to be sad, then we are likely to see sad things in life. If we choose to be happy and accepting of life's events, then we are likely to perceive the world with happiness and acceptance. The state of our mind is a choice.

The group support in childbirth classes offers an ideal opportunity to talk about pregnancy, labor, and birth with a positive viewpoint. People have a tendency to cling strongly to their beliefs, with the result of a vision that is narrow-minded. The discussion in group settings allows birthing parents to hear other opinions that can help change beliefs that may not be helpful for birth. Beliefs are very powerful, for they lead us to take action. A good action, for example, is a pregnant woman who learns the dangers of drinking alcohol while pregnant and stops for the sake of her baby.

To act against a belief is to go against the core of our own being. When beliefs are developed that

don't serve us well, they become self-limiting. It is essential that in childbirth class settings women have an opportunity to explore beliefs they have about birth and to become aware if those beliefs will serve them well or not. This needs to happen early in pregnancy, or even before conception. In classes, I ask which one of the following statements is true for participants: that birth is a dangerous and frightening experience, or that birth is a wonderful and safe experience. The belief that birth is a dangerous and frightening experience presents a completely different picture than the belief that birth is wonderful and safe, and actions taken for either vary immensely.

Consider the contrast in beliefs about birth in the following statements:

- I would have had the cesarean again anyway. I feel a cesarean is safer for the baby. The certainty—knowing how it's going to go—is a good thing. With labor, you have absolutely no control—you don't know when it's going to happen. You don't know how it's going to go.

- I view birth as a very natural process that reinforces my confidence in my own body. My midwife said to me, "There's no question you're going to deliver this baby naturally; and when it's all over, you're just going to be amazed at how important it was to you." Well, I did, and she was right. Afterward, I had a feeling about my own strength that I'd never felt before.

In the first statement, the belief is that birth is not safe. In the second statement, the belief is that birth is safe. In addition, the second woman received empowering words from her midwife.

It is common to have women in childbirth classes with both types of beliefs, and it is the job of the childbirth educator to facilitate discussion to help identify beliefs so they can be expressed. Never underestimate the power of a discussion where birth is discussed in a positive context that empowers women. Saying, "Your body is so wise—it already knows how to give birth and will be your guide in labor," can have a great impact on pregnant women, especially when repeated.

Suppose a woman in a childbirth class holds a belief that "My body doesn't work for me." There are many thoughts associated with that statement. The childbirth facilitator might ask, "When are times in life when your body hasn't worked for you?" The woman might say, "Well, when I was young, I couldn't keep up with my classmates when running in gym," or "I get sick a lot." With a history of her body not working for her, and then hearing friends' stories about how difficult labor was for them, her belief that her body doesn't work for her is strengthened. Such beliefs may result in a difficult labor that requires the help of medical interventions.

But if the woman has very positive communication from her birth team, she may pull through and have the experience of her life for which she is proud, and which empowers her for the important work of parenting. A woman who believes, "My body works for me," is likely to go into labor with confidence that her body knows how to do the job of giving birth, and few if any interventions may

be necessary. If her birth requires medical intervention, she will still have confidence that she did the best she could and will likely have a positive memory of her birth.

Other thoughts and beliefs that may affect labor adversely include, "I am afraid of pain," "Hospitals aren't safe," "The sight of blood or needles scares me," "I'm afraid of becoming a mother," and "I'm afraid I'll lose control and make a fool of myself." Beliefs that are helpful in labor include, "I am a strong and capable woman," "My body knows how to give birth," "I ride long contractions like waves that always come to shore," and "My body knows how to relax."

Societal beliefs in birth

A new societal belief surfacing today is that a cesarean is safer than a vaginal birth. In "More Women Turn to Cesarean Section," a *Philadelphia Inquirer* article from March 20, 2005, Marie O'Neill— obstetrician and gynecologist at the Thomas Jefferson University Hospital—was quoted as saying that she "chose to deliver Benjamin by cesarean section to avoid damage to her pelvic area." Another quote in the same article quotes a physician as saying, "Vaginal birth may be nature's way, but nature's way has always been hazardous."[2]

When authoritative figures reinforce a belief that major surgery is safer than vaginal birth, women believe it must be true. Even ten years ago, few women would have accepted such a belief. With a cesarean rate in the US of 30.2 percent in 2005,[3] more women now perceive the procedure as being relatively safe and do believe it will avoid damage to the pelvic floor. But with correct positioning this damage can be avoided, along with other risks associated with surgery such as infection, embolism, and hemorrhage. Women need to remember that though we can be thankful that a cesarean is safer today than fifty years ago, it *is* and always will be major surgery. The decision to perform a cesarean should never be taken lightly by either medical professionals or birthing parents.

Cultural beliefs in birth

There are various beliefs about birth depending upon the culture of a pregnant woman. It is often not clear in any particular culture where the line between fact and superstition lies; however, if a woman has accepted a particular belief, she is likely to adhere to its practice. To give you an idea of the immense variety of beliefs in some cultures, I have listed a few cultures and some of their beliefs.

Common beliefs in Chinese culture[4]

- Pregnancy is believed to be a "hot" condition, and so a balance of "ying and yang" cold foods must be consumed throughout pregnancy.
- Pregnant women are advised not to touch anything adhesive or with glue, as it might cause birthmarks on their babies.

- Pregnant women are advised not to criticize others, or their babies will look and act like the person criticized.
- Eating pineapple can cause miscarriages.
- The spouse is not allowed to be present at delivery, for it is not a male's role.
- The father gives the baby its first bath.
- If the woman cries out during labor, it will attract evil spirits, so silence is recommended to protect the baby.
- Women are advised to squat when giving birth, as lying on their backs will not give the baby any energy to come out.
- After birth, women are advised to abide by the "sitting month" (the first thirty days to three months after birth).
- Women are advised to lay babies on their backs to sleep to produce the desired flattened head, which is considered beautiful.

Common beliefs in African, Asian, and Latin American cultures[5]

- The abdomen of a pregnant woman is massaged prenatally, in labor, and to expel a retained placenta. It is also massaged after the birth, and the woman is kept indoors for eight to forty days. She is kept warm and is given herb infusions to drink.
- In prolonged labor, the abdomen is rubbed with herbs and vomiting is induced by inserting a spatula into the woman's mouth. If she has been unfaithful to her husband, she is urged to confess this.
- The umbilical cord is cut with bamboo or a razor blade a long distance from the umbilicus.
- Taboos exist on "protective" foods—ones that contain vitamins and minerals—during the antenatal period for fear of miscarriage. Toward the end of pregnancy there are taboos on "foods for growth" (protein) and "energy-producing foods" (carbohydrates and fats) due to fears that the fetus will grow too big and cause a difficult labor.
- It is believed that upright positions are preferred for birth.
- More folk beliefs of Latina women:[6]
  - An unsatisfied pregnancy craving causes birthmarks.
  - Milk causes large babies and difficult births, and is to be avoided.
  - Chamomile tea makes labor more effective.
  - Exposure to an eclipse will result in a child with a cleft lip or palate. Some women wear a red string around their abdomen to protect against cleft lip or palate.
  - Inactivity during labor and delivery causes the fetus to stick (se pega) to the uterus.
  - Fear of unnecessary or dangerous medical interventions with resulting separation from loved ones results in women laboring at home for much of their labor.

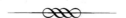
- Both children and unborn babies are vulnerable to *mal de ojo,* the "evil eye," which places a curse on the individual by such things as staring at her abdomen or paying her a compliment. To counteract the curse, the person must touch whatever part of the body that she or he looked at or admired.
- Vocalizing during contractions is encouraged, with many women releasing a rhythmic and high pitched *ay-ay-ay* chant as contractions increase in intensity. Some have been told that yelling helps to increase oxygen to their baby.
- After the baby is born it must be kept warm, as it is believed to be extremely sensitive to cold. In fact, the baby can easily catch a cold if part of the body is wet without getting the hair wet too. A binder is often placed around the newborn's abdomen, covering the umbilicus and making cord care difficult. A coin is sometimes placed over the umbilicus to prevent an umbilical hernia.

Cambodian culture[7]

- Prenatal visits are avoided by pregnant women because they require many physical examinations. (This is gradually changing with education about the importance of prenatal visits.)
- Pregnant women drink homemade rice wine, herbal medicines, coconut water, and beer—all believed to make the baby healthy.
- Pregnant women avoid taking showers at night and drinking milk, as these practices are believed to make the baby fat with a resulting difficult delivery.
- Most women give birth at home with midwives.
- The postpartum period is considered very important and is called the *"Sor Sai Kjey."* The woman lies on a bamboo bed with a constant fire underneath for one month after giving birth. During this time there is no bathing and she drinks only hot water, homemade wine, or herbal tea and eats hot fish and pork, as these are believed to help repair her tendons and regain her strength.
- During the first three days postpartum, others will breastfeed her baby and they will continue caring for the baby for a full month after birth.
- Sexual intercourse is avoided for six months to one year to allow women's bodies to recover and heal from pregnancy.
- Breastfeeding is believed to make their babies strong, smart, and obedient to their parents.

Culture of the Bedouin tribes of the Negev, Middle East[8]

- The evil eye is possessed by anyone whom Allah wishes to punish, and such a person is "empty-souled." Pregnant women must not walk by accursed landmarks that are associated with having the evil eye.

- The baby's forehead is smeared with indigo to protect it from the evil eye.
- A balanced mixture of the four humors in the human body—warm, moist, dry, and cold, which correspond with fire, water, air, and earth—must be received for a person to be healthy.
- Male babies are honored over female babies. Birth of a male baby is a joyous occasion and is accompanied by a ceremony, the *muruq isbu,* to celebrate. No ceremony is held when a female baby is born.

Indian culture[9]

- Pregnancy is viewed as a "hot state," a time of increased body heat. Becoming overheated is believed to cause miscarriage. Women are taught to avoid "hot" foods such as meat, eggs, nuts, herbs, and spices, and instead eat "cooling" foods such as milk products, fruits, and vegetables.
- Overeating is believed to produce a large baby and subsequent difficult delivery.
- To protect themselves from evil spirits, pregnant women wear a type of amulet called a *valai*—which means "to surround"—which is believed to create an invisible barrier for protection.
- Pain medications are believed to complicate the delivery and are avoided if possible.
- The sex of the child is told to the mother only after the placenta is delivered, due to fears that the birth of a girl may upset the mother and inhibit uterine contractions. Boys are highly preferred.

LIVING IN OUR HEART CENTER

Whatever the beliefs of a given culture are about birth, one thing remains the same and that is the overriding concern for the safety and welfare of the baby and mother. Beliefs women hold about childbirth are traditionally entrenched from early childhood, stories from older family members, expressions used in daily conversation, or from seeing live births. Women will hold onto beliefs tenaciously and really have to *want* to change them in order to do so. When they believe that what they are doing in birth is helpful to themselves or their babies, they feel good about themselves. Feeling good about themselves means they are living in their heart center.

When awareness is in our heart, words that are spoken are filled with compassion, kindness, and love, and those with us will feel safe, open, and relaxed. This is important in any area of life, including birth. In childbirth classes, when parenting, with relationships, and on the job, speaking from our heart center brings harmony to the mind and body. When challenges occur, having practiced this concept in daily life will make it easier to remember so that in times of stress and fatigue, we won't forget.

We use words all our lives in order to communicate, but have you ever wondered where they come from? If there is no such thing as "mind," then where do words that we associate with the mind originate? Some might answer, "The larynx," but the larynx only produces vibration, not words. Over the years I have come to realize that wherever awareness is in my body, that is where my words come from. This concept is best explained using the analogy of a guitar.

Imagine the strings of a guitar. If you press a finger on one fret, you hear one sound. If you move your finger to another fret, you get a different sound. So, whenever you put your fingers on different frets, you get different sounds. The key word is *awareness*. Now, picture imaginary strings of the guitar stretching from your head down the spine to the sacrum. In the same way as placing your finger on the guitar string to get a sound, wherever you place your awareness in your body is where words emerge. The heart is located in the upper part of the body, so when awareness is there, words are kind, compassionate, and loving. Understanding this concept has important carryover to pregnancy, labor, and birth.

Upon reading the following two scenarios of a dialogue between a doctor and a woman who is working through contractions in very active labor, see if you can identify which words are heart-centered and which ones are not.

First scenario

Doctor: "You've been laboring a long time and progress is very slow. I think you need some Pitocin to get things going."

Laboring woman: "I really don't want that, but what will happen if I don't?"

Doctor: "Well, I'm afraid something could happen to your baby."

Now the woman in labor is scared. Her baby's life could be threatened. Instinctively, she will do anything to protect her baby, and accepts the medication.

Second scenario

Doctor: "You've been working hard in your labor and are doing a good job."

Laboring woman: "But it's taking too long and I don't know if I can keep going!"

Doctor: "The baby's heart rate is fine and your body has its own time clock for birth. I believe in you. We need to be patient. Just keep working through the contractions one at a time."

Words that induced fear in the first scenario were "aren't making progress" and "afraid something could happen." Women often hear only these frightening words and go into an emergency mode even though no emergency exists. Words that were heart-centered in the second scenario were "doing a good job," "heart rate is fine," "I believe in you," and "your body has its own time clock." Even though the woman in labor expressed doubt that she could continue working through contractions, her

doctor's words carried much weight and she was likely to continue. Other good phrases are "You are doing beautifully!" "You are strong!" and "Your baby can't wait to meet you." These generate feelings of love, courage, and positive anticipation that empower women giving birth. During the prenatal period, comments such as "You look great!" and "You're going to be a mother soon!" help empower pregnant women.

A mother's love is special, and mothers and daughters who have good relationships and who are together at birth are very fortunate. The loving and encouraging words of a mother are invaluable to her daughter. A mother who says phrases such as "I'm so proud of you," and "You're doing a great job," can give her daughter the strength and courage she needs to keep working with contractions. A mother's love is deep and pure. Her praise is sincere and her prayers are powerful beyond measure, for the love of a mother towards her child is like no other.

CHANGING BELIEFS

Since all beliefs are learned, they can be unlearned. This is called state-dependent learning. We have the power to change any beliefs we want to change, but to do so, conviction and willpower are required. The most effective way of changing beliefs is through the use of affirmations.

Affirmations

Affirmations are simply positive thought patterns. In childbirth preparation classes there should be time devoted to helping women realize what beliefs they have about birth and changing any that they feel are not helpful for birth. Affirmations always work because they have action, and according to the laws of physics, what has action also has reaction. Affirmations may not always work in the way or at the time that you expected them to, but they do work in their own time and will surely impact your life in a good way.

When developing an affirmation, it is important to follow three general rules:
1. Keep all words in the present tense.
2. Keep all words positive.
3. Use the first-person singular.

These rules are based on the fact that the brain interprets words literally. This means that in the affirmation "My body *will* work for me," "will" means it will always be, projected into the future, but won't be in the present moment when needed. A woman in labor wants to know that her body will be able to do the work of labor. If she has doubts about this, the affirmation "My body works for me," is helpful. Note that all words in this affirmation are in the present tense and positive.

I used this affirmation when I gave birth to my son. However, the thought that my body didn't work for me when I had my daughter by cesarean was still strong in my mind. When changing a belief, an affirmation can often feel untrue at first because it is not infused with much energy, being

a new and thus weaker thought. To change a belief, focusing on the one you are trying to change actually draws more attention to it, reinforcing it. It is important to just let that belief alone and instead focus on the new affirmation. Ways to infuse this new thought with more energy are to write it down ten times before going to bed at night and placing it on a piece of paper by a light switch used frequently during the day, or in your car on the dashboard, or on your refrigerator. Saying over and over again, by pure repetition, "My body works for me; my body works for me; my body works for me," will eventually give this thought more energy, and it will then gradually manifest itself in your life. Whatever thoughts we infuse with energy must have a result.

There are many affirmations helpful for birth such as "My body is full of vibrant energy," "I am confident in my body's ability to give birth," "I attract all good things to me in my life," "I am a strong and powerful woman," and "The spirit works through me and gives me strength." It is best if you develop your own affirmations because they are then specific and more meaningful for you.

Reframing

Taking a negative thought and making it positive is called reframing. For example, the belief "I am afraid of pain," could be reframed in an affirmation such as "Contractions are healthy and normal." Another example of reframing can be seen during labor when contractions are becoming stronger and harder. A natural tendency is to want to run away from them, but if a woman is told, "The stronger your contractions, the sooner your baby will be born," she can be redirected back to the work of labor and birthing her baby, and welcome the contractions instead of running from them. The value of reframing is not to be underestimated.

A BIRTH STORY

As you read Lisa's birth story, see if you can identify what beliefs she holds about birth and what misinformation she has about birth. How do they affect the outcome of her birth? The story portrays how good childbirth class preparation can make a difference in birth by helping to dispel myths, build confidence, release fears, and reframe birth as a positive experience for women who are afraid.

The baby was two weeks overdue when my water broke. I went to the hospital but was sent home with the instructions to relax and rest and eat lightly. At 6 p.m. I returned to the hospital, only to find out that all the regular contractions I had had over the last twelve hours only achieved one degree of dilation of my cervix. My doctor told me to walk around the hospital corridors and not worry. I walked for three hours but my cervix only dilated to three centimeters. He gave me Pitocin to get labor going, and after four hours I asked for an epidural. I slept through the night toward dawn, when all of a sudden my doctor and staff members entered my room. The electronic fetal monitor strapped to my belly to track my baby's heartbeat was registering

decelerations. They inserted an internal fetal monitor to make sure the baby was okay. This fetal scalp blood sample indicated that the baby was okay. I labored more hours and watched TV. My legs felt cold, clammy, and uncomfortable and I didn't like not being able to move them. My cervix was near full dilation now, and so they let the anesthetic wear off. I was unprepared for the sudden strong contractions I was feeling. But the baby would not descend. By now I was in my thirtieth hour of labor. "It's time to do the cesarean," my doctor said. "You don't want to visit this baby in the intensive care unit, do you?" There was no way I wanted a cesarean, but then something happens and you say, "Do whatever—I don't care—do what's best for the baby."

Lisa believed that the first twelve hours of labor was active labor. Actually, it was prodromal labor, which means it was not yet active labor. She needed to know that active labor is defined as four centimeters of dilation and/or dilating regularly with time. Therefore, at the time she received Pitocin, she was not yet in active labor. However, if someone had complimented and encouraged her about all the good work she was doing to thin out her cervix (effacement), she would have felt she accomplished something good in those twelve hours.

She thought an epidural would make her comfortable, when actually the cold, clammy, heavy feeling in her legs was very uncomfortable and she couldn't sleep. It also kept her from being able to work with her body, moving into various positions to help her baby descend into her pelvis. She did not know that decelerations on the electric fetal monitor are infamous for being very subjective. The fetal scalp blood sample was an example of a medical procedure that confirmed the baby was okay, but that could have been prevented if there had not been so much trust in a tracing from the electronic fetal monitor.

When the anesthetic wore off, Lisa was suddenly faced with and unprepared for the very strong contractions that she could now feel. She became discouraged especially when the baby wasn't coming down. Not feeling sure that she could continue with labor, the doctor's comment about the intensive care unit tapped into her fears. At that moment she sacrificed all her hopes and dreams of the birth she envisioned and consented to a cesarean for the supposed "safety" of her baby.

In childbirth classes I ask participants, "What is so important about a vaginal birth? Why don't we just all go and have cesareans as more and more women are doing today? Scheduling a cesarean means we know when the baby will be born and also avoids labor."

Common responses are: "Surgery hurts and it is scary." "I want the experience of giving birth." "A vaginal birth is safer, far less painful in the long run, and more fulfilling." "I want my strength and energy to return quickly." "I want to laugh; it hurts too much to laugh after a cesarean." "I read in Dr. Michel Odent's primal health research that surgery affects milk production adversely, and I want to breastfeed." Having a group response such as this helps birthing parents to think through their choices more clearly and effectively.

PRACTICAL TIPS IN MANAGING THOUGHTS

Just as we learn to manage our money, time, energy, and food, we must also learn to manage our thoughts. Concentrating on the wrongs of others pollutes the mind with negative thoughts that take us away from the heart center. This results in anxiety, worry, and decreased clarity of vision. Such confusion makes it hard to set goals and attain them. Here are some steps you can take.

1. ***Become more aware of what you believe.*** Taking consumer-oriented childbirth classes can help you to do this. They will also inform you about options that are available. Writing down your beliefs helps to formulate them.

2. ***Learn to regulate your life in such a way that you do not have ill feelings and negative thoughts about others.*** When the mind concentrates on virtues and the well-being of others, it is cleansed and entertains only good thoughts.

3. ***Learn to forgive others for what they have done to you.*** No evil thought can penetrate the mind of a person wholly given to love and compassion. Forgive yourself. Forgive the doctor or nurse. Forgive the midwife or doula. Forgive the medical system. Forgive your husband or significant other. Just say, "I forgive you." Not to do so is to become the victim yourself, for it leads to a troubled mind. Forgiveness is the path to peace.

4. ***Live in the present: it is a gift.*** The past is gone. Let it go. Wake up each day with a fresh start.

When you open yourself to the spirit, the goals you may truly believe in are more likely to come true, but may also turn out somewhat differently than you imagined. This is because the spirit knows more about us and our needs than we do ourselves. Therefore, if we take the first step with heart-centered awareness, the spirit is sure to take us where we need to go. In the end, we may wonder how we didn't see the exact outcome ourselves.

It is only when the mind changes that the current crisis in birth will improve. The greatest challenge we face is that of understanding the nature of our own mind. Keeping the mind calm through slow breathing, reducing desires, taking thoughts first to the heart, and carrying out all actions with the idea that the spirit is working through us are positive ways to begin. Using the acronym **WATCH** (Words, Actions, Thoughts, Character, Heart) is another good way to start working on controlling the thoughts of the mind.

Words

Awareness is the key. Patience wanes thin at long labors when people become very tired, and behaviors become affected. Words may get short. People may become irritable. The laboring woman is working hard to ride the contractions and may not be making progress quickly enough to satisfy her caregivers. It is crucial, in spite of emotions, to maintain an atmosphere of safety by using words that are kind, compassionate, encouraging, and full of love.

Actions and thoughts

During pregnancy a woman needs to think good thoughts. This is sometimes difficult with hormones raging inside, causing mood swings, or with false-positive results coming back on prenatal tests. The best way to seek optimal health during this time of great transition and during the gestational period is to eat healthy foods, get good sleep, and exercise. It is a time to be conscious of breathing when anxiety or worry surface, and to send thoughts of love to herself and her baby.

Character

A person of character has a good sense of truth and bases all actions on truth. Such a person is dependable and trustworthy. Some people may refer to such a person as someone who has her act together. A man or woman with character stands out from others in a good way. Birthing parents will seek out such people to be with them at their birth if possible.

Heart

What is there if there is no compassion, warmth, or caring? Heartfelt communication means everything, and can come with a smile, a gesture, eye contact, and kind words. Verbal or nonverbal communication that is heart-centered feels engaging and safe. We all deserve to be treated with the dignity and respect that a heart-centered approach offers, and this is especially important during the childbearing period.

Our entire destiny is based on thoughts. They are the source of all our beliefs and actions, and we become whatever they are. When they are based on our dharmas, then all that we do becomes right action and we can know that we are making right decisions. A pregnant woman who puts this into practice will go into labor and birth with much wisdom, and she will come closer to realizing the full potential of all that birth has to offer her. She will find herself transformed in delightful ways that will lead her with confidence into her next role of parenting.

Birthing in the Spirit

To me, birthing in the spirit means bringing new life into the world through the Holy Spirit.
It gave me peace that God's will was being revealed through me and that I was partaking in the

experience of having a child that He gave me. The baby was His gift to me, and finally meeting my child gave me excitement and exhilaration. I couldn't wait to get to know each child that God gave me. I visualized the contractions as my body doing its work, like a flowing river, pushing the baby out.

—MITZIE BARTON, WHEATON, IL

CHAPTER 15

Pelvic Bodywork

Successful reproduction, or survival of the species, is built into every
living thing on the planet. Human babies are no exception.

JEAN SUTTON, MIDWIFE, IN *LET BIRTH BE BORN AGAIN*

There can be no right action more helpful in childbirth than an understanding of pelvic bodywork. The way in which a fetus moves down through its mother's pelvis is truly an engineering feat. Because it is an engineering feat, women need to learn what positions will help their baby the most when it makes the descent through the pelvis to be born. To understand this concept it is helpful to take a look at traditional cultures of the world, for they have much to teach us.

TRADITIONAL VERSUS MODERN LIFESTYLES

You may have seen pictures of women in traditional cultures carrying water jugs or baskets of food or clothing on their heads. In addition, they often have one or two hands on the object balanced on their heads to help keep it steady. This is an important image, because in such women the back must be "tall," or in anatomical terms, extended. The back can only be extended when the pelvis is forward. Try this yourself. Sit in a chair and slump forward. Note how your pelvis has moved back into a posterior position. Now shift your pelvis forward and note how your back begins to get taller. In addition, when one or both arms are upward, it puts a stretch on the entire trunk, stimulating the entire proprioceptive system with its tissue stretch mechanisms, helping the forces going up to balance the forces going down. This is why in traditional cultures you will see women in labor hanging from a tree branch or bar when in labor. In this way, the forces going up (upward stretch of the trunk) balance the forces going down (weight of the body downward with gravity).

IMPORTANCE OF AN ANTERIOR PELVIS

The fetus will move into whichever place gives it the most room. In our modern culture we have many practices associated with luxurious lifestyles that make this more difficult for the baby. Think about the large, comfortable sofas and lounge chairs that we like to sink back into while watching movies and television shows. Think about those comfortable bucket seats in cars, where we sit for

long drives. Think about even sitting in a chair and crossing your legs. These are all ways that make the pelvis tilt backward, moving it more posteriorly. When there is a posterior pelvis, there is less room for the baby. When there is an anterior pelvis, there is more room for the baby in which to move around.

In the last six to eight weeks of pregnancy it is essential that pregnant women avoid positions where the pelvis is posterior. Instead, they need to sit in chairs without crossing their legs, letting the weight of their abdomen shift forward. They need to sit on pillows if in the bucket seat of a car to position their pelvis forward. They need to avoid sitting back in soft, comfortable sofas or lounge chairs, instead choosing to sit in a regular chair with a flat seat. When the pelvis is forward, there is a clear passageway through which the baby can move.

Imagine a water hose. When there is a kink in the hose, the water gets stuck. When it is opened, the water flows freely. In the same way, a woman in labor needs to keep her passageway open without any kinks. This is best accomplished when her pelvis is forward. When you see a woman near her due date whose abdomen protrudes very far forward, you can know that her baby is likely to be in a good position to be born.

THE PELVIC OUTLET DIAMETERS

Many pregnant women envision a small opening for their pelvic outlet and wonder how on earth their baby can fit through it. They also envision birth as a more anterior experience, with the baby coming out more towards the front of their bodies. These are both incorrect. The pelvic outlet is actually quite large, just the size of a baby's head, and birth is more of a posterior experience, toward the back of the body.

Some women are told by their doctors in a prenatal visit that they have a small pelvis. This woman watches her abdomen grow larger day by day, and the seed of doubt that she can deliver her baby naturally has been planted. By the end of pregnancy she may already have prepared herself for a surgical delivery.

All childbirth classes should educate pregnant women about the size of the pelvic outlet, the space the baby has to emerge into the world. This can be done by asking women to place the palm of one hand on their pubic bone and reach back towards their tailbone. This will usually be to two-thirds of the way along their middle finger. This is the vertical diameter of their pelvic outlet. Next, they should place the fist of one hand between their "sit-bones," or ischial tuberosities, which are small projections off the large pelvic bone called the ileum. This is the horizontal diameter of their pelvic outlet.

Now have them hold one hand with fingers together in front of themselves. Trace a circle from the palm around the little finger to two-thirds down the middle finger, down around to the thumb, and back to the palm. Lo and behold, it is the perfect size for a newborn baby's head! It should also be pointed out that in the newborn, "bone" is actually immature and considered more cartilage, which is very flexible and pliable. A woman who understands this will go into labor with a completely different perspective of her body compared to someone who doesn't. She will be able to visualize a wide pelvic outlet that knows how to open just the right amount of space for the baby to be born. She will have confidence in her body and believe in its ability to open to give birth.

DIAMETERS OF THE PELVIC OUTLET

ANATOMICAL POSITIONING OF THE HIPS

Another very important concept in pelvic bodywork is keeping the hips in a neutral, anatomical position, meaning neither in internal nor external rotation but with the knees pointing straight forward. Here, knowledge of the sit-bones is very important. As mentioned above, the sit-bones form the horizontal diameter of the pelvic outlet. The baby must pass through the sit-bones to be born. If the sit-bones are closer together, it will be more difficult for the baby, and the mother will labor longer. If the sit-bones are farther apart, the baby will have an easier time passing through them and the mother's labor may be shorter, especially if the baby is in the correct occiput anterior (OA) position with its head down and its back on the left side of her abdomen. When a woman's hips are in external rotation, her sit-bones are closer together. The hips are in external rotation in the "stranded beetle position" when a woman in labor is lying on her back with her legs wide apart. This is one of the most disadvantageous positions a woman in labor can assume.

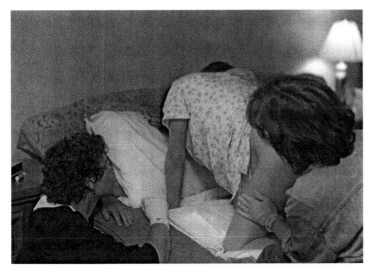

HANDS AND KNEES BIRTHING

THE HANDS AND KNEES POSITION

In labor, the hands and knees position has many advantages. In this position a woman's hips are in neutral position, keeping her pelvic outlet open. The pelvis is tipped forward especially with the weight of the baby, and the sacrum moves upward, allowing for more room for the baby to pass under it. The baby can pass in front of the pelvic floor muscles and easily through the sit-bones.

The hands and knees position

is so important that Jean Sutton, a midwife from New Zealand and author of *Let Birth Be Born Again*, advises women to crawl around on their hands and knees, perhaps washing the kitchen floor the old-fashioned way every day during the last six to eight weeks of pregnancy. This gives the baby optimal space to assume correct positions inside its mother and changes the direction of pull of weight on the mother's back. It is also a position one might assume when in prayer, lending itself to a sense of humility and surrender to the spirit. Doing this before labor can help a woman become familiar with the position and she may find herself wanting to assume the same position in labor.

Squatting helps to increase the pelvic space by opening the symphysis pubis, a fibrous joint located between the pubic bones of the pelvis up to two centimeters. Fibrous joints are not known to open, but the symphysis pubis does only for women during pregnancy and labor. However, a mistake that pregnant women make is positioning into a low squat where their knees are higher than their hips. This has the effect of narrowing the angle between the spine and the brim of the pelvis, closing the available space in which the fetus can move.

In the dangle squat position, the woman in labor stands between two other people who are sitting on higher surfaces and places her arms on their legs. She then allows herself to drop down, taking some but not all weight off of her feet, staying there during the contraction. In this position there is a stretch in her trunk, with the forces upward balancing the forces downward, encouraging the baby to move down into the pelvis. The same principles apply in the supported squat position, except here the woman in labor stands with her back against another person, who holds her hands at shoulder level. She drops down, taking some weight off her feet for the duration of the contraction, and then stands up again. Kneeling with arms over a birthing ball is still another position that keeps the knees lower than the hips and ensures more space for the baby to move.

BREATHING A BABY OUT

There is a belief in our culture that at the end of labor a pregnant woman must push her baby out. The typical scenario is of a woman lying on her back on a hospital bed, legs spread wide apart in the "stranded beetle position," numb from an epidural and with an IV in her arm. She is unable to move freely and lacks any ability to feel how to move her body in response to the baby's movement inside. She is in a position where there will be pressure of the baby on her pelvic floor muscles, with a possibility of damage to them. The position requires that she push, as the baby must move up—against gravity—to emerge from the vagina. But there is a much better way.

When a woman is on her hands and knees, or even left sidelying, with her pelvis forward and without any numbing drugs, the engineering aspect of birth becomes much easier. The baby passes in front of the pelvic floor, keeping the pelvic floor muscles safe from any trauma. The woman is also in a position where her pelvis is forward and the baby has a clear passage out into the world. A birthing woman in this position can simply breathe her baby out with minimal pushing. No need

for anyone yelling, "Push! Push! Push! One, two, three, four, five, six, seven, eight, nine, ten!" This is archaic managed birth and not birth as it was ever meant to be.

RHOMBUS OF MICHAELIS

At the base of the spine there is a rich reservoir of nerves around the three lower lumbar vertebrae and the sacrum, an area called the Rhombus of Michaelis. This pelvic plexus reservoir of nerves (inferior hypogastric, clitoral, and pelvic splanchnic nerve) does not play a role in defecation or purposeful pushing and is specific to the "fetal ejection" reflex. The Rhombus of Michaelis plays a crucial role in the second stage of labor, especially in positioning. The sacrum moves as a unit, causing the entire posterior pelvic wall to move together. The action of the Rhombus of Michaelis "seems to be triggered in a normal birth by the back of the baby's neck pressing on these nerves as he begins to lift his head."[1] This causes the fetal ejection reflex.

In women giving birth naturally, you will always see them arching their back in the moments just before birth, moving the wings of their ilea bones (largest of the pelvic bones) outward in a flaring motion for the final opening of the body for birth. Jamaican midwives taught Sheila Kitzenger that "the baby will not be born until she opens her back."[2] Women lying *on* their backs have difficulty moving their bodies in this way, and those with epidurals cannot move this part of their bodies at all.

BIRTH IS SEX; PUSHING IS DEFECATION

Sutton describes the concept of breathing a baby out by saying, "Birth is sex; pushing is defecation." She maintains that when the body is in the correct position for birth, it is an intimate and sexual experience. Women lying in supine or backlying positions have no choice but to push their babies up, against gravity, simply due to their positioning. Women on their hands and knees are positioned in such a way that their babies can slide out with the assistance of gravity. There is no counting and holding breath, no purple faces, and few sore muscles the next day.

SUMMARY

When a woman has kept her pelvis in an anterior position during the last six to eight weeks of her pregnancy, the baby has its best chance to find its way down into her pelvis correctly. If she assumes correct postures in labor, constantly moving her body into different positions, the baby can pass in front of the pelvic floor and she can literally breathe him or her out. Such a position is not routine in hospitals today and may require advance planning on the part of birthing parents by discussing this with care providers.

I'll never forget my sister's births of her four children. She gave birth on her hands and knees on

the hospital bed. There was nobody telling her to push. It was quiet, and her children came into the world with wide, curious eyes. It was peaceful and serene and filled us all with the wonder and beauty of birth.

Labor is hard work, but it doesn't have to be as difficult as it often is. With correct positioning based on pelvic bodywork knowledge, a woman can work with her body and give her baby optimal space in which to move and enter the world.

Women often refer to giving birth as being orgasmic. "I lost all sense of time and space and felt orgasmic," said one woman. When a woman is in her inner world that already knows how to give birth and has her body in correct positions, the baby slides out. This is a peaceful birth, and as the baby opens its eyes, the baby finds its first experience to be quiet, peaceful, serene, and full of love. There is no fear here, just pure love.

Birthing in the Spirit

My first birth was a revelation to me. I felt like I lost touch with the world for those hours I was in labor; sounds seemed distant and nothing else mattered except for the contractions. I followed my instinct and found myself walking all the time, even when the contractions were so hard that I barely moved a centimeter per step. I sat on the toilet a long while and would suddenly feel like walking. Everyone had to keep up with me and what I wanted. Surprisingly, I didn't want anyone to touch me or talk loudly because this brought me back to Earth.

I kept my wrists relaxed and let my body give into contractions. I remember asking how much longer it was going to be, and my husband answered that I was doing great and that the baby would come when it was ready. The midwife agreed, saying that my body was on its own clock. I let go of time.

Following my instincts, I gave birth on my hands and knees. (The midwife later told me that she had to quickly figure out how to do things backwards because she usually worked from the other way around.) So, although I didn't know what I wanted before labor I found out that I really did know what I wanted when I was in labor. It was a truly beautiful birth.

—TRUDY SULEIMAN, MOTHER IN NEW JERSEY

CHAPTER 16

Nutrition and Our Health

Let us bless the source of life that brings forth bread from the Earth.
Let our lives be a blessing to the Earth that sustains us,
and to all the creatures that, like us, call this planet home.

JOHN ROBBINS, AUTHOR OF *MAY ALL BE FED*

Health is wealth. Good health is required to do anything, including growing and birthing a baby. As is the food, so are the mind, thoughts, conduct, and health. Two good reasons for pregnant women to eat healthy foods are: to grow healthy babies, giving them an optimal start in life; and to be healthy themselves so they can take care of their babies. But in today's world, many women who are pregnant are not eating enough nutritious foods, and this impacts their health and the health of their babies. In fact, our entire society is at risk for diseases that result from eating foods with poor nutrient quality, in excess quantity.

The foods that are promoted by advertisers as tasting good are often high in sugars and saturated fats that promote obesity and cardiovascular diseases. These foods are highly processed junk foods and fast foods that are affordable and convenient but that wreak havoc on our physical, mental, and spiritual well-being. There is strong and mounting evidence that they have adverse effects on the fetus of a pregnant woman as well.

NUTRITION: A NEW SCIENCE

Until recently, few medical schools included nutrition in their course of study. The field of nutrition is thus a complex and rapidly changing one as we learn more about the wonders of the human body and how it interacts with the foods and nutrients we eat. Health letters, nutritionists, popular books, and the media often give contradictory advice regarding what they profess to be sound and healthful nutrition. Consumers often don't know which way to turn as they choose their foods. Now major medical schools publish nutrition newsletters to help educate the public so they can understand the

great influence of foods on their health and the prevention of disease. We are starting to gain an appreciation of the biochemistry of foods, but still there is much that remains to be learned.

In this chapter I am presenting basic information on nutrition that is applicable to all people and especially a pregnant woman, for she is growing a baby. Good nutrition should begin well before a woman becomes pregnant so that healthy eating habits will already be established when she conceives. By the time a woman realizes she is pregnant, the fetus may already have a beating heart. All fetal organs have sensitive growth periods. There is increasing evidence through primal health research that if essential nutrients are missing during such sensitive periods, it can result in permanent changes in the organ's size, structure, and function that will adversely affect life as an adult.[1] A good example is how a subtle deficiency of folic acid during pre-conception and early conception can result in neural tube birth defects.

You may be surprised to know that nutrition for a pregnant woman is not much different from nutrition for everyone else. The basic advice remains the same: eat a variety of foods, eat whole foods, and eat in moderation. In addition, a pregnant woman needs additional protein, calories, iron, calcium, folic acid, and fluids to grow a baby. General advice for all people includes minimizing their intake of refined sugar, saturated fats, and trans fats.

Despite not yet fully understanding the details of how various foods and nutrients affect a growing baby in the womb and how various foods work to keep a body healthy or cause disease, we can draw many important conclusions from nutrition research. Three of these well-established truths that are applicable to all people, and especially pregnant women, are:

1. Fruits and vegetables in quantities of four to ten servings daily should be consumed for optimal health.
2. Moderation of the quantity of foods eaten is necessary for a healthy and balanced life.
3. Eating foods as close as possible to their natural fresh state confers maximal nutritional benefit.

Fruits and vegetables contain phytochemicals, which are natural chemicals made only by plants and which include antioxidants, plant hormones, and enzyme-activating sulfur compounds. Their nutritious effects range from slowing down the normal wear and tear on body cells and improving heart and immune function, to strengthening bones and preventing cancers. A diet rich in fruits and vegetables (including dark, leafy greens) is rich in fiber, which helps food pass through the intestines more quickly. High-fiber foods are also more filling, decreasing the appetite for other foods that are more calorie-dense.

HOMEOSTASIS: CREATING A BALANCE

When metabolic, circulatory, and excretory systems of the body are in balance, there is a state of homeostasis and we feel healthier. Eating too much, eating too little, drinking too little water and

fluids, or eating unhealthy foods can all upset this balance. Certain basic life-sustaining nutrients, listed below, are necessary to maintain homeostasis, and they include:

- Carbohydrates to supply energy
- Fats and oils to supply energy and protect internal organs
- Proteins to grow and maintain lean body tissue
- Vitamins to provide components that are necessary for proper cellular function
- Minerals that are vital in many functions, including water balance and bone, blood, and soft-tissue health
- Water to carry nutrients and remove wastes

Protein

Protein requirements for pregnant women are 30 grams per day *above* the ordinary requirement to support growth of the fetus. Calorie and protein needs increase in the event of multiple pregnancies. Adequate protein intake often helps to decrease sugar cravings. Dairy foods and eggs are excellent sources of protein. Most of the protein in eggs is found in the white. Too much protein interferes with the absorption of calcium, so moderation is the key.

Calories

Pregnant women are advised to add 100 calories to their daily intake in the first trimester, moving to 400 by the third trimester. In other words, they should gradually eat more as the baby grows. If they are eating healthy foods, their bodies will likely guide them in how much to eat. If they are eating too much junk food, they will be consuming empty sugar calories that won't nourish their growing baby. Pregnant women should never go on a diet to lose weight because this can lead to nutrient deficiencies that may lead to low birth weight and other complications of pregnancy.

Iron

Hemoglobin in the blood carries oxygen from the lungs to the organs and tissues. Since plasma fluid volume nearly doubles by the last trimester of pregnancy, hemodilution occurs. Hemodilution means that even though the body fluids are nearly double, the hemoglobin does not increase proportionately, making it look like there is a drop in hemoglobin during pregnancy. Thus women may not be as iron-deficient as it appears. However, doctors recommend that pregnant women supplement their foods with at least 18 milligrams of iron per day during the last trimester of pregnancy.

Since it is hard to get this in foods, supplements are usually prescribed by practitioners. Iron in meat is easily absorbed, whereas iron in plants is more difficult to absorb. Eating vitamin C along with iron-rich foods or a supplement tablet will enhance the absorption of iron. Cooking in iron pots adds iron to the body, especially when cooking acidic foods such as tomatoes. Phytic and oxalic

acids can interfere with iron absorption, but this is not a concern in the presence of an adequate and varied whole-foods diet.

Calcium and vitamin D

The need for calcium increases to nearly 1,300 milligrams a day during pregnancy. If a pregnant woman does not meet these needs, the baby's calcium needs will pull from its mother's calcium, especially the teeth and bones. Yogurt is high in calcium and is also a fermented food that provides probiotic bacteria that enhances intestinal and immune health for both the baby and mother.

Vitamin D is necessary for the absorption and utilization of calcium. The body makes vitamin D from sunlight or receives it in fortified foods, the primary source now being fortified milk. Although dairy products are a good source of calcium, they are lacking in fiber and phytochemicals. Dark green leafy greens are good sources of calcium and they do have plenty of fiber and phytochemicals. Other good sources of calcium besides dairy products are sardines and calcium/vitamin D-fortified orange juice.

Recent research indicates that most people do not get enough vitamin D, especially in the winter months. Taking a walk in the sun or resting in sunlight for a half-hour three times a week is one of the best ways of getting the sun's ultraviolet rays, which make vitamin D in the body. It is also a good way to get a little exercise or simply to rest the mind in our busy lifestyles. However, there is a trade-off with more sun exposure given the increasing rates of skin cancer, especially if you don't use sunscreen; so again, moderation is the key. Most researchers now recommend 1,000 IU of vitamin D daily, and the only reliable way to achieve these levels of vitamin D intake is through supplements or vitamin D-fortified foods.[2]

Folic acid

Folic acid is a vitamin that helps to produce healthy red blood cells. All women of childbearing age should be taking at least 400 micrograms of folic acid a day as a supplement to prevent neural tube birth defects such as spina bifida and anencephaly, as this is needed well before conception actually occurs. Most multivitamins contain 400 mcg of folate, but read the fine print to be sure. Total intake in foods and supplement should be 800 mcg per day for pregnant women. Asparagus is a good, natural source of folic acid and also contains vitamins C and A, glutathione (an antioxidant that helps protect against cancers), and rutin (a bioflavonoid that may strengthen blood vessels). One more bonus—it is also low in calories. Many breads and cereals are fortified with folic acid, but don't count on these to get enough.

"Eating for two" or more

When a woman is pregnant, it is often said she needs to "eat for two." This intake of food and fluids

should continue as she breastfeeds, to support the production of milk. Even though the need for nutrients does increase over the course of a pregnancy, just because a pregnant woman is "eating for two" doesn't mean she should eat twice as much. Her body becomes more efficient at absorbing nutrients in the digestive system and it knows how to build up stores of vitamins and minerals for the baby. Also, the baby is small and doesn't need what an adult needs. It is the quality of the food, rather than the quantity, that matters.

A woman carrying twins or triplets needs to know that her nutritional needs will increase as the babies grow in size, and she will need to eat more. A baby who is not getting enough food may send an early signal to its mother to be born, as its survival is at stake. I worked with a woman pregnant with triplets. She ate food and drank fluids around the clock. Her babies were born at thirty-six weeks' gestation, with two weighing over five pounds and one over four and one half pounds! Nutrition is life-giving.

Good nutrition: Are you confused?

Because a pregnant woman wants to have a healthy baby, it is a time in her life when she is more likely to make changes in what she eats. However, she may be confused on what exactly constitutes good nutrition. For example, she may have read the cover title on a *Newsweek* magazine in March of 2006,[3] which said, "Diet Hype: Confused? From Fat to Calcium, How the Media Collides With Science." The inside article began: "Fat is bad, but good fat is good. What about fish? Wine? Nuts? A new appetite for answers has put science on a collision course with the media." In one place she may read it is okay to eat fats, and in another place reads cautions against doing so.

The following newspapers had these headlines:

New York Times: "Low-fat diet does not cut health risks, study finds."
Atlanta Journal-Constitution: "Reducing fat may not curb disease."
The Boston Globe: "Study finds no major benefit of a low-fat diet."
Los Angeles Times: "Eating lean doesn't cut risk."

This leads to the confusion of not knowing who or what is right, and results in people deciding to keep life simple and continue eating what smells and tastes good and is convenient.

Food preferences are formed very early in life, and the color of a food can determine the perception of its taste. In addition, aroma and memory are closely linked together. The certain smell of a food can remind us of a vacation or past event. As soon as we eat a certain food, its gases are released, which flow out of the mouth and up the nostrils to the back of the mouth to a thin layer of nerve cells called the olfactory epithelium, located at the base of the nose, in between the eyes. This is so automatic we don't even think about it. The brain then lets us know if it is something we want to eat or not.

Our likes and dislikes of certain foods are so well established and deeply entrenched by early life

that it may be difficult to change them. In fact, the market-research firm AC Nielsen found that Americans *are* very resistant to changing their lifestyles. In their study, Nielsen found that although people knew that what they were eating wasn't good for them, and were advised as to which foods were more healthy—e.g., water instead of soda—few actually followed this advice. Their reason for going ahead and eating unhealthy foods was living in a "modern convenience culture" where it was too inconvenient to follow lifestyle changes.[4] A woman may pass on a liking for high fat and sugary foods to her baby in the womb and on into its young life. This child will be so accustomed to eating a high-fat and -sugar diet that he or she may struggle with this the rest of their life.

Our changing foods

"What we eat has changed more in the last forty years than in the previous forty thousand years,"[5] says Eric Schlosser, author of *Fast Food Nation*. Aromas play a large part in our selection of foods to eat. Schlosser says that much of the aroma of the fast foods we eat today is manufactured at a series of large chemical plants off the New Jersey Turnpike. This means a strawberry drink with natural flavor is likely to have no strawberries or strawberry juice in it at all, yet it will taste like strawberry. In addition, we are adding more to our packaged foods in terms of artificial dyes, sweeteners, and preservatives than ever before, and we are also modifying foods through genetic engineering.

Genetic engineering is the removing of genes from one organism, such as a plant, animal, or microbe, and transferring them to another for the purpose of achieving a desirable trait. Genetic engineering has its advantages and disadvantages. It has helped millions of people through gene-altered bacteria that produce life-saving drugs and safer pesticides, less harm to wildlife, more nutritious foods, and increased quantities of food to feed the world's hungry nations. Scientists are currently working on crops that can resist droughts and survive in salty, marginal soil to produce higher yields.

A downside of genetic engineering is that allergens can be unwittingly transferred into the products, triggering allergic reactions in the people who eat them. Genetic engineering can also produce toxic foods because when a gene is transferred from one organism to another, there is no way of knowing which chromosome the gene will adhere to and how it will react with the genes around it. This is why all genetically engineered foods need to be tested before being put on the market.

Still another way foods have changed is due to improved transportation, which no longer makes us dependent on seasonal foods. We can now eat foods shipped or flown in from around the world, meaning that many are picked green and have not ripened on the vine.

What impact these have on a pregnant woman and her baby in the womb remains largely unknown. It is best to eat organic foods if possible, but there is a place for both organic and genetically engineered foods, as they can produce improvements over conventional agriculture.

FATS

There are good fats and harmful fats. To be healthy, our bodies need good-quality fats to make tissue and manufacture biochemicals such as hormones. The challenge is to balance the right amounts of good (poly- and monosaturated and omega-3) fats in our daily meals and avoid the harmful ones. Moderation and balance are the key. Too much of any kind of fat increases the risk of heart disease. Too little fat risks the body's ability to absorb and use fat-soluble vitamins, protect vision, bolster the immune system, and keep reproductive organs functioning.

The Dietary Guidelines for Americans recommend that no more than 30 percent of our total daily calories come from fat and that no more than 10 percent come from saturated fat. Without obsessing about the numbers, a good rule is to avoid fats that are solid at room temperature as much as possible (cheese, meat fats, Crisco, lard) and eat oils that are liquid at room temperature in moderation (fish oils, nut oils, vegetable oils). When possible, choose low-fat versions such as skim milk, non-fat yogurt, and part-skim cheese.

Good fats

Good-quality fats are crucial for fetal brain development. The brain is composed largely of fats, and in the last trimester brain development of the fetus is a primary emphasis. Growth spurts for fetal brain development occur at mid-gestation and in the ninth month. At birth, the brain is already 25 percent of the size it will be in adulthood, whereas the total birth weight is only 6 percent of adult weight. Olive oil, canola oil, safflower oil, fish oils, and flaxseed oils are all good-quality fats, but again, should be consumed in moderation.

In the last trimester pregnant women need to be sure to increase their intake of omega-3 fatty acids, especially docosahexaenoic acid (DHA). DHA is a long-chain polyunsaturated fatty acid of the omega-3 family that is very important for brain development, and the nervous system in particular. During the last trimester of fetal life, more than 50 percent of the fatty acids that incorporate the brain are represented by DHA. The chickens that produce DHA-enriched eggs have been given a special feed containing marine algae, which increases DHA levels in the egg. DHA is preformed and abundant in the seafood chain and also in human milk. The developing brain also needs polyunsaturates from the other family (omega-6) fatty acids, which are abundant in the land food chain.

Harmful fats: trans fatty acids and saturated fatty acids

Trans fatty acids are polyunsaturated oils that are industrially processed with hydrogen to make them more stable and resistant to spoilage. They then become "partially hydrogenated vegetable oils" added to foods to improve shelf life. Some junk food products in the grocery stores that are loaded with trans fats have a longer shelf life than the human body! These trans fats are even worse for the heart than saturated fat.[6] In fact, they are associated with the highest heart risk of any type of

dietary fat,[7] and in amounts typically consumed by Americans, they alter basic metabolic pathways, affect cell membranes, and generate free radicals that suppress the immune response.[8] A strong immune system helps to keep the body healthy.

Dangers of trans fats have been known for over ten years. Even though the Center for Science in the Public Interest asked for labeling of trans fats ten years ago, and the food industry spent three more years analyzing foods for trans and print labeling, it wasn't until 2006 that the government required labels on packaged food to disclose trans fats. This has had an immediate effect on food manufacturers, as we are now seeing packaged items stating "No trans fats." Still, if you see any ingredients that say "partially hydrogenated," you will know it contains trans fats and you would be wise to avoid buying such foods. Foods typically high in trans fats are French fries, Danish pastries, doughnuts, margarine, and most junk foods. But if the package says "No trans fats," be careful about how much saturated fat is in the product. Also know that manufacturers are allowed to say "No trans fats" on labels if there is 499mg or less of trans fats per serving in the product. For a substance that is felt to have adverse effects on our health at levels of two to five grams a day, 499mg per serving is a worrisome amount.

Saturated fats

Saturated fats are also detrimental to your health in proportion to their presence in your diet, but probably not at quite as low a level as trans fats. In a typical or standard American diet (SAD), saturated fat constitutes 13 percent of calories but trans fat contributes only 2 percent of calories, so there is more opportunity to cut saturated fats from our diet. The best indicator of whether a product contains a large proportion of saturated fats and trans fats is whether it is solid at room temperature. Thus, foods such as margarine and butter, shortening, cheese, meat fats, French fries, pizza, ice cream, and doughnuts are all high in saturated and/or trans fats and provide ample opportunity to cut back on these unhealthy fats. A pregnant woman should minimize her intake of such products.

Fatty streaks in fetal aortas

Does excess consumption of harmful fats impact the health of pregnant women and their babies? The answer according to recent animal and human research is a resounding yes. A study carried out on rats at the University of Buffalo gives us clues. In this study, female rats were fed a high-fat diet, and it was found that the chronic consumption of a high-fat diet by female rats adversely programmed the male progeny for glucose intolerance and development of increased body weight in adulthood. Researchers went on to conclude that this high-fat diet bears a resemblance to dietary habits in western societies with associated human obesity and related disorders.[9]

In another study,[10] human fetal aortas from mothers with normal cholesterol, with high cholesterol associated with higher-fat diets, and with high cholesterol only during their pregnancy were analyzed for fatty streak formation. It was found that though all fetal aortas had the formation

of fatty streaks, the fetal aortas from the high-cholesterol mothers contained more and larger lesions. Furthermore, the size of the lesions increased with age but increased much faster in the high-cholesterol mothers.

EFFECTS OF HARMFUL FATS AND EMPTY CALORIES— BODY MASS INDEX (BMI)>30

Today, about 44 million American adults are obese and an additional six million are super-obese, with a body mass index (BMI) greater than 40. No other nation in history has gotten so fat so fast, and the US has the dubious distinction of having the highest obesity rate of any industrialized nation in the world.[11]

A fetus is already familiar with the tastes of its mother from the food she consumes while pregnant. A taste for fat in childhood is difficult to lose as an adult, and this may have something to do with the characteristics of early fat cells. It seems that a characteristic of fat cells is that they only divide in the first one to two years of life. If so, it appears that early infancy may be the most important period for weight control on a permanent basis.[12] "Because obese infants have larger and more fat cells than non-obese infants, they are apparently more prone to becoming obese adolescents and obese adults."[13] This tendency is backed up by still another study showing that rapid weight gain in both infancy and early childhood is a risk factor for adult adiposity and obesity.[14]

Metabolic syndrome is a cluster of abnormalities that includes insulin resistance, being overweight, high blood pressure, high triglycerides, and low HDL (good) cholesterol. This syndrome is exacerbated by a high intake of refined carbohydrates (empty calories) and a sedentary lifestyle. It is associated with cardiovascular disease and diabetes and is reaching epidemic proportions. Substantial evidence was found to suggest that a poor *in utero* environment caused by maternal dietary deficiencies or placental insufficiency may "program" susceptibility in the fetus to later development of cardiovascular and metabolic disease. This "programming" is associated with any situation where a stimulus or an insult during the fetal development establishes a permanent physiological response.[15]

Putting this all together, we have a mother eating a diet high in trans fatty acids and saturated fatty acids as well as refined carbohydrates. Her fetus has increased and larger fatty streak lesions in its aorta. Early fat cells are larger and more numerous in these infants as compared to normal infants, making them prone to obesity and various associated diseases such as diabetes and hypertension as an adult. A child who learns to enjoy the taste of high-fat and refined-carbohydrate foods while young will have difficulty losing that as an adult, predisposing the individual towards obesity, diabetes, and cardiovascular diseases.

This epidemic of obesity and associated disease results in an increased cost of healthcare to society and the likelihood of another generation of children with similar problems. These considerations

make it apparent that there should be no place for junk food (foods high in trans fatty acids, saturated fatty acids, and empty calories) in a well-supervised program of nutrition for women, infants, and children, and that education of mothers regarding these nutritional truths is essential.

LIFESTYLE TRENDS ENCOURAGE OBESITY

Our nation has changed its way of eating and living, supporting a trend towards obesity. More and more people are eating meals outside the home and are thus consuming higher quantities of empty calories and solid fats and less fiber. In addition, portion sizes are usually much larger than necessary for both adults and growing children. Along with eating foods higher in sugars and fats, people are exercising less, and as a result they are gaining more weight.

Obesity now ranks second only to smoking as a lifestyle cause of mortality in the United States. The Center for Disease Control estimates that about 280,000 Americans die every year as a direct result of being overweight and that this has been linked to heart disease, colon cancer, stomach cancer, breast cancer, diabetes, arthritis, high blood pressure, infertility, and stroke.[16] Eric Schlosser documents that the obesity epidemic is spreading to the rest of the world, and wherever fast food restaurants proliferate, waistlines are getting bigger.[17] In fact, the eating habits of American children are examples to other countries of what should be avoided for their own children.[18] Yale University obesity expert Kelly Brownell states, "Our diet is deteriorating and physical activity is declining. Our current lifestyle with modern conveniences conspires to make both worse and worse."[19]

Diabetes

The danger of developing diabetes begins in the womb. Pregnancy changes a woman's metabolism and makes her more susceptible to developing gestational diabetes, which has profound implications for the health of the woman and the baby she is carrying. A woman, pregnant or not, who eats a diet high in sugar and refined carbohydrates is at risk for becoming obese and/or developing diabetes. Since 1990, type 2 diabetes has jumped by 33 percent nationwide,[20] and the epidemic of type 2 diabetes is the disease most closely linked to being overweight. Though it tends to be more a disease of adulthood, it is now beginning to show up in adolescent children. The rapidly multiplying fast food restaurants that serve foods high in sugars, refined carbohydrates, trans fatty acids, and saturated fatty acids are contributing to this problem. Diabetes is a disease that, once established, is difficult to reverse or even control with lifestyle measures alone. It can often be prevented simply by choosing to eat healthy foods and keeping physically active.

If you feel your foods contain too much sugar, here are some ways you can begin lowering the sugar:

- Begin to retrain your taste buds to enjoy healthy, whole foods that are naturally sweet, such as fruits and veggies. The mind is more trainable than you realize.

- Stevia, an herb used for sweetness, comes in small bottles, and very little goes a long way to sweeten your foods.
- Stop buying soft drinks. Instead, choose to buy drinks that say "100% fruit juice." If you want carbonation, natural markets sell spritzers—carbonated drinks with natural fruit sweeteners—or mix seltzer water with juice to make your own.
- If you need a drink without calories, then water is the best, but mineral water or flavored seltzer waters are good, zero-sugar, zero-calorie drinks for variety.

WHAT IS NOT NUTRITIOUS?

Let's take a more detailed look now at what foods are unhealthy for all people, including pregnant women, new mothers, and their babies. This will be followed by what foods are nutritious, along with some strategies for promoting healthier eating.

Foods high in sugar. We are programmed to like sweet foods! Even the baby's first food, breast milk, is sweet. In the womb it is known that a fetus will reject a sour substance but accept a sweet one, and a young baby will do the same. We like sweet foods so much that as we grow older, we tend to eat too much of them. Too much sugar is harmful in that it upsets the homeostasis of the body. It interferes with the body's regulatory system that lets us know we are full, and this leads to overeating. People then gain weight with empty calories that do not provide nutrition for the body. This places a pregnant woman in danger of not giving her growing baby optimal nutrition for growth. Many junk foods, doughnuts, candy, ice cream, and most desserts are high in sugar.

a) Soda. One of the leading culprits of overconsumption of sugar is soda, which is basically liquid candy. Sodas contribute more sugar to the average American's diet than any other food.[21] Soda has ten teaspoons of sugar in one eight-ounce serving.[22] It also contains high doses of phosphates that de-mineralize bones and lead to fractures, and caffeine, a stimulant.

Twenty years ago teenage boys drank twice as much milk as soda; now they drink twice as much soda as milk.[23] According to Schlosser, one-fifth of the nation's one- and two-year-olds now drink soda. Michael Jacobson, the author of "Liquid Candy," reports: "Pepsi, Dr.Pepper, and 7-Up encourage feeding soft drinks to babies by licensing their logos to a major maker of baby bottles, Munchkin Bottling, Inc." A 1997 study published in the Journal of Dentistry of Children found that many infants were indeed being fed soda in those bottles."[24] The average pH of soft drinks such as Coke and Pepsi is 3.4, an acidity strong enough to dissolve teeth and bones.

b) High-sugar foods. Ingredients listed on labels of products are in the order of their percentage by weight. If sugar or sweeteners are one of the first four ingredients, it is a good idea to put the item back on the shelf. Foods that are high in refined sugar tend to be lower in beneficial nutrients due to the disproportion of empty calories.

    a.   *Foods containing predominantly refined carbohydrates.* If white flour, as opposed to whole wheat flour, is one of the three or four primary ingredients, the food is best left on the shelf.

161

Substitute brown rice for white rice, and whole grains or qinoa pasta for pasta made from durum wheat semolina.

b. *Foods containing more than 250mg (0.25gm) of trans fatty acids per serving or more than 1000mg (1 gram) of saturated fatty acids per serving.*

c. *Foods containing heavy metals and other known toxins.* Examples are mercury in some types of fish and lead, dioxin, and pesticide residues typically found in non-organic peaches and strawberries.

WHAT FOODS ARE NUTRITIOUS?

1. Eat nuts. They are good for you! The story of nuts is one that demonstrates the changing trends in the science of nutrition. A few decades ago, nuts were valued for their protein, vitamins, and minerals. Then in the 1980s, they became compact sources of fat and calories that were to be avoided. Now in the 1990s, studies are showing that nuts are good to eat, as they contain good-quality fats and may actually protect against heart disease as well as lower blood cholesterol levels.

Nutrition researchers at Loma Linda University in California studied more than 25,000 Seventh Day Adventists to estimate how frequently they ate sixty-five foods from fruit to fish. A decade later it was determined that of all the foods, nuts was one of the most important links to good health. In addition, a recent study showed that consuming more nuts and peanut butter helped to lower the risk of type 2 diabetes in women.[25]

Nuts are rich in fiber and magnesium, mono- and polyunsaturated fats, vitamin E, folic acid, and other B vitamins (believed to lower blood levels of homocysteine, which has been identified as a risk factor for heart disease), and have a relatively low glycemic index. They also contain copper, potassium, and certain phytochemicals that may act as antioxidants or to lower cholesterol. The nut protein amino acid, arginine, protects arteries from injury and stops blood clots from forming. Nuts are so dense with nutrients that they satisfy hunger on fewer calories. Thus, research is showing us that nuts were and always have been safe and healthy to consume, and in fact are accepted as an essential food for our bodies.

Use nuts in meals rather than as a snack, when larger quantities might be consumed. I include walnuts in salads and stir-fry, and in banana and zucchini breads. Consider the nutritional content in the following variety of nuts:

- Almonds: rich in calcium, vitamin E, and fiber
- Brazil nuts: rich in selenium
- Cashews: rich in copper, iron, and folic acid
- Chestnuts: the only low-fat nut; rich in fiber
- Hazelnuts: rich in vitamin E and folic acid
- Macadamia: highest in fat

- Walnuts: rich in vitamin B$_6$ and heart-healthy oil
- Peanuts: not true nuts, but legumes

Of all the nuts, walnuts are especially rich in one kind of fat, the alpha-linolenic acid, which is converted in the body into omega-3 fatty acids, which are important for fetal brain development. Walnuts are a good source of these fatty acids for vegetarians who do not eat meat, fish, or poultry. The omega-3 fatty acids are found in fish oil as well. Note that cashews and hazelnuts are natural sources of folic acid, which is known to prevent neural tube defects such as spina bifida if taken before conception. Eating nuts by the handful right out of cans or jars can give an unexpected calorie surprise, as 100 grams (3.5 ounces) of nuts typically contain 500 to 700 calories. So go for those nuts—in moderation, of course.

2. Water and watermelon. The body does not store water, so we must drink a new supply every day. Most of us don't drink enough water. It is said that when we first have the thought that we are thirsty, we are already dehydrated.

The body is composed of approximately 70 percent water, which helps to move nutrients and cells around the body. A pregnant woman doubles her plasma fluid volume by the seventh month and needs to drink plenty of water to sustain that increase. A nursing mother should continue to drink plenty of fluids, including milk or soy milk, water, and fruit juices, to support the production of breast milk.

But we don't have to get water only from drinking a glass of water. There are fruits with high water content. Watermelon is named appropriately because it is 92 percent water. In addition to the water, it is also a good source of vitamins A, B$_6$, and C, has less than one gram of fat and no cholesterol, and is very high in fiber. You may be surprised to read that other foods that have 90 percent water content include green beans, cauliflower, celery, cucumber, lettuce, zucchini, onion, and pumpkin. While caffeinated and alcoholic beverages provide water, they also increase its elimination from your body, as they are diuretics (chemicals that increase urination), which may lead to dehydration.

3. Fruits and vegetables. No matter which nutrition health letter I read from which medical school, the consistent conclusion is that people who eat more fruits and vegetables in their meal plans are healthier than those who don't. The Heart, Lung and Blood Institute in the DASH (Dietary Approaches to Stopping Hypertension) diet and the American Cancer Society recommendations to prevent cancer both place eight to ten servings daily as the optimal goal for fruits and vegetables combined. Thus, the word is out and people are responding by eating more fruits and vegetables.

I have included a short description of the role they play in keeping our bodies healthy. They should be washed well to decrease chances of bacterial contamination and to attempt to remove pesticide residues. The following guidelines are recommended:[26]

- Buy fresh produce only if it is refrigerated or surrounded by ice.
- Store fresh fruits and vegetables in a clean refrigerator at 40 degrees Fahrenheit or below.

- Wash both your hands and the produce thoroughly.
- Scrub firm produce and let it air-dry before cutting.
- Remove outer leaves of heads of leafy vegetables.
- Drink only pasteurized milk, juice, or cider.
- Refrigerate or freeze leftovers within two hours of cooking.
- Store food at a shallow depth to speed chilling.
- Use leftovers in the refrigerator within four days or throw away.
- Organic produce is preferred over conventional produce, as there are fewer chemical fertilizer and pesticide residues and they are more environmentally friendly.

Some people wonder if soil mineral depletion makes the food we eat from the plants less nutritious. "Not so," says Dr. Gary Banuelos, a soil scientist. He explains that vitamins in plants are created by the plants themselves. Minerals such as phosphorus, potassium, iodine, calcium, copper, iron, selenium, fluoride, molybdenum, and zinc must come from the soil. If they aren't there, the plant droops, fails to flower, and may die. Thus, if the fruits and vegetables we buy look healthy, we can be certain they contain the nutrients they should.[27]

Eating a variety of fruits and vegetables as close to their natural state as possible helps maintain good health. Here is a list I have compiled of some "High-Power Foods" for pregnant and nursing women, gathered from various publications including Whole Foods Market[28] and Environmental Nutrition.[29]

a) Papaya. One-third of a papaya contains 100 percent of your daily vitamin C requirement. Vitamin C keeps your skin, bones, teeth, and tendons healthy. Its strong antioxidant qualities help the immune system fight against infection and assist in wound healing. Cantaloupe, strawberries, oranges, and kiwis are also high in vitamin C.

b) Dark, Leafy Greens. These greens are nutrient powerhouses containing easy-to-absorb non-dairy calcium, fiber, and vitamins A and C. They are also high in antioxidants and are an important source of folic acid and lutein. Other foods high in folic acid include oranges, beans, asparagus, avocado, and berries. Dark, leafy greens such as kale and collard greens are easily added to soups, stir-fry, and quiches. I chop them in my food processor and add them to mashed potatoes and, even better, to mashed sweet potatoes.

Spinach and Swiss chard contain oxalates that interfere with calcium absorption. If eating them, it would be best not to consume dairy products high in calcium until afterward. Lutein is a phytonutrient found in dark green, leafy vegetables such as spinach. It has the ability to filter out some of the sun's damaging light. Though lutein is present in eye tissue, it can only be obtained from food and cannot be made by the body.

c) Carrots. If you have a choice of what to snack on, choose carrots. Cut them up and cover with water in a container, and they are there ready for you to eat all week! They are especially beneficial

for eye health. Carrots are a leading source of beta-carotene, a compound the body converts into vitamin A as needed. Vitamin A helps the eyes to adjust from darkness to light and also aids in bone growth, reproduction, cell division, and cell differentiation. Sweet potatoes, peaches, spinach, and broccoli are other sources of beta-carotene.

d) Quinoa (KEEN-wah). Quinoa was a staple of the Inca civilization. It cooks faster than rice, is more nutritious, and has a nutty taste. It is technically a seed, not a grain, and has up to 11 grams of protein in just one-half cup, with a better balance of amino acids than many grains. It has a delicate flavor and is also high in fiber (5 grams). Quinoa also contains ample magnesium, potassium, zinc, vitamin E, riboflavin, copper, and more iron than true grains. Make this your staple during pregnancy and lactation! At natural food markets you can find spaghetti noodles made with quinoa.

e) Blueberries. Blueberries rank number one in their antioxidant power, i.e., their ability to neutralize cell damaging free radicals. Blueberries also have 4 grams of fiber per cup and lots of vitamin C. They are instrumental in the development of brain and visual tissue and help prevent urinary tract infections. Fresh or frozen are fine. Freeze them in the containers during blueberry season and enjoy them all winter long in smoothies, muffins, pancakes, salads, or simply in a bowl of milk or yogurt or on whole grain cereal.

f) Broccoli. Broccoli is a member of the cabbage family and is a powerhouse of nutrition. Its extensive list of nutrients includes vitamins C, K, and A, folate, dietary fiber, manganese, tryptophan, potassium, vitamin B_6 (pyridoxine), vitamin B_2 (riboflavin), phosphorus, magnesium, protein, omega-3 fatty acids, vitamin B_5 (pantothenic), iron, calcium, vitamin B_1 (thiamin), vitamin B_3 (niacin), zinc, and vitamin E. And all this with only forty-three calories in one cup of steamed broccoli! Make this wonderful vegetable a part of your daily meal plan by putting it in salads, stir-fry, quiches, stews, soups, or just as a side dish.

g) Sweet Potatoes. Sweet potatoes are an excellent source of vitamin A (as colorful beta carotene) and vitamin E. Eating them with a little fat increases the absorption of these nutrients. Baking them not only brings out the natural sugars but also makes your kitchen smell wonderful. Eating the skin gives you fiber and increases nutritional benefits. Fiber is important to help food move through your intestines, preventing constipation.

h) Avocados. These are excellent for all childbearing women due to avocados' potassium, folic acid, and vitamin C. They also provide an array of other essential vitamins and minerals including magnesium, thiamin, riboflavin, niacin, biotin, pantothenic acid, vitamin E, and vitamin K. Avocados are nutrient-dense and contain healthy monounsaturated fats. They also contain the antioxidant lutein, shown to be beneficial for eye health. Try cutting up some fresh onions and tomatoes, sprinkling them with a little olive oil and basil, and placing them on top of an avocado sliced in half with the nut removed. It is delicious!

i) Legumes (beans). Legumes are loaded with protein and fiber. Many varieties are also sources of iron, folate, and magnesium—important minerals especially for vegetarians. Kidney beans, garbanzos (chick peas), pinto beans, and black beans are high in health-promoting antioxidants.

Serve them in wraps and tortillas or soups and stews. Freeze and serve on busy nights during the week.

j) Grapes. Grapes are not only delicious but also protect your health. They contain two beneficial flavonoids, proanthocyanin and catechins. They assist the body's circulatory system—helping blood vessels to maintain their elasticity—and help to reduce cell damage. A single grape can hold more than 1,000 flavonoids. They also provide potassium, which benefits nerve and heart function. Other flavonoids are found in citrus, onions, and fruits. I don't buy grapes from South America, as DDT pesticide sprays are still used there, unless the grapes are organic.

k) Kiwifruit. Like broccoli, this fruit is also a powerhouse of nutrition. Two medium kiwifruit have more potassium than a banana and twice the vitamin C and fiber of a small orange, plus some folate, magnesium, vitamin E, copper, and lutein.

Color Coding

One of the easiest ways to know we are getting good nutrition is by how many colors of foods we have on our plate, and keeping the quantity of food there in balance and moderation. Choosing to eat from the spectrum of colorful fruits and vegetables is a concept called color coding. Most of the pigments that make the color in fruits and vegetables are potent antioxidants that help your body to fight disease. "Almost across the board, the most intensely colored fruits and vegetables have the highest levels of protective phytonutrients," says endocrinologist Daniel Nadeau, director of the HealthReach Diabetes, Endocrine, and Nutrition Center in Hampton, NH.[30] He gives the example of spinach, which has the yellow pigment lutein that helps prevent macular degeneration. A one-cup serving of raw spinach contains about three-quarters of our daily vitamin A, a quarter of our folic-acid needs, and a whopping 185 percent of our vitamin K—a nutrient correlated with bone strength. In contrast, pale iceberg lettuce has virtually no nutritional value. When I'm making a meal, I am always conscious of how many colors of foods I have on my plate.

4. Fatty Fish. Fatty fish are high in the omega-3 fatty acids so important for brain and visual development. Good sources of fatty fish are salmon, sardines, black cod, anchovies, herring, and trout. Due to the harmful effects of mercury on a baby's developing nervous system, the following guidelines should be followed by pregnant and lactating women:[31]
- Do not eat any shark, swordfish, king mackerel, or tilefish (also called golden or white snapper) because these fish have high levels of mercury.
- Do not eat more than six ounces of "white" or albacore tuna or tuna steak each week.
- Do not eat more than two servings or twelve ounces total of fish per week, making sure they are different types of low-mercury-containing fish.
- Choose shrimp, salmon, pollock, catfish, or "light," tuna as they contain less mercury.

As an alternative to eating fatty fish, fish oil supplements that have been processed to remove contaminants are available.

For those who do not have access to the sea food chain (or do not eat fish for personal or cultural reasons), it is important to eat foods containing catalysts for the development of unsaturated long-chain fatty acids such as magnesium, calcium, and zinc. Only the precursor to the long-chain omega-3 polyunsaturates (alpha linolenic acid) is provided by the plants of the land food chain.

5. Salt. Salt helps to maintain fluid volume. By the seventh month of gestation, the pregnant body nearly doubles its fluid volume. Salt intake in pregnancy should not be increased or restricted. People eating less healthy packaged and processed foods typically receive plenty of sodium. Adequate sodium is found in fresh natural foods so that adding salt is usually not necessary. A sufficient amount of salt tends to moderate the stimulation of the renin-angiotensin system (sodium pump) and is also necessary for the adaptive blood dilution in late pregnancy.

6. Vitamins. Varying opinions exist about whether or not to take multivitamin nutritional supplements during pregnancy. Some women believe eating well-balanced foods gives them all the nutrition they need, while others take the vitamins "just in case" they aren't getting the vitamins they need in their foods. If a pregnant woman takes vitamins, they should never be a substitute for eating nutritious foods and should never be consumed as a safety net. Healthy foods provide adequate vitamins for our health, and experts say there is a synergy between chemicals and nutrients in foods that can't be reproduced synthetically.

The only vitamin for which there is definite data of a benefit is folic acid, which prevents neural tube defects and which has to be taken prior to conception as well. For practical purposes, having all women take a reliable multivitamin with 400mg or more of folic acid throughout the childbearing years would make the most sense from a public health point of view.

ALCOHOL, NICOTINE, CAFFEINE

Pregnant women should avoid any consumption of nicotine, caffeine, and alcohol, as they all have adverse effects on a growing fetus and are known blocking agents, or inhibitors, to placental growth. They are all risk factors for low birth-weight infants (less than 5.5 pounds) and other poor infant outcomes. Alcohol is linked to fetal death, growth abnormalities, mental retardation, and fetal alcohol syndrome (FAS).[32,33,34] Many people use such stimulants in times of stress, when the body is already producing stress hormones such as cortisol. Cortisol is known to be an inhibitor to placental growth as well, so taking a stimulant during a time of stress has a double impact on fetal growth.

Tobacco decreases oxygenation to the fetus and leads to low birth weights and at-risk infants. Secondhand smoke is now viewed to be as dangerous as primary smoke, so a pregnant woman who breathes in the smoke from others is increasing risk for the health of herself and her baby. Policy makers have recognized that the environment must be free of pollutants and smoke, and responded by banning smoking in most public places in the US.

Caffeine addiction in our society is rampant. By its very nature as a stimulant, it will "pick you up," giving a boost in energy, but then it will also "drop you down." Because you still want to feel that boost, you reach for more caffeine. In this way, caffeine affects the central nervous system.

A hallmark of good health is the ability to have a steady mind. It is difficult to keep a steady mind under the effects of caffeine and other stimulants due to their physiological effects, for after they give you a high, they also send you low. Current available evidence suggests that pregnant women would be wise to limit their coffee consumption to three cups per day and no more than 300mg per day of caffeine to avoid the possibility of spontaneous abortion or impaired fetal growth.[35] I've never had a cup of coffee in my life, not only due to not liking the taste, but also because I haven't wanted to become addicted to caffeine.

FLAXSEED OIL AND ESSENTIAL FATTY ACIDS

Using flaxseed oil in your diet is one of the most important changes you can make in your meal plans! It is an all-star provider of essential fatty acids. Add it to cottage cheese, to olive oil in your salads, or over pasta. For vegetarians, foods that grow on land and contain catalysts such as magnesium, calcium, and zinc should be eaten so your body can make its own long-chain fatty acids.

MORNING SICKNESS AND HEARTBURN

If a pregnant woman has morning sickness (nausea and vomiting in the first trimester), she should practice "grazing" (eating small meals during the day); eat dried foods such as crackers or pretzels; avoid greasy, fried, or spicy foods; drink plenty of juice and water; and get rest. The same advice applies to heartburn, which is a reflux of food into the esophagus that gives a burning feeling. This is more common later in pregnancy, when the fundus of the uterus is high, pressing against the lower lobes of the lungs. In addition, drinking milk, avoiding liquids at meals, and elevating the head of your bed on four-inch blocks at night can help to decrease heartburn.

EATING MINDFULLY

Have you ever eaten a meal while engaged in delightful conversation, all of a sudden realizing the food is gone but you hardly remember eating it? This is not the practice of mindfulness. The practice of mindfulness means being more aware of all that is happening in the present moment, thus making the present more real. Eating mindfully means being more aware of food while eating it, and also sensing how we feel while eating it. Eating an apple mindfully means fully enjoying its taste, texture, and smell, eating it slowly, and sensing the elements of the sun, water, and soil that helped it to grow.

When we are not eating mindfully, we are more likely to eat too much. Eating too much creates an imbalance in the stomach. Imagine your stomach as a flat balloon that has no air in it. Now as you begin to inflate the balloon a little, that is your stomach with some food in it. Then imagine blowing more air into the balloon. How does your stomach feel with that much food? Blow more air into the balloon. It is quite big now. How does your stomach feel now? Blow even more air into the balloon. How is your stomach now? Can you remember overeating at a meal such as Thanksgiving and feeling very heavy from having eaten too much? Your body has produced insulin to counteract the blood sugars, and the resulting hypoglycemia or low blood sugar makes you feel lazy, tired, and lethargic. Perhaps you are thinking, *I wish I hadn't eaten so much!* This state is not healthy for anyone, and certainly not for pregnant women. A good rule of thumb is to get up from a meal with the same light feeling in the stomach as you had when you sat down.

There is a piece of advice from the people of Okinawa, an island off the coast of Japan where people live to be very old. Their secrets have more to do with how we live than who we are, which means they are applicable in any culture. The Okinawans eat plenty of fish and many vegetables, along with some meat and soy. However, their most important advice is to always keep one-fifth of the stomach empty. In other words, "Never, never be too full!" A sign in their community expresses their belief: "At 70 you are still a child. At 80 you are a young man or woman. And if at 90 someone from Heaven invites you over, tell him, 'Oh, just go away, and come back when I am 100.'"[36]

We often take food for granted because in the US it tends to be plentiful. But there are families of low income and single and teen moms in America who live day to day not knowing if they will have enough food to eat. Their basic priorities are to survive. Few take childbirth classes. How can they be concerned about positions in labor and good choices in food when they and their children are not getting adequate nutrition?

If a woman has a high-risk pregnancy and requires frequent visits to the doctor throughout her pregnancy, it may mean losing a desperately needed job to make ends meet. Some women are homeless and change their sleeping place on a monthly, weekly, or even daily basis. Prenatal care is a low priority when such a basic need as shelter is lacking. Outreach groups are making a difference, but it is slow and requires patience, creativity, and ingenuity.

HOLISTIC NUTRITION

People who are healthy in mind, body, and spirit have a countenance of happiness and good energy. In general, unhealthy foods and poor recreational habits are two primary causes of ill health.

Good nutrition involves more than knowing what kinds of food to eat. The ability to digest foods also makes a difference in how much food reaches the body and the growing baby. Even if nutritious foods are eaten, if they are not digested well, of what use are they to the body?

The stomach is the governing organ of the body. All the food we eat first goes into the stomach, and from there to the other organs by way of the bloodstream. During digestion, particles of food are

broken down into smaller and smaller components that are eventually absorbed from the intestine into the bloodstream. Some of the food we eat is excreted. Other parts of the food provide nutrients and energy to organs and blood, which in turn have an effect on our moods and thoughts. Therefore, there is a connection between the foods we eat and the mind. The human body itself is derived from food. Thus by the foods we choose, we can manifest or stifle our own bliss.

In cells, when oxygen from the lungs combines with food molecules such as simple sugars, there is a release of energy to the body. The amount and quality of energy released depends on the type of food we eat, our state of mind while eating it, and our current state of health. Try not to feel rushed. It is best to eat your largest meal in the middle of the day, when the sun is highest in the sky and the digestive fire is the strongest.

Eating while feeling upset affects how well the body is able to digest and excrete food. Breathing slowly at meal times and playing relaxing music improves digestion of foods. Overeating stresses the stomach, so we should try to eat only to satisfy hunger and not to appease an appetite. Besides being relaxed and breathing slowly, another way to improve digestion is to embrace the sanctity of the meal. Appreciate and give thanks for your food by saying a prayer. Be grateful to those who made it possible for you to eat it, from the farmer to the manufacturer and to whoever prepared it, even if it was yourself. Be grateful to the sun, which gave life energy to the plants.

Emotionally and mentally, we also nourish the heart and spirit with "food" taken in through not only the mouth but also through the other four senses of seeing, hearing, touching, and smelling. In fact, all of the five senses can be considered our "food" because they impact our health in some way. Thus, holistic nutrition connotes more than what is taken in through the mouth. What is seen through the eyes, heard through the ears, smelled through the nose, and felt by the skin is all a form of nutrition for the body. This food taken in through the senses may affect how the food taken in through the mouth is processed. Try to avoid eating in front of the television or eating on the go all the time so that you can eat mindfully with a steady mind. In this way, you can gain full benefit from the foods being eaten. A good nutritional spiritual practice is to:

See only what is good.
Hear only what is good.
Eat only what is good.
Touch only what is good.
Smell only what is good.
This is the way to good health
For the mind, body, and spirit.

To maintain good nutrition, it is essential for all people, especially pregnant women, to be more aware of what they are eating. It is never too late for people to make changes in their eating habits.

I grew up in a family that ate meat, potatoes, and vegetables at most meals. When in my late twenties I realized that a vegetarian diet was healthier; I have remained vegetarian to this day. I gave birth to my two children while vegetarian, and they have remained vegetarian as well. We are all very healthy.

Childbirth educators, doulas, midwives, and other caregivers who are knowledgeable about good nutrition can make a difference in the health of our future generation by helping them to make positive changes in choosing the foods they eat.

The body has been given to us for the purpose of carrying us through the journey of life, and for women, to bring forth life. It is our duty to sanctify our lives with good food that will bring forth good thoughts and deeds. This in turn has an influence on the fetus of a pregnant woman.

One way we can begin making changes in our own meal plans and intake of food is to choose one or two things that make sense and feel manageable. Healthy eating is a continuum. Experiencing success motivates us to make more changes. The bottom line is that we feel good about ourselves and what we eat.

Horatio Daub, MD, developed the following *Common Sense Nutrition*[37] guidelines to eating healthfully. Perhaps you may want to choose one or two items on the list and put them into practice. The guidelines are part of the *Common Sense Nutrition* brochure, available from the Birth Works® International online store (www.birthworks.org/store.phtml).

A Guide to Common Sense Nutrition
By Horatio Daub, MD

NUTRITIONAL VALUE IS GREATEST WHEN FOOD IS CONSUMED CLOSEST TO ITS NATURAL FRESH STATE
Overcooking/reheating foods depletes them of their nutritional value and life-giving energy. Every step of transporting, processing, or packaging food has an impact on its nutritional value. It is wise to avoid highly processed foods that have no resemblance to the original foods they were made from, i.e., chips and fries.

CHOOSING COMPLEX CARBOHYDRATES (WHOLE GRAINS & FOODS) RATHER THAN REFINED CARBOHYDRATES (SUGARS AND REFINED STARCHES) BENEFITS HEALTH
Read labels and avoid buying and eating foods where sugar (especially refined) or refined white flour (wheat, rice, or semolina) is one of the first few ingredients.

HIGH-FIBER FOODS HAVE MULTIPLE HEALTH BENEFITS
Fiber helps food to pass through the digestive system quickly. A diet high in meat, which has little fiber, and low in fresh fruits and vegetables is not as healthy, especially for the colon and bowel.

MODERATION OF THE QUANTITY OF FOODS EATEN IS NECESSARY FOR OPTIMAL HEALTH
One should eat only when hungry and until hunger is satisfied. A distinction must be made between appetite and real hunger. Balance is the key to health. When the stomach is two-thirds full, it is better able to digest food, and therefore the body obtains more nutritional benefit.

CHOOSING FOODS LOWER IN FATS (ESPECIALLY SATURATED FATS) ENHANCES HEALTH A CERTAIN AMOUNT OF GOOD-QUALITY FATS SUCH AS OLIVE OIL, OILS OF NUTS AND CERTAIN SEEDS, AND FISH ARE GOOD FOR THE BODY
Foods that are deep-fat-fried or contain hydrogenated and trans fats have an adverse affect on the body and a growing baby. Check food labels and avoid buying foods with hydrogenated or partially hydrogenated oils that contain trans fats.

CHOOSING FRESH FRUITS AND VEGETABLES BENEFITS HEALTH AND WELL-BEING
These foods are high in fiber, vitamins, minerals, and trace minerals. The more green the leafy vegetable, the higher the nutritional value. Broccoli is a powerhouse of nutrition, especially when eaten raw or lightly steamed.

EATING FOODS LOWER ON THE FOOD CHAIN AND WASHING ALL PRODUCE CAN DECREASE EXPOSURE TO PESTICIDES, TOXINS, AND BACTERIA
Toxins and pesticides are concentrated in the fatty tissues of animals and fish that eat plants and plankton or other animals. The lower the foods are in the food chain, the closer they are to the sun, which is the source of the energy that goes into the foods.

GETTING ADEQUATE VITAMIN D AND CALCIUM AND AVOIDING EXCESS PROTEIN AND PHOSPHATES INCREASES BONE DENSITY AND DECREASES THE RISK OF OSTEOPOROSIS
Dairy products, tofu, and certain greens such as kale and collards are good sources of calcium. Vitamin D helps the body absorb calcium. Current researchers in vitamin D are recommending higher intakes of 1,000 IU daily, the bulk of this from supplements or fortified foods. In addition, vitamin K in the amount of 200mcg daily is optimal for bone health and can be found

in leafy greens such as kale, collard greens, and spinach, and also in broccoli and brussels sprouts.

KNOWING HOW TO READ LABELS AND SELECTING FOODS CAN BENEFIT HEALTH AND TRANSFORM YOUR SHOPPING AND EATING
The first item listed on a label is present in the greatest percent by weight. Look for the words whole and organic (not refined or enriched) on the ingredients list. Avoid foods where sugar is listed as one of the first four ingredients.

READ CURRENT INFORMATION ON GMOs OR TRANSGENICS (GENETICALLY ENGINEERED FOODS) AND THEIR POSSIBLE HARMFUL EFFECTS

A pregnant woman who eats healthfully lays the foundation for growing a healthy baby, with good eating habits likely to continue through the years of parenting. Eating foods that enhance health rather than create more risk can help her pregnancy and labor progress more smoothly. It also lays the foundation for a more balanced mind, body, and spirit.

Birthing in the Spirit
vestibule to life
hot passionate enjoyment
unfolds for crowning
—VALORIE AKUFFO CD (BWI)

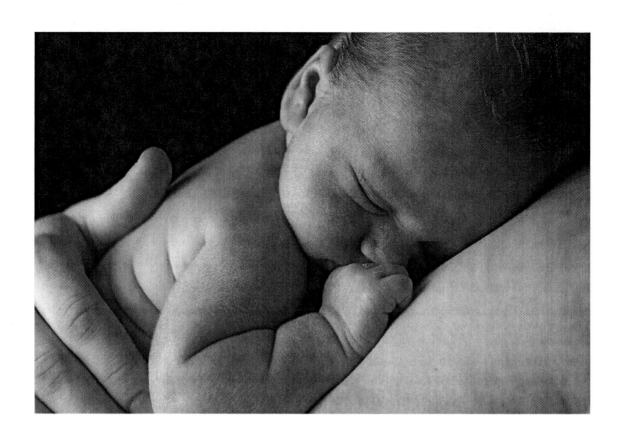

CHAPTER 17

The Power of Sleep

Pervasive sleep deprivation and undiagnosed and untreated or misdiagnosed and mistreated sleep disorders collectively are America's largest, deadliest, and most costly health problem.

DR. WILLIAM DEMENT, AUTHOR OF *THE PROMISE OF SLEEP*

P regnancy is a time of great change in a woman's life. One of the most significant changes is how it affects a woman's sleep. Few women pregnant for the first time are prepared for the effects that interrupted sleep patterns and sleep debt will have on their moods and daily functioning during their pregnancy and on into the early years of parenting. I was certainly one of them. Nobody had ever mentioned how tired I would be after I had my baby.

While visiting my son in college at Stanford during a parents' weekend, I started to learn more about sleep and realized how little the average person knows about its important effects on our lives. This is not limited to new parents. The importance of quality sleep and the impact that sleep deprivation has on our lives is under-recognized by physicians as well,[1] many of whom are unaware of the degree to which they suffer from it themselves. Because there is limited literature on the subject, and because I wish I had known more, I have decided to include this chapter in my book. Dangers of sleep debt will be described first, followed by sleep debt in pregnancy, labor, and parenting.

At the Stanford parents' weekend, various professors taught classes for the parents. I found myself sitting in one offered by William Dement, MD, PhD, one of the world's leading experts on sleep. He began by asking, "How many of you think you are in sleep debt?" Some people in the amphitheater raised their hands. "How many of you remember a time when you were driving when it was hard to keep your eyes open?" More than half the people now raised their hands. In a stern tone he said, "For the rest of your life, the words 'Drowsiness is red alert!' should leap into your mind automatically whenever your eyelids start to get heavy, whenever you would like to close your eyes for just a few seconds because keeping them open is getting difficult. When you begin to feel drowsy, you have arrived at the edge of the abyss. Step back! Get out of harm's way. Drowsiness is red alert! Stopping and getting some sleep could save your life!"

He went on by telling us that he has observed people staggering through their lives in a daze, not even recognizing that they are sleepy. It seems impossible that people could be very sleepy and not know it, but Dement notes that study after study has shown that people who are chronically sleep deprived can be completely unaware of the root cause of their overwhelming fatigue.

———— ∞∞∞ ————

Most people know when they are about to fall asleep, feeling their eyelids getting very heavy and having a hard time keeping them open. They have difficulty concentrating. They may fight drowsiness by opening the window, turning on the radio, or drinking caffeinated beverages, but if they are driving they are risking their lives. Drowsiness means that a large sleep debt is winning the battle over the mind and brain. Someone who is feeling that drowsy while driving should immediately pull over to the side of the road and sleep. It is completely irresponsible to drive while feeling drowsy, risking not only your own life but also the lives of others. In a survey by the National Sleep Foundation, 23 percent of the people who were polled admitted falling asleep while driving in the past year.[2] Over the long term, no quantity of coffee and no amount of willpower will keep you awake if your sleep load and your biological clock are working together to put your brain to sleep.[3]

On an everyday level, sleepy people make math errors, drop things, and become emotionally distant from their friends and families. In the postpartum period, many women remember it as being a time of burnt meals and having a confused state of mind as they adjust their schedule and sleep patterns to take care of a new baby. Dement cautions that what's dangerously deceptive is how awake we can feel even when we're carrying a heavy sleep load.

A large sleep debt cannot be worked off with one night's good sleep. Stimulating activities, excitement, and stress can override effects of large sleep debt, but sleep deprivation cannot be ignored and will eventually catch up with us. At that moment, which is undetermined, we are in grave danger of being rapidly overcome by sleep no matter where we are or what we are doing.[4] Parents in such a state risk great harm to themselves and their children.

As I listened to Dement talk, my mind flashed back to a birth I attended where the woman had a very long labor. I had difficulty keeping my eyes open while driving home, and nearly had an accident, suddenly finding myself driving in the other lane of the road. Dr. Dement says, "Drowsiness—that feeling when the eyelids are trying to close and we cannot seem to keep them open—is the last step before we fall asleep, not the first. If at this moment we let sleep come, it will arrive instantly."[5] I was lucky.

At the end of Dement's lecture I bought his book *The Power of Sleep*, which I highly recommend reading and of which I have included numerous excerpts. After years of research, Dement concluded, "My most significant finding is that ignorance is the worst sleep disorder of them all. People lack the most basic information about how to manage their sleep, leading to a huge amount of unnecessary suffering."[6] He says that millions of people are walking around living their lives at a less than optimal performance, carrying a sleep debt they don't even recognize.[7]

OUR BIOLOGICAL CLOCK AND CIRCADIAN RHYTHMS

Dement explains that over millions of years the human body has developed a precise biological clock that ticks like a metronome to regulate sleeping and waking. He likens it to a tiny mirror of the celestial clock—much like our Milky Way spiral galaxy spinning through space—with our protons,

neutrons, and electrons spinning in their orbits around the atom like the planets rotate around the sun. [8,9] At a cellular basis and at microscopic levels, we are a system of rotating orbits ourselves and our bodies are in constant motion, even while we are sleeping. In fact, these circadian rhythms (coined by Franz Halberg of Minnesota) can be seen in almost every function in the body, down to the smallest cellular processes.

Every aspect of our daily lives—our eating, thinking, and exercising—are all based on this internal celestial clock. Studies show that people who are out of synch with their clocks, such as workers on shifts (includes obstetricians, midwives, and doulas), under-perform both physically and mentally. [10] I would add to this list women in late pregnancy and those with new babies.

Scientific research has enabled us to know the precise location of our biological clock. The biological clock is the term applied to the brain process which drives twenty-four-hour oscillations in body temperature, hormone secretion, and a host of other bodily activities. It is housed deep in the brain in two tiny, pinhead-sized clusters of nerve cells called the suprachiasmatic nuclei, or SCN. They sit in the midline of the brain directly above the optic nerves, and though they are composed of about 10,000 nerve cells, they have a direct influence on 10 million other brain cells that function as a control center for trillions of cells in the body. [11] The biological clock fosters the orderly twenty-four-hour alternation of sleep and wakefulness.

In the third trimester, a pregnant woman's baby is growing significantly larger and moving more. Polls show that up to 97 percent of pregnant women report sleep disturbance during this time due to physical reasons such as low-back ache, restless legs, leg cramps, nocturia, and abdominal discomfort. [12] At this time women typically have more difficulty finding a comfortable position in which to sleep and often need to urinate more often during the night. Sleep patterns begin to change with the development of increased light sleep and a suppression of dream sleep known as REM—or rapid eye movement—sleep, which is probably nature's way to prepare new mothers to wake up to their baby's cries at night after they are born. When there is less REM sleep, moods and energy levels are affected. [13] In the third trimester, women should be encouraged to take naps whenever they can to get the rest they need.

If a pregnant woman has poor sleep patterns or has a large sleep debt before she goes into labor, it can not only affect her ability to do the hard work of labor but can also compound additional sleep debt acquired in the postpartum period. We live in a day and age when many pregnant women are either working in their jobs right up until their due date or taking on an enormous task, failing to get the rest they need before going into labor. Labor is active and hard work, and if a woman goes into labor exhausted, she will find it hard to endure the work required, especially if it is a longer labor. She needs to be well rested.

Take the case of Julie, who was expecting her first baby. Two days before her due date, she and her husband moved into a new house. At the time labor began, her new house was disorganized, her body was exhausted, and her life was in chaos. Too tired to cope with the labor, she requested an epidural that turned into a spinal, as she had a contraction while it was being administered. She

developed the infamous spinal headache and was flat on her back the first nine days after giving birth. The first blood patch provided no relief, but the second was successful. We are left to wonder how different her birth may have been if she wasn't in sleep debt and exhausted before labor began.

Much of the sleep debt acquired by new mothers is unavoidable because they need to be taking care of their babies, who are on different sleep-wake cycles. Before a baby is born, it spends up to sixteen to twenty hours a day asleep. However, Dement continues, "The fetus is more active while asleep than we are, which explains why pregnant women can feel kicking at almost any hour."[14] We often think that the baby is awake when it is kicking inside the womb, but it is actually asleep much of the time! Its nutritional needs are met continuously while in the womb, and after birth these needs continue through the day and night.

Studies on rats and mice show evidence that a mother even prepares her baby for the rhythms of life outside the womb before birth via signals of melatonin levels across the placenta to the biological clock in the fetal brain. Human circadian patterns mirror those of such animals. Dement relates that a mother's circadian rhythm also seems to act as a gatekeeper inhibiting birth during the day (when she is active) and promoting it at night (when she is more relaxed), which may be why so many women begin a "false labor" a night or two before the actual birth. With the era of "daylight" deliveries, we may be interfering with circadian modulation in mothers and babies.[15]

REM AND NON-REM SLEEP AND SLEEP PATTERNS

Watching a newborn baby sleep, we are fascinated to see little smiles, eye flutters, and twitches of its arms and legs. Newborns spend about 50 percent, or eight hours of their daily sleep, in REM sleep as opposed to our 25 percent as adults. During REM sleep, the heart rate and breathing increase, brain waves become more intense, and though the body is still, there is eye movement under the closed lids, and facial and finger muscle twitches. An infant's facial expressions are associated with the releases of hormones and chemicals, and it is believed that infants actually learn to smile and cry in their sleep.

At birth, infants sleep sixteen to eighteen hours a day with six to seven brief sleep periods that have both REM and non-REM sleep. Non-REM sleep is quiet sleep when the baby is sleeping still, quiet, and limp. Babies can pass directly from wakefulness to REM sleep. REM sleep is usually accompanied by muscular paralysis, but this is not yet fully developed in the infant and so it is called active sleep.[16]

Marshall and Phyllis Klaus in their book *Your Amazing Newborn*[17] identify the various types of sleep in a newborn. There are two sleep states, that of quiet sleep and active sleep. There are three awake states—quiet alert, active alert, and crying. The final type of sleep is that of drowsiness, a state between sleep and wakefulness. These sleep states are all accompanied by specific behaviors to help a mother identify what her baby is feeling or communicating, and this takes some of the guesswork out of the early months of parenting. Within the first hour of birth, an infant is in a quiet alert state

for about forty minutes, during which she intently studies the faces of her mother and father and responds to their voices.

Both REM and non-REM sleep are important. REM sleep is crucial to the developing brain, as it is believed to be important for brain growth and maturation during infancy.[18] Gradually the baby will begin spending fewer hours in REM sleep and more in non-REM sleep, when growth hormone is secreted. Growth hormone spurts at night are triggered by deep sleep. When we fall asleep, the body begins its job of energy and tissue conservation. Body temperatures decrease, sugars are stored, growth hormone repairs tissue, and the immune system is strengthened. Good sleep is essential to the health of both babies and adults.

The cycle of REM/non-REM sleep becomes stabilized into a regular pattern at about three months of age. Infants at this age change from a polyphasic sleep-wake pattern to a circadian one. This is associated with maturation of the brain.[19] By six months of age or earlier, babies are usually able to sleep through the night. Research has shown that throughout life, REM sleep is so important that when the brain is deprived of REM sleep, it tries to have longer REM sleeps and to have them sooner.[20] Maybe this explains why a person in sleep debt will fall asleep within minutes of lying down on the bed. Both new and experienced mothers know how to do this well!

Mothers can get more of their needed sleep by keeping their babies close to them after they are born. A Swedish researcher found that babies who maintained skin-to-skin contact with their mothers in the first ninety minutes after birth cried much less as compared to those who were wrapped in a towel and placed in a bassinet.[22] Such findings led UNICEF (United Nations International Children's Emergency Fund) to promote mother-infant contact as a priority both at birth and throughout the hospital stay. When babies are quiet and peaceful, their mothers are more likely to be able to take naps or microsleeps. Even these are successful in lowering their sleep debt.[23]

Newborns lack the physiology to handle long stretches of sleep and so wake up every few hours to be cuddled, fed, or changed. Their small stomachs can only hold so much food and so they need to feed frequently during the day and night. Their mothers wake up to their baby's cries and groggily get out of bed night after night to feed and comfort their little ones. For a while the mother has to adapt to her baby's irregular sleep, taking catnaps when she can until her baby's biological clock matures and can keep track of the time of day.

INFANT POSITIONING IN SLEEP

A good example of successful public education concerns how to position newborn babies when they sleep. Since 1992 with the "Back to Sleep" campaign in the US, which promotes the backlying position for sleeping babies, there has been a great reduction in the rate of Sudden Infant Death Syndrome (SIDS).[24] All women should be educated about ways to decrease the incidence of SIDS, which are to place their babies on their backs for sleep to prevent accidental suffocation, to breastfeed, and to stop smoking in pregnancy.

By the end of the first year of life, an infant still sleeps fourteen to fifteen hours a day, taking only one nap by eighteen months, and sleeping only about 50 percent of the time by the end of their second year. Between two and five years of age, they tend to stop napping completely.[25]

WILL I SPOIL MY BABY BY PICKING HIM UP WHEN HE IS CRYING?

In the first year of a baby's life, new parents both younger and older are typically in turmoil, not knowing whether to let their babies cry it out or to pick them up and nurse them back to sleep. They are afraid they will spoil their babies by picking them up every time they cry, and yet they feel distraught at hearing their babies cry when they try to let them cry it out. I believe that babies who are cared for and comforted when they cry are more likely to feel secure enough to go back to sleep on their own in time. I believe that responding to their needs at this young and tender age is reassuring to them and helps them to develop into more secure adults. At least in my experience, my grown children were not spoiled by picking them up whenever they cried as babies. At nighttime feedings, it is important to keep it a time for feeding and not for play.

DISTURBING NATURAL SLEEP CYCLES

Once outside the womb, a baby gradually adapts to the earth's rhythms, sleeping at night and being awake in the daytime. But as children grow older, soon the natural sleep cycle can be abused by staying awake late into the night—perhaps watching television, staying up late with friends or to do homework, or being out with the family—with the result of children not getting the sleep they need to be alert and energetic during the day. By the time they are teenagers, they are universally sleep deprived.[26] In fact, approximately 15 million American children are affected by inadequate sleep, according to a recent study.[27]

In addition, many children live in troubled families. Such parents report that their children have problems at school with severe headaches and other depressive symptoms. Reasons for these symptoms were cited as parental anger, heated arguing, family disagreements, and parental concerns, and were such that the child did not always feel safe at home, at school, or in their neighborhood. When children feel safe, they sleep better and are healthier in mind, body, and spirit.

Although it is impossible to avoid sleep debt towards the end of pregnancy and as a new mother, there are a number of good strategies that can help cope with fatigue.

1. *Sleep when your baby is sleeping.* The most important strategy is for mothers to learn to sleep when their babies sleep. It doesn't matter if this is fifteen minutes or an hour. Microsleeps and short naps all help to decrease sleep debt.
2. *Avoid drinking caffeinated beverages.* Avoid drinking coffee or other caffeinated beverages in the hours before bedtime, as they are stimulants and keep us awake. People who say,

"Coffee doesn't keep me awake," are probably the same people who say, "I can sleep anywhere."

3. **Deal with insomnia.** Insomnia is very common in pregnancy and happens when a woman wakes up after going to sleep. It can be caused by physiological changes of pregnancy or shortness of breath from backlying. Try side-lying positions in late pregnancy, and use pillows for support behind the back and between the legs. Positioning the top leg forward very far helps keep the pelvis anterior, giving the baby more room in which to move. If this continues after birth, try to decrease worries and learn the beauty of a quiet mind.

4. **Go to sleep earlier.** Resist the temptation to stay up and watch movies or read a book or do dishes. Learn to adapt to your baby and child's sleep schedule so that you can be more awake the next day and have energy to take care of them. You can always do some of the household chores while your baby is awake.

5. **Pay attention to your sleep debt.** Be smart about sleep by being more aware of when you are alert or drowsy, and pay attention to how you feel. Most people do not believe sleep debt has any adverse effects on health, but this is ignorance. It has been shown that sleep debt has a harmful impact on carbohydrate metabolism and endocrine function.[28] Sleep debt builds up if you aren't getting enough sleep, and at some point you will reach a steady state of sleepiness. Believe that you can work down your sleep debt, even if this means hiring a babysitter so you can take a nap. Keeping your sleep debt down as much as possible gives you more energy during the day to enjoy your children.

6. **Develop a bedtime ritual.** Find rituals that feel comforting and relaxing, such as a hot bath, yoga, meditation, soft music, or a short walk in the moonlight. Then relax into your soft, warm bed.

7. **Don't let your bedroom be your entertainment room.** Keep your bedroom a place for sleeping only. Don't let a television compete with your desire for sleep, even if it feels relaxing to watch a movie.

8. **Limit your social life.** Managing your sleep debt means making sacrifices. You may need to turn down invitations for social engagements. Your circle of friends may change to include more women with babies and young children. If you go to a party, it may mean leaving early.

9. **Keep sleep debt low.** When you have a chance, get extra sleep to make up for your short nights. Once your sleep debt is decreased and you start feeling good, be careful not to slip into the late life again, as the sleep debt will increase once again.

10. **Exercise.** Exercise, but do so earlier in the day and avoid exercising three hours before you go to sleep. This is because exercise stimulates the body's arousal system, which opposes the sleep process.

11. **View sleep as a gift.** A dreamless sleep is the most restful sleep and corresponds to non-REM sleep, or deep sleep. Deep sleep is the time of the body's greatest production of prolactin.

This is important for nursing mothers, as prolactin is known to stimulate milk production, but it is not yet known how it is important for non-nursing adults and children. In deep sleep the body also releases growth hormone and cortisol to mobilize energy stores to get ready for energy demands of the coming day.

Right action means following the fundamental triumvirate of good health, which is physical fitness, good nutrition, and healthy sleep. However well we think we are, we must realize that we are not healthy unless our sleep is healthy. This impacts every aspect of our daily lives, our births, and our work. Sleep is altered when a woman is pregnant, and may not return to pre-pregnancy quality for several years after birthing a child. Implementing sleep strategies can make a significant difference in helping a woman to enjoy the years she has with her young children.

Birthing in the Spirit

My "due date" has come and gone. "No, everything is great," I tell my midwife. I don't tell her what is really on my mind. With a first baby on the way, I had never really opened up to my midwife about my history, my very personal and well-kept secrets of childhood. Oh, others knew. I had long since dealt with the memories and confronted those who I blamed for not protecting me. I had even healed those relationships. But, I hadn't really put the pieces together that this thing, this thing that had gone on in my childhood, would weigh so heavily on my mind as I approach the birth of my baby. So, I lingered … that is what we do. We linger, waiting, praying for someone to ask, What is on your mind?

I completely trusted that my body knew how to give birth. But it took a real leap of faith to get this trust to extend beyond my body, my arms. Somehow, I needed to find the strength to let go of this baby to the world, a world that from experience I knew was an uncertain one. How could I reconcile the need to protect with the inevitable letting go that giving birth required? Knowing full well the connection between mind and body, I soon realized that that was indeed what was keeping labor from starting. Birthing in the spirit for me meant getting past fear and trusting birth. It meant going deeply into a "spiritual space" where calm, confidence, and acceptance reside. Once I found this place of equanimity, I was ready to give birth and open my heart to the lessons that birth had to offer.

It was inevitable. Labor did start, and as I allowed myself to give in to each and every contraction, I marveled at how beautifully my body was designed for this work. I learned that for some of us, believing in birth is the critical first step to believing in life itself. That life, as hard as it can be, is also wonderful at the same time. I learned that just as my body has the knowledge

to give birth, that same knowledge will help guide me in parenting and bringing my child to adulthood; and, ultimately, in letting my child go, contraction by contraction, to find her own special place in the world.

—DEBRA MENDELSON CCE (BWI)

CHAPTER 18

Peace and Equanimity

Finish each day and be done with it. You have done what you could.
Some blunders and absurdities no doubt creep in. Forget them as soon as you can.
Tomorrow is a new day. You shall begin it well and serenely.

RALPH WALDO EMERSON

BIRTH STORY

The man stood at the door of Sandy's bedroom, having rushed there responding to a 911 call. He knew she was having a baby but he never expected what happened. He was literally stopped at the door by something he felt but couldn't see. It felt pure, serene, still, and was as if an invisible sacred boundary that could not be crossed. So he just stood there on the edge of what felt like a sanctuary, a holy place. The stillness almost felt like it could be touched and was so quiet he could have heard a pin drop. All was quiet. In that moment, even though it was a 911 call, he suddenly felt completely safe and without worry. Sandy had just given birth to her baby, who was lying on her abdomen. She was stroking his back, feeling his soft skin. She looked up at the man and smiled. He felt his breathing slowing down. It was the first birth he had ever witnessed, though the baby had been born moments before. He continued standing at the door, realizing that everything was okay, and he waited. Nobody said anything. He found himself thinking, Birth is sacred.

Sandy looked up at him and gave another reassuring smile. This was the birth she had dreamed of. Still there was silence. It was as if everyone present wanted the feeling they were experiencing to last a little longer because it felt so good. It was as if the spirit itself was touching everyone in mysterious ways with its invisible fingers.

Sandy knew she would feel safer giving birth at home than in the hospital. Her midwife had not arrived in time for the birth, so knowing birth was imminent, she called 911 just in case her baby needed help. Soon the midwife arrived, and after awhile they all went to the hospital to have the baby examined.

Peace is precious and is essential for everyone. Having peace is having everything. One can have much wealth and many comforts, but without peace, life will feel as if it is in pieces. In the absence of peace, there is agitation, tension, and a feeling of being thrown up and down in life as if on a roller coaster that won't stop. In this state it is harder to concentrate and focus on work that needs to be done. It also wreaks havoc on the mind, which is unable to experience quiet. Peace cannot be seen,

but it can be felt. The man responding to the 911 call expected an emergency with chaos, confusion, and turmoil. What he found instead was peace and serenity.

PEACE

Words that describe peace include calmness, equanimity, and serenity. Looking into a baby's eyes is an experience of peace and wonder. A newborn baby is unaffected by the forces of envy, greed, anger, and hatred. There is no egotistic desire, no anxiety to impress others or to show off. There are no plans for the future and no regrets for the past. It lives completely in the present, and its faith in the love and strength of its mother is unshakable. It cries only to communicate needs until it learns to say words.

I wonder if there are times you can remember feeling very peaceful. I think about times when I have walked along the ocean at dusk. Sometimes there is hardly a breeze. The little sandpiper birds are scurrying at the ocean's edge and the waves are lapping gently to shore. At such times I feel like I can almost "touch" the stillness of peace with my fingers, as if the air is heavy with a peace that passes all understanding.

In moments of peace there are pleasing physiological responses in the body. Breathing slows down, the pulse rate and blood pressure lower, and digestion is efficient. A general feeling of goodness pervades the body as it experiences calmness and relaxation. These are perfect conditions for labor to progress, and so every effort should be made to help a woman in labor to relax. Her ability to relax is much improved when she has a mind-set that feels confident in her body's ability to give birth. Herein lies the value of good childbirth class preparation.

It is well known that meditation produces even deeper physiological effects on the body, such as a decreased metabolic rate, increased basal skin resistance, decreased respiration rate, and a decrease in the stress-related hormone plasma lactate.[1] We experience some of these same effects when we lie down in bed to go to sleep, when standing in a warm shower, or when immersed in a tub of warm water. Many women in labor find that laboring in a pool of warm water helps them to relax into the contractions.

EQUANIMITY

Equanimity is a state in which a person is not agitated or ruffled by anything that happens. Such a person has a steady mind and experiences peace. Although we search for peace, we encounter difficulties that are a part of life, and nobody can escape them. However, what we *can* do is change our reaction to them. An ideal is to reach a state of equanimity where, throughout the ups and downs in life, we remain calm, treating them as passing clouds and avoiding states of both elevation and despair. Such a person tends to live more in the present moment and experiences equanimity.

My father happens to be such a person. He is eighty-five years old now, and in all my life I cannot

remember a single time when he was angry. That is quite remarkable! He has had his share of troubles, but always looks for the good that comes out of them. He is a model for me to this day. He is grateful for his family, his home, and his backyard, and he enjoys food. He is at peace with himself and flows with the ups and downs of life. Anyone who exhibits such qualities will be remembered by many people.

When a woman in labor doesn't think she can handle another contraction, living in the present moment helps her to let go of worrying about the contractions that have happened or those yet to come. Instead, she accepts each one as it comes, knowing that when it is over, it is finished, just like a wave coming to shore.

Peace can only be found within. It cannot be learned from a book or any other external means. From the moment we wake up until the moment we go to sleep, most of our day is consumed with activity in the external world. Few people really spend time developing their inner vision. Birth is an inner journey, and if time is not spent practicing this during the prenatal period, it may be unfamiliar and difficult to access during labor.

Just as the ocean has waves and agitation at the surface yet is calm and still at its depths, so our external world is full of constant change, confusion, and chaos, but deep within lies the peace we seek. It is useless to search for peace in the outer world where all is in a state of flux. The contractions of labor are like the ocean surface, with "waves" coming one after another. A woman in labor must dive deep within herself to find that state where all is still and peaceful. This can be described as an inner wakefulness, a state of complete alertness, non-duality, silence, and inner peace.[2] Tapping into that state is nourishing to the mind, body, and spirit. I believe a woman in labor who has surrendered completely to the spirit within and who has found the depth of her soul is oblivious to anything going on around her. She seems as if in another dimension, yet is in this deep state of inner wakefulness.

WAYS TO FIND PEACE WITHIN

There are nine strategies that I believe are helpful in finding the peace within and which can have a very positive impact on birth.

1. Two rules

The first way is to put things into perspective by remembering the short quotation from Michael Mantell, who said there are two rules. Rule number one is "Don't sweat the small stuff." Rule number two is "It's all small stuff." We tend to make mountains out of molehills, adding more fuel to emotional fires. Just stepping back figuratively and looking at the situation with detachment is a way to put it into perspective and find a sense of peace and equanimity.

2. Reducing ego and desire

A second way is to look at three words: "I," "Want," and "Peace." Have you ever found yourself thinking thoughts such as, *I need balance in my life*, or *I'd like to be content at each moment*? The first word "I" stands for ego. The second word "Want" stands for desire. Simply let go of the "I" or ego, and the "Want" or desire, and what is left is the "Peace" that has been waiting to be expressed all along.

The ego is only interested in selfish gains and self-gratification. The ego feels inflated when praised and devastated when blamed. It sees itself as separate and different from others. When ego enters, envy and jealousy follow fast and occupy the heart: "You only had a three-hour labor?!" or "You're lucky to have a girl. I've only got two boys," or "I wish I could get my shape back as well as she did!" It is best to work to improve ourselves and be happy with who we are, not comparing ourselves with others. Loving ourselves is not ego. It means knowing that we are our own best friend and cultivating a selfless love toward ourselves and others. It means taking care of the body physically, the mind mentally, and the soul spiritually.

The second word "Want" stands for desire. Desires are bundles of impulses that make the mind jump out at everything that passes by. It wants this; it wants that. It wants it now! Maybe it is a chocolate dessert, or chips that you can't stop eating. Maybe it is a desire to keep buying clothes you don't really need. Other common desires may be power, fame, and wealth. Desires need to be controlled if there is any chance of experiencing peace. When we have many wants and desires, we never have enough; and the minute one desire is met, we seek another. As desires are cut out one by one, peace manifests itself more fully.

When desires are not fulfilled, anger may be the result. Anger is one letter short of danger. It is a destructive emotion that heats the internal body temperature and causes words to be said that are harmful to others. Anger looks strong and powerful but it is actually debilitating in its effect. The nerves become weak, blood temperature rises and its composition changes. Anger also demands an expenditure of energy and reduces our stamina. Anger is very weak when compared to the power of love. When we put a "ceiling" on desires, we find the peace within beginning to surface in life. Letting anger begin to become a thing of the past that is no longer a part of us helps us find the peace which we have been seeking, and also improves our health.

3. Understanding duality

A third way to find peace is to understand the concept that pain is the interval between two pleasures. Orgasm in intercourse is often described as a moment of bliss. A woman may conceive at that time and gradually grow a baby. She then experiences labor pains to birth her baby. Then at the moment of birth, she holds her baby, delights in its little fingers and toes, gazes into its eyes, and forgets everything in a moment of sheer bliss.

Pain and pleasure are opposites and represent duality. Duality is a concept that means we cannot

know one thing without being able to compare it to another, because otherwise there is no reference point. To know one is to know the other. We wouldn't know day without night or joy without sorrow. We wouldn't know pleasure without pain or happiness without despair. We live in a world of duality and so will experience all the emotions associated with it.

We make mistakes and feel devastated, but can learn to see them as life's lessons. Darkness, defiance, anger, violence, chaos, agitation, tears, selfishness, and hatred are all life's teachers. When they come our way, we have a choice. Instead of becoming depressed, we can choose to learn from them and see them in a positive light, making changes in our lives for the better. The world can throw us up and down like a roller coaster if we allow it to do so. Seeing the good that comes out of both joy and sorrow leads to the cultivation of equanimity. One who has equanimity says, "Whatever happens is good for me. I have learned as much as I can, and I've made the best decisions that I can. What more can I ask of myself than this?" A woman who adopts this philosophy can have good memories about her birth regardless of the outcome.

Imagine these philosophies being put into practice by members of the birth team and the birthing woman. She must open not only her body but also her mind to give birth. This makes her very vulnerable to all the energies surrounding her in the labor room. If the birth team is consumed with anxiety, it will affect her because all is reaction, reflection, and resounding. If they are calm and believe in her ability to give birth, that will influence her and give her inner strength to cope with contractions. A woman who feels safe will give birth more easily than one who doesn't feel safe.

4. Practicing integrity

A fourth way to find peace is through the practice of integrity, which is having unity in thought, word, and deed. Saying one thing and doing another is not integrity and results in inner conflict. When there is unity in thought, word, and deed, the peace within begins to flow without any effort on our part. Affirmations or positive thought patterns are examples of integrity, so long as they are carried out. For example, a pregnant woman might say, "I am eating healthy foods for myself and my baby," or "I'm giving birth where I feel safe." To practice integrity and feel a sense of peace, the woman must then come through with her promises to herself of eating healthy foods and choosing a birthplace that feels safe. Practicing integrity means becoming more aware of our thoughts so that we can make sure we follow through on them. Taking thoughts first to the heart ensures that they are right action. Right action results in peace.

5. Steadying the mind

A fifth way to find peace within is to begin the practice of steadying the mind. The importance of having a steady mind is illustrated in the following true story.

A spiritual teacher once asked a group of people, "What is youth?" They answered, "Youth is being young, having much energy, and practicing simplicity." The teacher responded, "No, youth

is determination." A year later, the teacher was speaking with the group again and asked the same question, "What is youth?" They were excited that they knew the answer and said, "Youth is determination!" But then the teacher looked at them and said, "Determination for what?" and they didn't know what to say. He continued, "Youth is the determination to have a steady and unwavering mind."

Youth is not limited by age. Though in one sense youth is a reflection of a younger person, it is also defined by steadiness of the mind. An elderly person who has a steady mind will appear youthful in the eyes of others. Some may believe that the ideal of having a steady mind is beyond the reach of anyone, but the mind is trainable, and developing a steadier mind is not beyond our reach. If we begin with the simple things in life, like becoming more aware of negative thoughts we might be saying, or finding ourselves saying one thing and doing another, then we can begin to find peace within. We can't make changes unless we are first aware of what we want to change.

6. A "life is perfect" attitude

A sixth way to start working on slowing down or even getting off the "roller coaster" of life to experience more peace is to adopt a philosophy of seeing life as perfect at every given moment. This means that no matter what comes our way, we have faith that it is meant to be at that given moment in time. I don't believe in coincidence, and see everything that happens to me as life's teacher.

7. Affirmations

A seventh way is to take a good look at what we believe and use affirmations to change our vision, letting go of old habits. For example, if we are criticized, we need to learn not to criticize back. When we criticize back, we take in the negative energy from the person we are criticizing. In addition, we are causing harm to another with our negative words, and that is not conducive to feeling peace. Alternative responses would be to drink a glass of water or go for a short walk and cool down. There is a saying that God tests us with a little to see what we'll do with a lot. Life is constantly presenting us with tests to teach us more about ourselves. They can be welcomed as such.

8. God's grace

An eighth way is to regard anything that happens as a gift of grace from God or a higher power or life force. We cannot know what will happen to us at any given moment. When problems, difficulties, and disappointments occur, instead of succumbing to them, work to overcome them. See the greater scheme of things and believe that events of life come to make us wiser. We can choose to believe that whatever happens to us is for our own good, helping us to develop a more optimistic view towards life.

9. Breathing

The ninth strategy I would like to discuss is that of breathing. We breathe about 21,600 breaths every day, depending on our state of mind. We normally breathe six to seven breaths a minute. When very relaxed, the number can go down as low as three to four. Slow, deep breathing is relaxing and is how we breathe while drifting off to sleep. Tension, on the other hand, increases the rate of breathing.

A beautiful way to give birth is to breathe the baby out. Practicing pushing in childbirth classes is a waste of time because pushing is instinctive, and what is instinctive cannot be taught. And if the mother is in gravity-helping positions, she may hardly push at all and actually breathe her baby out. Keeping the breath long and slow during each contraction allows the body to do its work and is a much more gentle way to work with the body. Here are a few ways to work with slow, relaxed breathing during the prenatal period. Practicing at least one of these each day will help them to automatically be part of your labor.

Upper lung expansion and vocalization

Placing your hands on your upper chest over both upper lung fields, feel yourself breathing into each of your hands. Next, exhale; and as you do so, say "Ahhhhhhhh," feeling the vibration in your hands as you breathe all the way out. Follow the vibration all the way down into your pelvis. Repeat and remember to breathe deeply and slowly. In labor, this is a way to breathe your baby out. You can turn the vocalization into a mantra for labor by saying, "Downnnnnnnn," or "Come…" or "Love…" or "Ommmmm," or whatever feels good to you.

Lateral costal expansion

Next, place your hands on either side of your lower rib cage where the lower lung fields lie. Press in as you exhale slowly and deeply. Then as you breathe in, feel your rib cage pressing out against your hands. Make sure that your shoulders are staying low so that you are not using accessory muscles of breathing. Repeat for several breaths, again breathing slowly and deeply.

Diaphragmatic breathing

Next, place just a few fingers just below the xyphoid process located at the base of the sternum in the front of your chest. This is where the ribs come together in front of your body. Right there, with just light pressure while breathing, you can feel a pouching out of the diaphragm muscle as you breathe in. You are feeling the diaphragm contracting to pull down the rib cage when inhaling. It then relaxes as you breathe out, with the exhale requiring no conscious effort on your part. Breathe several times with this awareness.

Pelvic breathing

Moving on down the body, now place your hands over your lower groin area. This is where you can feel air moving all the way down into the pelvis. It is subtle and is felt as part of the contraction of the abdominal muscles with the diaphragm. Thus you can have the experience of breathing all the way *down* into your pelvis.

Breathing is not just for the lungs; it is a whole body experience, especially when you consider that the molecules of oxygen are being carried by the blood throughout the body very quickly. The slower the breathing in labor, the more effective the contractions will be in dilating the cervix, and the better a woman can feel her body guiding her through labor.

RELAXATION TECHNIQUES: HELPFUL AND NOT HELPFUL ASSOCIATIONS

In childbirth classes, techniques are often taught to help women learn how to relax into pain, believing this will help them be familiar with relaxing into labor contractions. We have to be careful about what we do because the associations a woman makes with what is taught in classes will likely be carried over into birth. In general, what is warm and comforting feels safe and brings a feeling of peace. What is cold and hurts induces a protective response that constricts. We instinctively relax when we are warm, whereas when we are cold we instinctively bring the arms and legs closer to the body, trying to stay warm. In addition, prenatally, endorphins—the body's hormones that are natural painkillers—have not been secreted as they are in a natural labor.

What to avoid

1. *Hurting others.* I believe that it is our duty to be helpful and kind to others and that doing so encourages others to be kind and helpful to us. Religions of the world teach the concept, "Do unto others as you would have them do unto you." Therefore, I do not believe any techniques, even for learning purposes, should be taught that inflict pain on another. These include trying to relax into pinching or squeezing of the skin, or clothespins on the ears.

2. *Ice.* Ice is cold! The rationale behind *not* using ice has to do with associating cold with labor. Words associated with ice include *cold, hard, burning,* and *numbing.* Some childbirth classes tell women to hold ice in their hands, or feel ice poured down their backs, or even stand in a bucket of ice and see if they can relax and breathe slowly while enduring the burning sensation of the ice. Other times, while holding ice in their hands, they are told to try and relax while being given a massage on their backs. But the body instantly responds to the touch of ice instinctively with constriction of blood vessels.

    The palms of the hands and the soles of the feet are areas of the body that have the most cortical representation in the brain. When ice is placed on such places of the body (or on any part) in the context of learning with the purpose of trying to relax into the pain of

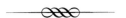
labor, an association of ice is made with labor. The body's immediate physiological reaction is to pull inward and constrict in response to the cold. An association of ice with labor has now been made and may be triggered when the woman is actually in labor, with resulting constriction and a "holding-in" energy. This is the antithesis of the "letting go" that a woman needs to do in labor. Promoting these kinds of exercises in any childbirth classes shows a lack of understanding and respect for body physiology and energy dynamics.

Good associations

1. *Keeping the feet and hands warm.* Warmth brings forth relaxation. Having a woman in labor wear socks helps to keep her feet warm and indirectly warms the entire abdomen. This is a common practice of midwives in Central America. They also dip cloth in warm oil and apply it to the perineum to help increase vascularity and promote greater ease of tissue expansion through increased blood supply.

2. *Relaxed hands.* In this very short but powerful exercise, all are invited to begin by squeezing their hands and calling out other parts of their bodies that are tightening in response to the squeeze. At first they will mention the arms and shoulders, and then quickly they will feel tension in their jaws and down into the pelvis, realizing how connected the body is. They are then told to open their hands and see if they can sustain tightening in other parts of the body without squeezing their hands. They will find it difficult to do so. Therefore, a great job for men in labor is to make sure that as a contraction comes, the hands of the laboring woman are open and relaxed. However, at the very end of labor, because of the paradoxical effects of adrenalin, a woman will feel like clenching her fists just before the baby is born. This is not only fine but also exciting, for it means the baby is about to be born.

3. *Creating a safe atmosphere.* When birthing parents experience a childbirth class setting that feels intimate, open, and safe, they are more likely to express deeply held fears. The degree of safety that they feel in classes may well be one they are likely to want around them when in labor. Simply the experience of being in such a class where they do not feel judged, but rather, empowered is one of the most powerful relaxation techniques for birth.

4. *Affirmations.* One way to begin feeling more peace is to say an affirmation as simple as, "I am peace." Saying this over and over again throughout the day infuses it with energy and becomes a part of us because it connects with that which is already within. Gradually we can note its calming effect through slower breathing and a general sense of well-being. By feeling peace, we are practicing equanimity, staying unaffected emotionally by either praise or blame.

5. *Prayer.* Connecting with a power greater than ourselves and in whom we believe or hope knows all, confers a sense of peace. Most people, even if they are not religious, pray in one way or another by saying, "God help me!" or "Oh, God!" Prayer is a way of putting

estrangement and suffering and death into a context that makes them part of a meaningful life.[3]

There are many reasons why we pray. We pray to ask for guidance. We pray during worship services, to be in the presence of the Almighty. We pray for strength and courage when faced with crises such as death and suffering. We pray for healing, wholeness, and comfort. We pray before meals to purify the food and offer thanks to God. We pray for reconciliation from having hurt or offended a loved one. We pray for strength to deal with moral obligations. We pray with gratitude for our very existence. When standing on a mountain top or at the edge of the ocean, we feel a small part of something much greater than ourselves.

A mother's prayer for her child is special because no one can love a child as much as its mother. In pregnancy, a woman prays for the safety and health of her baby. She prays for help to make it through the next contraction. She prays that her needs will be respected. She prays that she will be a good mother. In a hands and knees position in labor, her head is down in a position of humility, just as she might lower her head in prayer. Visual distraction is decreased in such a position and she may want to send prayers to her baby, connecting with it while it moves through her body and out into her waiting arms. Practicing prayer on a daily basis helps a woman to remember to pray during her labor if she feels the need. Being able to pour out fears, inadequacies, and doubts to the spirit brings solace and helps strengthen us.

OBSTACLES TO FINDING PEACE IN LABOR

1. *Invasive techniques.* In birth, we are applying invasive procedures far too often, which cause a woman to tighten and constrict her body. These include intravenous lines, fetal scalp sampling, internal monitors, internal exams, forceps, vacuum extractors, needles for administering anesthesias and analgesics, and even hands inside the vagina helping to birth the baby's head. Though any one of these may be medically necessary in some instances (and may bring a sense of peace in that case), certainly their routine practice is unwarranted, unnecessary, and counterproductive to feeling peace at birth. The newest device on the market, the CLM or continuous labor monitor, is attached to the cervix and requires rupture of membranes and a wire screwed into the baby's scalp.

2. *Anxiety.* Reducing anxiety allows more and more of the peace already within to flow. Anxiety is reduced with encouraging words, warm water, keeping the feet warm, good positioning, and having a safe and loving atmosphere. These are all conducive to a laboring woman feeling more peaceful, relaxed, and safe to let go and give birth. She is then free to focus her attention inward, be more in touch with her instincts, and surrender to the forces in her body that are birthing her baby. She enters a spiritual realm that is vast, peaceful, and subtle, where the miracle of existence can be touched.

3. **Doubt.** So many women today carry doubt into labor, being unsure that they can make it through labor. One woman only thirteen weeks pregnant recently said to me, "I'm not good with pain. I don't know what I've gotten myself into, but I can't get out of it now. It's too late. I don't know what I'm going to do." Such women can benefit greatly from the support of a good childbirth education class where they can express fears, learn affirmations, and learn to have more trust and faith in their body's ability to give birth.

During pregnancy there are tremendous hormonal changes as a woman's body adjusts to growing a baby. These hormones may swing her into moods of joy and tears all in the same day. When fears, doubt, and anxiety compound the situation, she will find it difficult to steady her mind and experience peace. But if in those moments of distress she surrenders to the spirit and prays for its guidance, she can find redirection and courage to continue on each day, one at a time. If she can do the same in labor, she will have less fear and more strength to keep relaxing into and working through contractions, making dilation more effective. The way this sounds in labor is, "Another contraction is coming and I am opening to it, welcoming it, since it is helping my baby to be born." Peace is a treasure if we can find it.

The yearning for peace is in everyone. Peace comes from the depths of the soul and is an expression of the spirit. It is felt mostly when there is complete silence, absolute safety, and pure love. It cannot be learned from books and it cannot be bought for any amount of money. It is the precious treasure within us. Those who have the experience of such peace will never forget it, and their yearning for it will become even greater.

Birthing in the Spirit

Right from the start of labor I found birthing to be a really amazingly intense and wonder-filled experience. I quickly discovered that the labor "pains" that had been so often mentioned but never explained vividly were truly beyond explanation, as was the feeling of fullness during birthing and the joy of seeing my son for the first time. I think this is what is at the root of how birthing is a spiritual experience.

I found myself turning inward in a much more meditative way than I (a rather extreme extrovert) ever do normally, and relied on prayer to make my way through each wave of contractions. I sang, in my head, "I Surrender All" and a few other worship songs and internally repeated phrases to help me envision the change my body was going through. During the most intense moments, I just prayed by focusing on the name of "Jesus." I really enjoyed my labor experience, which surprised me, and one main reason is that I had this rare inward and upward connection with God. I'm actually looking forward to birthing my next child someday.

—CAITLIN LITTLETON, NEW MOTHER

CHAPTER 19

Fears and Worries

Thou shalt not worry, for worry is the most unproductive of all human activities.
Thou shalt not be fearful, for most of the things we fear never come to pass.
Thou shalt not cross bridges before you get to them, for no one
yet has succeeded in accomplishing this.
Thou shalt face each problem as it comes. You can handle only one at a time anyway.
Thou shalt not take problems to bed with you, for they make very poor bedfellows.
Thou shalt not borrow other people's problems. They can take better care of them than you can.
Thou shalt not try to relive yesterday for good or ill—it is gone.
Thou shalt concentrate on what is happening in your life today.
Thou shalt count thy blessings, never overlooking the small ones,
for a lot of small blessings add up to a big one.
Thou shalt be a good listener, for only when you listen do you hear ideas different from your own.
It's very hard to learn something when you're talking.
Thou shalt not become bogged down by frustration, for 90 percent of it is rooted
in self-pity and it will only interfere with positive action.

AUTHOR UNKNOWN

PRIMAL FEARS

There are two primal fears of all mankind. The first is that of being abandoned in a time of need. The continuous presence of a birth doula, a birth companion, partner or significant other, or close friend or family member, helps a woman in labor to know that she is not alone in a time of need and that there is help if she needs it.

The second fear is that of being restrained against one's will. I have heard a number of birth stories told by women who had epidurals that did not take effect and who felt the entire cesarean surgery. Their cries of anguish were not heard and their arms were restrained (necessarily) so as not to touch a sterile area of the surgery. One woman told me that when this happened to her, memories flooded her mind when she was abused by an adopted brother. She felt helpless being unable to stop it then, and now felt helpless again, consumed with pain from the surgery with her cries for help being ignored. We bring many life experiences to our births and giving women (and men) an opportunity to talk about traumatic experiences during a class focusing on grieving and healing helps to facilitate normal birthing.

FEARS IN BIRTH

Fears women bring to their births are often so deep and scary that they have difficulty expressing them. A woman whose sister died before birth due to a tight umbilical cord around her neck was fearful of this happening in her own labor. Another woman had her membranes ruptured at six centimeters and experienced such intense contractions that in a subsequent birth, she was fearful when she became "stuck" at six centimeters. Still another woman was afraid of becoming a mother because her mother had died at childbirth. The power such fears hold over the human body are tremendous and have the potential to adversely affect labor in unforeseen ways due to a tocophobic fear of labor. Never underestimate the healing that comes from helping a pregnant woman to feel safe enough to express and release such fears.

A woman who is told there may be something wrong with her baby during either pregnancy or labor will make any sacrifice for the safety of her baby. The feeling of vulnerability may prevent her from recovering emotionally the rest of her pregnancy, for if her body has failed her now, it is capable of doing so again. This can happen with false- positives in any prenatal test, or the reading and interpretation of external fetal monitor strips in labor that are very subjective. The woman will instinctively go into a protective mode, secreting the stress hormone cortisol, which can affect her in both pregnancy and labor.

Other typical fears and worries that women have about birth include: "Can I trust my doctor to do what he/she says?" "Where should I give birth?" "What if my midwife doesn't arrive in time?" "What if my husband can't handle the sight of blood?" "How will my body change with this pregnancy?" "Should I quit work and stay home with my baby?" Fathers may wonder, "What if I lose my wife at birth?" "What will it be like to see her in pain?" "How will this baby affect my relationship with my wife?" "Will she still have time for me?" "If she stays home from work, how will that affect our current lifestyle?"

We live in a day and age when if a woman doesn't want to feel pain in labor, she doesn't have to. However, the fear of labor pain has led to a number of medical procedures that also have their own associated risks and consequences. Birth is not without pain, whether it is vaginal or cesarean. If it is a cesarean, there will be pain afterward from the incision.

What is behind the fear of labor that leads so many women to request epidurals? Though reasons may range from a belief that medical technology has advanced to the point where labor contractions don't have to be felt anymore, to simply not wanting to feel pain or being afraid of an inability to cope with pain, I find another interesting reason during role-plays in classes:

Instructor: So, what plans have you made for your labor and birth?
Jenine: Oh, I'm going to the hospital and I have a really good obstetrician.
Instructor: I'm glad you like her. And what do you plan to do in labor?

Jenine: Well, I'm going to walk first, and then when the contractions get strong, I'm going to have an epidural. They say it's important not to get the epidural until labor is going well.

Instructor: That's good that you're planning to walk, as it helps the baby to move around and position itself well.

Jenine: Yeah, I feel good about that.

Instructor: And do you think your baby will be able to move around when you have the epidural?

Jenine: Not as well, I guess.

Instructor: How will the epidural help you in your labor?

Jenine: I'm told it will take away the pain.

Instructor: The pain . . .

Jenine: Yeah, lots of my friends have had epidurals and say they're great. You don't feel pain and still have the baby!

Instructor: What would happen if you felt the contractions?

Jenine: I don't know if I could take it. I don't know if I could deal with the pain.

Instructor: What's the worst thing that would happen if you felt the pain?

Jenine: I don't know.

Instructor: What would it be like for you?

Jenine (beginning to become teary eyed): I'm afraid I would lose control.

Instructor: Have you ever lost control before?

Jenine: No.

Instructor: What's the worst thing that would happen if you lost control?

Jenine: I'd get hysterical.

Instructor: And then what would happen?

Jenine (softly and starting to cry): I'd make a fool of myself in front of others.

A deep fear of many women is that during labor they will become hysterical, go out of control, or make a fool of themselves in front of others. Others fear they will get angry or that they might die. These are anticipatory fears and are normal occurrences when going into the unknown, because we don't know what to expect or what will happen. A woman who has never seen or given birth before may hear birth stories that sound frightening. She may hear of women passing out due to the intensity of contractions, or fatigue so extreme from a long labor that drugs were needed to help the cervix dilate. She may hear of women who cried, screamed, or cursed to cope with contractions. She may think, *What will it be like for me? Will I be able to do it? What will happen if I can't bear it?* Such fears are diffused and weakened simply by their expression, with the result that they have less of a "hold" on the psyche.

EMBARRASSMENT

Another common fear besides that of becoming hysterical is the fear of pushing out a bowel movement in front of strangers, which frequently happens when women are pushing their babies out. One woman said, "My husband has never seen me go to the bathroom and he's not going to now!" In childbirth classes, when women learn that others have the same fears, they don't feel so alone in their own fears. Such fears are so deep that women often have difficulty even expressing them. Their expression can be encouraged in a class setting simply by validating that whatever is expressed is valued and important. This helps women and men to feel safe and let go of their fears.

FEELING INTIMIDATED LEADS TO FEAR AND WORRY

Medical practitioners can easily intimidate pregnant women with fears of medical tests and also with the "what ifs." The following story is an example:

I am pregnant with my first child at the age of thirty-nine and my due date was last Friday. At my last checkup I was 80 to 90 percent effaced, but not dilated yet. The baby has been head down since approximately thirty-two weeks and moves frequently throughout the day and night. Her heartbeat is strong and steady (as is mine), and she has plenty of fluid to swim around in.

For a variety of reasons (e.g., ultrasound done two weeks ago, one hour glucose test results at 120+, my prenatal weight, etc.) my OB thinks I'm going to have a ten-plus-pound baby and seems to be rather in a hurry to deliver her as soon as possible. He has already suggested induction or just going ahead and scheduling a C-section. He cites shoulder dystocia and vaginal tearing, etc., as good enough reasons to avoid a vaginal birth, but I'm not convinced that the weight measurements are all that accurate. I'm 5'8" and my baby's father is 6'2". We're both of hearty stock; in fact, he has two older daughters, both of whom were over nine pounds at birth. Unfortunately, I'm adopted and do not know how much I weighed at birth.

I've been putting my OB off on inducing so far because I believe in my body's ability to give birth normally and naturally. At least I'd sure like to try first before just assuming that I can't do it. I also don't believe that inducing only a week past my due date is really giving my daughter (or my body) a chance to go into labor on its own first, which I know is the best thing for both of us.

I had always planned on a drug-free, intervention-free birth (I hired a doula to ensure this), but as my due date grew closer, it seems my OB's attempts to instill fear in me grew stronger.... He also thought I had gestational diabetes, but I've been testing my glucose levels four times a day (fasting in the morning and two hours after every meal) and my levels are in the 78 to 92 range. Perhaps because of my age and because I worked in a hospital for over ten years, as well as all the reading I've done, I am not easily intimidated or swayed by his fear tactics. I'm willing to go to at least the end of forty-one to forty-two weeks before agreeing to induction.

This woman is struggling to make the right decision. She is wavering between the confidence she has in her body's ability to give birth normally and fears instilled in her from her doctor, who wants to intervene in her birth. She is left wondering if she should be taking any chances for the sake of her baby, and this fear lingers.

THE NATURE OF FEAR

Fear is a paralyzing emotion. It makes us do things we never thought we would do and which sometimes make no sense to others. Take, for example, a woman who has had a traumatic birth with one doctor in a certain hospital and chooses to go back to the same place and the same doctor for her next birth. It may be that what is familiar to her feels safer than an unknown hospital and new doctor, regardless of what happened before. Or, she may be so paralyzed with fear that she is just going through the motions without being able to think clearly.

I remember once hearing a man from Croatia interviewed on television. The Serbs came into his village and herded the people together, separating the men from the women. "They took my mother, my wife, and my daughter," he said in anguish. "And we behaved just like sheep, doing what they said. I was taken on a truck with other men but escaped the slaughter. But I wish I hadn't. Now I can't live with myself. Why didn't I do something to try and protect my family! I did nothing!" he cried out. Fear of what would happen prevented any of them from taking action. They were literally paralyzed with fear.

How many times have you heard stories where women in labor described themselves as being "good little patients"? One woman said, "I smiled and joked, but there was terror inside and I let them do everything, *everything*, to me, including multiple residents doing internal exams, checking my dilation in front of others with my legs wide open. I felt raped! Now I'm so angry that I allowed it to happen. It's as if I wasn't thinking!" When paralyzed with fear, we lose the ability to act on our inclinations. It is a hard "brake" on any action.

THE "J" POINT

The "J" point is a state or condition that occurs when a person feels trapped, meaning that there is a perception of no acceptable solution. There is no change. In the systems way of thinking (seeing the whole "picture"), we can say that the system is static and the person is simply stuck. There is no movement forward or backward, either of which would be healthier than a static situation of no change.[1]

Annette was in my Birth Works® class and expressed a desire to stay at home to give birth because that is where she felt safer. However, her medical insurance did not cover medical backup for a home birth, and she and her husband could not afford to pay privately for a backup doctor at the hospital plus a midwife to come to their home. It became clear during class discussion that she was terrified of

hospitals. Although she wanted to have a home birth, she was also fearful of giving birth unassisted at home without medical backup. She felt stuck and was at the "J" point. If she went to the hospital, she would feel vulnerable in a strange environment and likely be subjected to medical procedures that she didn't want. On the other hand, if she stayed at home without backup, something could happen and she might not have time to get to the hospital. She felt trapped, believing that there was no option available or acceptable.

In class, she felt safe to express her fears. With the support and suggestions of others, and hearing herself voicing her own fears, she was able to work through them and she discovered there was an option she had not thought about before. Her insurance company had assured her they would be able to cover any option for birth. She went back and approached them, explaining that she wanted to give birth at home but needed the medical backup to be covered by the company. Since they had agreed to cover any option, they agreed to pay for a backup doctor who was not previously on their list. She hired a midwife and had a beautiful home birth.

Another woman couldn't find a hospital or doctor open to her needs in her own community. Through networking with others, she found a place that was a three-hour drive from her home. She moved beyond her J point by hearing about others who drove long distances a week before their due dates and stayed at a hotel near the place of birth they had chosen. She and her husband decided that since this was an experience they wanted to treasure the rest of their lives, it was worth it to them to do the same. They had a beautiful birth experience, in part because the place she had chosen felt safe to her.

CULTURAL PERSPECTIVES

Human beings have inhabited the earth for over 10,000 years. Women always gave birth in their homes or a familiar setting during these thousands of years. It is as recent as the 1960s that birth in the US have moved from the home to the hospital. Family members are now less likely to witness a birth because hospital policies usually place limits on how many people can be with the woman in labor. Important information and experience about birth once learned by other family members in the home is being lost in our culture and others where hospital birth has become the norm.

But the Latino (Hispanic) culture in the US is an interesting story that has something to teach us about birth. Despite their social disadvantages, Latina women have surprisingly favorable birth outcomes. This was shown to be true especially in Mexican women, according to one important study entitled "The Latina Paradox: An Opportunity for Restructuring Prenatal Care Delivery".[2] In this study, in spite of Latino infants having lower birth weights (6.5 percent) than the national averages of birth weights for non-Latino Whites (6.9 percent) and African Americans (13.4 percent)—a disadvantage, as lower birth weights are correlated with increased birth complications—they also had lower mortality rates.

The possible reasons for the better birth outcomes in Latino culture seem to be due to their

closely networked and intimate family social support networks that have provided informal systems of prenatal care. In spite of the social disadvantages Latina women often experience, this system of support offers them enough advantages to promote healthy births.

In this culture, giving birth is very special and the family system provides encouragement and values of love and compassion. Pregnant women from this culture benefit from the knowledge handed down through the generations, the support of their sisters and extended family members, and a feeling of belonging to their family and community. Mexican fathers also play an important role and display a willingness to take responsibility for those outside their own family. The culture also has its own lay midwives, called *"parteras,"* who have various levels of training; and because they are from the same culture, they understand the needs of their pregnant and laboring women. Latina mothers who had this support generally had better birth outcomes than those who did not.

Of great interest is the fact that these benefits began to disintegrate as Latina women acculturated to western lifestyles in the US, where the collective, community-based lifestyle was more difficult to maintain. At the same time, the study suggests a solution on a public policy level of the importance of protecting our communities.

I believe the importance of this study is that it shows how a sense of community and family support is instrumental in helping pregnant women to feel safe to express their fears and worries, and that the reassurance they receive from their loved ones is a powerful "medicine" that balances social disadvantages inherent in their culture. The need for a sense of community goes beyond us as individuals, says Dean Ornish in his book *Love and Survival.*[3] He believes that we are losing a sense of community in America and that this is reflected in the current state of how women are giving birth.

ROLE OF THE FAMILIAR

Women who have been raised on a farm usually have the wonderful opportunity of seeing animals being born. These women come to birth with an understanding of the birth process as very natural and normal. They tend to give birth more naturally as well, for just having observed these births makes it a familiar process. That which is familiar to us feels safer and less fearful. A Latino woman would likely feel safer with her partera than a strange, authoritative American doctor.

But in today's world most pregnant women having their first baby have never seen a live birth before, and so have fear of the unknown. A willingness to trust intuition and to trust process also involves a willingness to embrace difference, the unfamiliar, and accept risk. When going into the unknown, there is a perceived threat of what may or may not happen, bringing a sense of helplessness. This can be heightened by stories in the family about traumatic births or what has been seen on the television and in movies. Depending on the stories, women will either feel empowered or more fearful.

The media often generates fear and false impressions by portraying birth either as an emergency

or as an easy experience, birthing a baby after one or two pushes. Families and friends like to tell stories of births when women almost lost their baby or how the doctor didn't get there in time. Women may have heard that every labor is different, and so have no way of predicting exactly what their own births will be like. Childbirth classes should show only movies that empower expectant parents, helping them to have more confidence in their body knowledge that already knows how to give birth.

I once attended a doula workshop where a film was shown of a woman having a cesarean. The camera zoomed in to show the cutting of layers of tissue in the abdomen. There was no music, only the sound that the scissors were making as the tissue was cut. People in the room turned their heads away from the screen but could not keep out the sound of the scissors cutting the tissue. Showing such films weakens the psyche and induces more fear. It is not empowering to show such images to either birthing parents or birth professionals, because now that sound is in them forever and won't be forgotten. This is not unlike the story Dr. Ornish tells. When his father, who was a dentist, came to his classroom and showed pictures of decayed teeth from eating too much candy and sugar, Ornish says that immediately afterwards the kids snuck into the bathroom and ate their candy.

Most women today give birth in a hospital where the energy and atmosphere are very different from the home. Most of us associate hospitals as places to go to when we are very sick. As a pregnant woman enters a hospital, she may see people in wheelchairs or on stretchers with IV poles attached. To their credit, hospitals are trying to make their birthing rooms feel more like home with interior décor and Jacuzzis, but this has had limited success because of established hospital routines for labor and delivery. To another woman, the hospital may provide a sense of security where there is immediate help if needed. Choosing the place of birth is an important decision birthing parents need to make because the environment affects a woman's ability to give birth, and whichever it is, she needs to feel safe.

The nature of fear is constriction, and the nature of love is expansion. Fear can either slow contractions down or stop them altogether. Labor cannot establish itself well in the presence of fear due to the body's associated fight or flight reaction system being the dominating factor. Fear is often compounded by the interventions themselves, such as a woman who feels helpless, not being able to move her legs with an epidural in place. Birth is an experience of opening the body completely to give birth. It is an experience of love; it is an experience of spirit.

"It was quiet and the lights were low," said a woman. "I moved around the room and was conscious of the rhythms of my body. I worked with each contraction, one at a time saying, 'Yes, yes, yes,' opening fully to its power and following its crescendos and decrescendos. I felt labor as a song and began singing through the contractions. I had such clarity of mind and felt in tune with the spirit in my body. It was a power much bigger than myself, and I surrendered to it."

I believe that medical interventions are often used to override fears that women have about giving birth. For example, suppose a woman is so afraid of labor that she keeps her body in a state of constant alert. Her cortisol levels will be high, and she has prepared herself to "run away" from

labor. It is very difficult to establish labor with high cortisol levels. However, the baby has to be born. Being induced and then receiving an epidural in labor so she doesn't have to feel the contractions may help to decrease the woman's anxiety and thus her cortisol levels. However, now muscles that help to rotate and turn the baby are numb, and she may end up with a forceps delivery or a cesarean.

WORRYING

Worries and stress lead to a multitude of anxiety-ridden symptoms such as fatigue, lowered resistance to infection, lack of sleep, and unhealthy eating habits. They also cost us increased energy, which leads to a feeling of always being tired.

Worrying is an outcome of fear. Some of us worry more than others. Stop and think for a moment what worries you have had this day. Perhaps there is a health issue, a concern about your children, your job, your appearance, or something about the future. Maybe you worry about not getting enough sleep. The work of worrying is tiring because it consumes energy. Women worry what labor will be like, if the baby will be okay, and what life will be like with a new baby. Men worry, too, not sure how they will cope with watching their wives or significant others in labor, and not sure if after birth it will feel like "three's a crowd." Birth professionals fear malpractice suits and cover themselves by performing a multitude of medical procedures.

More fears and worries continue after a baby is born. I was at a birth of a woman who had a beautiful natural birth in a birthing center, but upon going home had to deal with a very difficult mother-in-law who was staying with her and her husband. She described the tension in the air by saying she was always "walking on eggshells." Her milk supply became affected and actually was reduced due to the stress. She tried everything and had lactation specialists come to visit, but nothing worked and she ended up bottle feeding. It was only when her mother-in-law left that the parents could enjoy their new son.

I had a similar experience when my daughter was born. She cried a lot, and my mother told me it was because I was vegetarian that she wasn't getting enough milk. The pediatrician backed this up by saying that the only way I could get protein was by eating meat. Both, of course, were wrong. I was emotionally distraught thinking I couldn't provide my daughter with enough milk. The anxiety I was feeling further limited my milk production. In addition, back then we didn't know that mothers who have had cesarean sections for birth tend to have difficulty with breastfeeding.[4] We now know that oxytocin plays an important role in milk production and that when it is decreased due to fear and anxiety, analgesics (pain relievers), or anesthesia such as epidural blocks, the production of breast milk is decreased.

A Swedish study found that two days after birth in natural deliveries, oxytocin was released in a pulsatile, effective way, whereas cesarean mothers had, on the average, fewer oxytocin pulses during breastfeeding in the first two to three days after birth.[5] It was also noted that the cesarean mothers

were less calm after birth, perhaps due to pain from the surgery. Not surprisingly, it was found that the duration of breastfeeding seemed to depend on how a baby is born, with cesarean mothers breastfeeding for shorter times.[6,7] In my case, it was probably a combination of the anxiety from my mother and pediatrician, compounded with effects from the cesarean delivery, that may have caused the problem. The problem resolved itself after the first four weeks of birth. I also learned too late that my multivitamin contained B_6 (pyridoxine), which is a lactation inhibitor. These events were all based on misinformation, fear, and worry.

HEALTHY FEAR

"Healthy" fear motivates us to make changes for the good. Take, for example, a pregnant woman who smokes and decides to stop smoking during pregnancy because she is fearful of the adverse effects it would have on her developing fetus. Others may refrain from drinking alcohol. Many women become more conscious of eating healthy foods when pregnant. If there is a medical emergency, fear motivates the birth team into action to help a baby and mother giving birth. Fear of being hit by a car makes us drive safely and check for traffic as we cross the street. But tocophobic fear, a fear of birth that reduces one to gripping and paralyzing submission, is much more severe and debilitating.

PHYSIOLOGICAL EFFECTS OF FEAR

It is essential to help women keep a positive outlook about birth and release fears they may have, because there are direct physiological effects on the mother and her baby. When anxiety emerges from fear, the body's production of cortisol increases. It is interesting that cortisol, which is secreted by the adrenal glands, and oxytocin, which is secreted in the pituitary gland located in the posterior aspect of the hypothalamus, have a direct effect on each other.[8] One is the stress hormone and the other is the hormone of love, and together (along with other adrenal gland hormones including adrenaline) they control the activity of the hypothalamus through a feedback system.

The ability to feel both love and fear seems to be a priority in fetal development because when the fetus is only eleven and a half weeks old, an intricate vascular link already exists on what will become the hypothalamus and the already-existing pituitary gland. This means the pituitary gland is a priority in the very early development of the fetus.

The effects of cortisol on the baby are greater than we may think. In fact, it is known to be a fetal growth inhibitor.[9] High levels of cortisol disturb the synthesis of prostaglandins, which are regulators of cellular activity. Prostaglandins are pervasive throughout the body, which is composed of millions of cells. In a baby or young child, a raised level of cortisol has a spectacular effect in reducing the size of the thymus and causing premature aging.[10] Levels of cortisol are even higher when there is no chance to flee in a fight or flight response, leaving submission as the only alternative.

If high stress continues over a period of time, especially during sensitive growth periods of the fetal

organs, it can have a negative effect on the fetus. Exposure to cortisol during fetal life can result in permanent high blood pressure and hyperglycemia as an adult.[11] Separation of the mother and baby at birth and during the hours after birth produces a state of high stress and high cortisol production in both the baby and the mother that is heart-wrenching. This in turn reduces milk production in the mother. The *Listening to Mothers II* survey (see Introduction) found that 39 percent of mothers polled were separated from their babies in the first hour of birth for routine care.[12] Babies who need care in the neonatal intensive care unit are separated from their mothers for longer times.

It is good to know that the body has its own check-and-balance system and is always seeking homeostasis. When stress levels become too high, causing increases in cortisol, the adrenal gland secretes DHEAs to oppose the action of cortisol, exerting a true anti-cortisol effect and thereby reestablishing balance.[13] However, when stress and anxiety overpower the check-and-balance system, we are out of balance and can become sick. As a society, we need to recognize the importance of keeping mothers with their babies as much as possible after birth and in the postpartum period to keep levels of oxytocin high, encouraging optimal health and well-being.

WAYS TO WORK THROUGH FEARS

There are ways that birthing women can work through fears, lessening their impact. Here are some suggestions:

1. ***Do a safe birth multi-sensory visualization.*** This visualization may be done in a childbirth class setting, and pregnant women may continue playing it out in their minds like a rehearsal for birth.

2. ***Say affirmations.*** Affirmations are positive thought patterns that help us to feel good energy. They can be practiced early in pregnancy and well before labor begins. Examples are, "I am a strong and powerful woman," "My body knows how to give birth," and "My pelvis has plenty of room for my baby."

3. ***Choose a birth team that feels safe.*** This requires prenatal screening and good use of prenatal visit time. A valuable member of any birth team is a doula, whose continuous presence throughout labor helps to decrease anxiety and fear. In addition, childbirth classes will review pertinent questions to ask doctors and/or midwives in prenatal visits. For example, a good question is, "What are things you believe disturb a woman's labor?" Such questions tell us much about the way a doctor or midwife practices medicine. A woman with a previous cesarean who is planning a VBAC might ask, "If you find a 'window' (small opening in the uterine wall from a cesarean incision) in my uterus after the birth, what would you do?" The correct response should be, "Nothing," for research has shown that windows, though rare, are safe even for future labors.[14]

4. ***Keep good company.*** There is an expression "You know a person by the company they keep." Just by observing facial expressions, we know if someone is anxious, worried, fearful, or

happy. We manifest more anxiety on a daily basis than we realize. What we talk about usually accompanies our expressions. And believe it or not, we actually imitate such expressions. We are experts at reading body language because we have done it since our first day of birth. Due to the principle of reaction/reflection/resounding, a pregnant woman who keeps the company of others who have many fears and worries about birth will tend to absorb some of these herself. It makes sense for pregnant women to find support groups who empower them with good thoughts about birth.

Take, for example, a woman seeking a vaginal birth after cesarean. Let's see how the company she keeps could make a difference in how she feels about birth.

Scenario 1

Melissa is three months pregnant and is planning a VBAC because she doesn't want to go through another surgery. She meets up with her friend Janice, who questions what she is doing because studies have found risks of uterine rupture and entire hospitals aren't even allowing VBACs anymore. Melissa tells Janice that uterine rupture is more of a risk with classical incisions and that hers is a low transverse incision, so it is safe.

But Janice tells her she has lots of friends having cesareans and they did okay, so it's very safe now. She tells her she can avoid labor completely by having a cesarean.In addition, she can even plan the time and date of her birth! But Melissa tells Janice she wants to feel labor contractions because God must know more than we do and she wants the very best for her baby. Besides, she has read that contractions help hormones to be produced, and these all help the baby in some ways too. But Janice tells Melissa that some of her friends had fourth-degree tears when pushing their babies out and also had pelvic floor damage. She reaffirms that pelvic floor damage is common in women who give birth vaginally. Now doubt is setting in as Melissa realizes she didn't think of that.

Scenario 2

Melissa is three months pregnant and is planning a VBAC because she doesn't want to go through another surgery. She meets up with her friend Jean, who acknowledges the fact that a cesarean is major surgery with all the risks of any surgery. Jean wants to know if Melissa's doctor is supportive of her plans. Melissa says he is and that some other women in his practice have had successful VBACs. She also says confidently that her doctor says the risks of cesarean surgery are greater than those from a rare but possible uterine rupture. Jean tells Melissa she has lots of friends having cesareans, and many have had infections in their incisions and that it takes weeks for the incision to heal. Her own baby was born naturally and she was up walking around within an hour after birth, able to take care of her new little daughter.

Melissa questions her about not having any damage to her pelvic floor. Jean replies that she knew pelvic bodywork techniques, and with good positioning mostly breathed her baby out in front of the pelvic floor, with little pushing required. She refers Melissa to Jean Sutton's booklet, *Optimal Foetal Positioning,* and her book, *Let Birth Be Born Again,* to learn more about good birth positions. Melissa questions her further about labor contractions and how they felt. Jean replies that they were a lot of hard work but it was good work. She adds that you can rest in between them. She also relates that she labored in a pool of water for awhile and had a birth doula who encouraged her and stayed with her through the whole labor.

Melissa starts to feel that labor is manageable with all these good ideas and begins to develop more confidence that her body can do the job. The vision of being able to take care of her baby right after birth instead of being in pain from surgery was something she hadn't thought through completely before.

5. *Attend childbirth education classes.* On the other side of every fear is freedom. In childbirth classes it is the simple expression of fears that helps to release them. The challenge lies in helping birthing parents to feel safe enough to let go of such fears, because if they don't feel safe, they won't express them. When working with women in childbirth classes and at their births, there is much we may not know or that they may choose not to share. Depending on how effective the instructor is in creating a safe space, people will share their deepest fears. Fears that are internalized and kept secret grow from little monsters to big monsters.

I remember a woman from my Birth Works® classes who attended a second class series for her second baby. It wasn't until the end of that class, two years after the time I met her in the first class, that she was able to tell me about an abortion she had had. I could see the relief on her face from having finally told someone. It was as if her resident monster had suddenly shrunk.

Doubts are a reflection of decreased confidence, and women with doubts can be easily swayed by what is heard and experienced from others, read in books, or seen on the television and movies. A good, quality childbirth preparation class is one that provides both an academic and emotional preparation for birth. It empowers women through accurate and current information and the sharing of experiences with others. The woman in the above scenarios would do well to surround herself with others in a class setting who convey a positive attitude about birth and who provide accurate information, helping her to be successful in having a VBAC. Caitlin recently gave birth to a little boy, Sam, and prenatally made it a point not to look at births on videos or television before going into labor. Instead, she read books that empowered her and described natural birth, and she also received Birth Works® training. From these preparations she envisioned what to do and had a beautiful natural birth in a birthing center.

A good technique to draw out fears in childbirth classes is that of the open-ended sentence exercise. In this exercise, participants complete sentences with one or two words. Examples are: "Labor contractions are . . ."; "One of my deepest fears about birth is . . ."; "Pain is . . ."; and "The sight of blood makes me feel . . ." Another technique to draw out fears and worries is to ask the same question more than once throughout the discussion. I like to ask, "What is your deepest fear about birth?" several times during the evening discussion, for each time a fear is expressed, there is certain to be an even deeper one behind it.

6. *Rest.* Resting lowers the breathing rate. When the breath is slow and deep, the body is more at rest. When we are fearful or anxious, our breathing rate increases. Taking time in the day to rest, we can reflect on what is making us fearful or worried and work to let it go, or at least put it into a better perspective. A walk in nature helps to nurture the mind, body, and spirit. Rest also helps to steady the mind. This is refreshing to the body and improves clarity of thought, which is so important in decision making that might have been causing stress. Meditation and relaxation exercises bring calm and rest to the body.

7. *Exercise.* Exercising brings a feeling of freshness to the body. For a woman who is pregnant, it helps to increase confidence, endurance, and muscle strength, which are all assets for labor. In addition, exercise is active work, and so is labor. A woman who exercises will be more familiar with the work of labor. Yoga, swimming, bicycling, and walking are all excellent types of exercise for pregnant women.

8. *Do the "releasing fears" visualization.* Here is a wonderful exercise that is simple yet profound, and that can help you release fears. You can do this exercise anywhere and at anytime. If you stop and think about your day, you might be amazed at how many times fears and worries enter the mind. Awareness is the key. It is only when we are aware of fears that we can begin to work through them and release them.

RELEASING FEARS VISUALIZATION

So, when you are ready, I wonder if you can identify a fear that you have inside you. Closing your eyes can eliminate visual distraction and help you focus. Take your time to find it, and when you have it, determine where it is sitting in your body. Yes, we store fear in the body, and it is in different places for different people. Common places are the gut, back, and head.

When you have found a fear, imagine a spherical globe, or a jack with points coming out of it, or any shape that works for you, and bring it down from space in front of your body, wherever the fear is sitting. Inside this sphere (or whatever shape you have chosen) there is a vast, dense, magnetic field, so dense that it is like a black hole, attracting into it all that comes near. If you are ready to release your fear, do so now, seeing the globe open and, with great power, suck in the fear into its dense magnetic gravitational field where it disappears, never to be found again. Fears have a way of surfacing again inside the body. Keep releasing them into the globe as many times as you need to.

Now around the globe is a golden light. When the fears are gone, accept the golden light around the sphere into your body where the fear was sitting. Allow this golden light to cleanse, heal, and make whole that part of your body. Keep sending more and more light until you feel at peace with yourself."

HEALTHY PAIN

Pregnancy is not an illness, and labor is a normal and natural function of the female pregnant body. The purpose of birth is to bring a baby into the world. A woman's body is so well designed to do this that it knows exactly what to do and when to do it. It knows how to conceive a baby, how to grow a baby, and how to birth a baby. The knowledge about how to give birth is already inside every woman. It is we who lack patience and faith, often trying to quicken the process.

The pain that is felt in labor is normal. It is caused by the uterine muscle contracting and shortening its fibers, which pulls up on the cervix, helping it to dilate little by little. When full dilation is reached, the baby passes out of the uterus and descends down into the pelvis. The body is kind to us, and in active labor produces its own pain relief via endorphins. This process is so well established over the thousands of years that women have been giving birth that we can trust it. We can believe that birth works because it's ancient.

In the English language, we have only the word "pain" to describe both a pathologic and a healthy pain. When there is pathology, pain serves as a warning signal that something needs medical attention, and we can be grateful to our body's ability to let us know this. Pain in childbirth is healthy pain, but people are often afraid to talk about it because they relate it to pathologic pain. Marathon runners and other high-level sports people view pain positively, as in the expression "No pain, no gain," and they learn to work through their pain to win a race. Ornish writes, "We are trained to view pain as an enemy and to kill the pain as quickly as possible...but the pain is there for a reason."[15]

There are different schools of thought about whether or not to talk about pain in childbirth classes. Some feel just mentioning the word *pain* induces fear in women and becomes counterproductive to empowering them for labor. Others feel that it is only by diving into fears that we can get to the other side of them, and so they believe pain should be discussed. Words for contractions vary, too, with some people calling them "rushes," "surges," or "waves" that tighten, apply pressure, or give squeezing sensations. I simply call them contractions. Perhaps it is because I am a physical therapist, but the word *contraction* brings me in touch with the magnificent uterine muscle that holds a baby and then knows how to shorten its fibers to contract, open the cervix, and move the baby down into the pelvis. I have great respect for a muscle that can do that! We want the baby, and without this powerful muscle we wouldn't be able to have it. I, for one, am grateful to it. I like the wisdom and spirit of one woman in labor who welcomed the strong contractions by saying, "Let it hurt more!" She knew that the stronger the contractions, the sooner her baby would be born.

There is a saying that "When you run from pain, it chases you." So the worst thing to do is try to

"run away" from labor contractions. Techniques of distraction are often taught to pregnant women, such as finding a focal point and using patterned breathing, but these are external strategies. Knowing more about birth physiology and the role of the neocortex, we can understand that patterned breathing stimulates the neocortex about what to breathe and when, which can inhibit labor. In addition, because the woman's focus is outside her body, she is less in tune with her instinctive urges of giving birth. In contrast, staying centered inside the body, riding each contraction as a wave, staying with it breathing slowly and deeply into the contraction, and feeling it crest and then washing to shore, gives a greater feeling of confidence and an "I can do this" attitude.

REFRAMING

This thought process is called reframing, and it is a powerful technique. Reframing means learning to view something perceived as negative in a more positive light. It means turning something perceived as fearful into something good. A good midwife or doula is trained in the technique of reframing and can help move a woman in labor through her fear.

In a previous birth, Janet had been "stuck" at five centimeters of dilation. It had been a long labor. The doctor artificially ruptured her bag of waters to help speed up labor, but this was followed by long and painful contractions. This memory was recorded in Janet's subconscious. Now she was pregnant with her second child and in labor.

Janet had been in active labor half the day. She was at home and had been at five centimeters of dilation for several hours. She was afraid the same thing that happened in her last labor would happen again in this labor. Eventually the contractions became very strong and intense, and she cried out, "No, oh, God, no." Maria, her doula, went behind her and began to breathe with her, synchronizing their rhythms with each other. Then as Janet cried out again, "No, oh, God," Maria began saying softly into her ears, "Oh good, oh good, oh goooood." Janet heard it and began saying, "Oh goooooood, oh, God . . . good God," as their voices rose in unison in primal rhythmic toning. In this way, her doula helped her bring a positive outlook to the labor contractions through reframing them as being good. With the single change of a word, Janet's tense body softened and she was able to relax into the contractions instead of fighting them. When fears and worries are reframed, they become empowering. Thus, contractions that hurt become powerful contractions that help a baby to be born.

PREPARING FOR BIRTH

Direct experience is our best teacher. Trying to explain what labor is like to a woman pregnant for the first time is like trying to explain what a fruit tastes like to someone who has never eaten it before. But we can give ideas. Here are some suggestions that can help women feel more familiar with birth, thus lessening fears.

1. *Attending a birth.* Attending another woman's birth is a good way for a new mother to become familiar with labor and birth, but is not always possible for many women today. Finding a natural birth may be even more difficult, but my niece just invited a new pregnant mother to be at her birth, and it was an empowering natural birth experience for both of them.

2. *Listening to labor sounds.* In classes, another effective way to give new parents a sense of labor is to play a CD of a woman making vocalization sounds during labor. I ask class participants to close their eyes and listen to a few minutes of the labor sounds from a few births. Afterward, I ask them how they felt in their bodies while listening to the sounds. This leads to a discussion of which labor sounds felt open and which ones felt tight. For example, high sounds are usually tighter and low, deeps sounds are more open. Most people, especially new parents, are surprised how "primal" the sounds are.

3. **Doing a multi-sensory birth visualization.** Information learned in an emotional context goes deeper into the psyche. A birth visualization that incorporates multi-sensory techniques provides a memory in the subconscious brain that can then be accessed during labor.

Understanding something helps us to be less afraid of it. When pregnant women understand what causes labor pain, they may see contractions in a more positive light. Our work in childbirth classes must be to educate and inspire women about their bodies, and clearly explain how it… *knows*…to give birth without our even having to think about it. I believe that hearing this over and over again, over the series of weeks of classes, inspires and empowers women. When they are in awe and wonder of their own human body, they come closer to believing it can do anything, even work with strong contractions in labor. Expectant parents would be wise to seek out childbirth classes that have such a philosophy. Here are some examples of concepts that empower women for birth:

- A woman's uterus knows how to grow a baby—continually adjusting its size as the baby grows—and her other organs know how to move and adjust their position to accommodate this expansion.
- Did you know that your uterus is a powerful muscle that is always contracting? In labor, its power moves the baby down into the pelvis to be born. It does all of this without your even having to think about it.
- At some point the baby knows when it needs to come out and sends signals to its mother through stretch proprioceptors and hormones, as if to say, "Mom, I'm ready to be born!"
- Remember that your body already knows how to give birth. All you have to remember to do is to let your body be your guide.
- In labor, as the uterus contracts it shortens its muscle fibers and pulls upward. This is what opens your cervix to give birth.
- Ligaments in the pelvis are softened by body hormones that give them more flexibility, helping to open the pelvis even more.

- We are full of electromagnetic power. Women giving birth are lucky to be able to feel this power inside them during the strong contractions of labor.
- Opening your hands to strong contractions helps your entire body to relax. With each contraction, all you have to remember to do is breathe deeply down into your pelvis, riding each contraction as a wave.
- Changing positions frequently during labor helps your baby to move down into your pelvis and out into your waiting arms.
- There is so much room for the baby to come out. Did you know that the diameters of the pelvic outlet are the size of a circle drawn around your hand when open—just about the size of a grapefruit and the perfect size of a baby's head.
- Contractions are like ocean waves, coming one after another. They gradually increase in intensity, reaching a point where the muscles won't get any tighter, and then they always come to shore as you rest and your baby rest.
- At the moment a woman sees her baby for the first time, she forgets all the work of labor in the moments of pure joy.

MOVING THE CONSCIOUSNESS

We are actually quite good at moving our consciousness in and out of the body. Most women have experienced pain of some sort during their lives by the time they give birth. This may be from surgery, dental work, serious falls, incest, rape, or loss of loved ones. A coping mechanism is often to "take ourselves out of ourselves." One woman said, "I don't want to bring up any memories of when I was sexually abused. It's just too painful." Yet this is the part of her body where she needed awareness in order to give birth. How can a woman give birth when her consciousness is not "present" in that part of her body?

I was teaching a Birth Works® childbirth education workshop and a woman described how difficult her birth had been. She had traveled to another country and while there, had sex with a man she didn't know. There were mirrors above the bed and she could see herself. She knew she should use some form of protection but had such low self esteem that at that moment, she simply didn't care what would happen. She told us she felt like she was watching a movie and that it all didn't seem real. She didn't know why she was doing it except that maybe she needed to feel loved. As she related the experience to those of us at the workshop, she suddenly realized, "That's why I couldn't feel myself in my birth! I wasn't in my body!"

Part of birth preparation is helping women to determine if they are "present" in their pelvis. If not, work needs to be done to help them come back in. In my experience, the feeling is first vulnerability. Then as the consciousness re-enters, there is reorganization, and finally refinement. Consciously moving the consciousness in and out of the body is an exercise that can help us realize what we often do subconsciously. I like to call it the life-force exercise.

LIFE-FORCE EXERCISE

Lie on your stomach in a very quiet place, making sure to place a pillow under your stomach to protect your back. Make sure your head is on a pillow and feeling comfortable. Dim the lights. Begin breathing slowly and deeply, following the breath all the way down deep into your pelvis. See if you can feel your breath filling your body slowly and deeply. Relaxing into the breath, see if you can feel yourself beginning to feel lighter and lighter, like a helium balloon rising slowly up into the sky. Now picture your life force as a blue cloud, hovering over the lower part of your back around the level of your lower vertebrae. It has been with you there since you were born. Invite this blue cloud to effortlessly enter your body. Since it doesn't need form to exist, it can easily pass into the body. See if you can feel it happening without forcing or pressing it to do so. Just let it be and feel the experience of it moving into you. Enjoy its exhilarating presence and then allow it to pass back out again; in and then out of you, taking whatever time it needs. It has done this without your conscious awareness so many times in your life already, and so can easily do so now. Feel the ease with which it can move in and out. Enjoy the experience. Continue as long as you want, enjoying the sensations. While doing so, realize how important it is to have your awareness inside your pelvic cradle when giving birth. Make sure that you have invited it back in before rolling to your side to sit up.

MOVING OUT OF FEAR

It is *not* our true nature to be constantly worried, anxious, and fearful. In fact, doing so leads to illness. We *can* train our mind to think of good thoughts no matter what the situation. Then it will see good, do good, and be good. Such a person experiences the peace from within that pours out, affecting every aspect of daily life. A person whose mind is full of worry, anxiety, and negative thoughts has no peace. A woman coming into labor with a feeling of peace will have a completely different experience in birth than one who comes full of fears and worries. A mind-set of fears and worries adversely affects the body's ability to do its work in labor, and medical procedures and/or obstetrical drugs will likely be needed to overcome such fears.

Birth practitioners often underestimate the degree to which emotions can interfere with a woman's ability to give birth. Fears of becoming a mother, of losing the pregnant body, or of the responsibilities and sacrifices that parenting requires may feel overwhelming and a woman in labor may not be sure if she is ready for it. Sometimes labor may be delayed even though the baby is in a good position. Addressing existing fears often help labor to progress again. It is the integration of the mind, body, and spirit that gives birth to a baby, and not just the body. This is why emotional preparation for birth is so important.

The more connected a woman is to the spirit within her, the less fear and anxiety she will have. In other words, the more open the shutters and doors of her "body-house" are, the more her light can shine. There is a spiritual hunger in us all, whether we realize it or not. This spiritual hunger is

actually a desire to know and experience more about the spirit and how it works within us. Just think of how precarious the internal temperatures and acid/base balance are that even allow conception to occur. Think of how the body knows to grow a fetus with different organs, each with its own specific purpose and function. Think of how the uterus knows to contract, pulling its muscle fibers up to open the cervix. There are atoms in all the tissues. Tremendous power is contained within the atoms. We are powerful beyond our wildest imagination and are capable of doing much more than we think we can. All women can realize how wise the body is and have more faith in its innate ability to give birth naturally. This empowers women to move out of fear and into a sense of wonder about birth.

When we are consumed by fears and worries, we are less able to listen or act on our own intuitive guidance system. In this state, we will lean more on others to make decisions for us. The practice of human values reduces fear and anger, making birth a place of love and beauty. Fear represents things that trouble or frighten us and cause us to become easily threatened, worried, and stressed under pressure. The spirit, on the other hand, represents all that is refreshing, new, and surprising. It is in the present moment. When a birthing woman lets the spirit work through her, she will have confidence for labor and will feel empowered not only by her birth experience, but also during her life as a mother.

To experience love, one must be fully open like an innocent, spontaneous child. Any residual fears or tension need expression in order for love to flow. The love within us wants to flow outward, but we often hold back and restrict this love in many ways. This is why childbirth classes that address fears and encourage their expression are vital in childbirth preparation.

ARTWORK

Artwork is helpful in releasing fears. Here are some ideas for classes:

1. *Drawing a cervix.* Women can draw a circle representing their cervix, and around the circle list anything they perceive as obstacles to its opening in labor. Have couples discuss the drawing together to see what can be learned from it. This provides insightful discussion that helps to work through fears and worries.

2. *The heart.* Have couples draw a heart. In the heart, ask them to list values they think are helpful to have in birth. Then for each value, describe how it can be used in birth.

3. *The birth place.* Ask women to draw a place where they feel safe. Have them share their pictures with their husbands or significant others. Have them determine if this is a place where they would like to give birth.

4. *Mothers.* Using clay, ask all class participants—including the men—to make a sculpture of themselves with their mothers. Next, have each of them describe their sculpture to others. As they are about to become parents themselves, discuss good things they learned from their mothers. Include what they learned from their fathers as well in the discussion.

5. ***Dispelling fears.*** Using crayons, have class participants draw a picture of what fear looks like to them. Have them describe their pictures to the class. Ask them what they can change in their picture to soften the fear. Instruct them to go ahead and do so. Repeat this process if needed to keep softening the fear. Next, have them draw a picture that represents love and share how it feels. This exercise can also be done with clay, forming a shape that feels like fear and then describing it. Next, they can form a shape that feels like love, and share its meaning.

When consciousness is released from the bondage of fear, it can move on in its evolution to higher levels. Learn the skill of listening patiently. When people feel safe and are given the opportunity to talk, they release fears and worries and can find solutions acceptable to them. The more love we give, the more we receive and the less fear and anxiety we will experience.

The Pouring Love exercise effectively helps birthing parents to experience this in classes, and as an exercise, it can be integrated into daily life with amazing results!

POURING LOVE EXERCISE

When you are ready, write down on paper all the good thoughts that you can think of about childbirth, parenting, and what makes people feel good. Keep writing as they enter your mind. Be sure all the thoughts you are writing down feel good as you write them. When you are finished, close your eyes and begin to visualize sending these positive thoughts to yourself and to your baby if you are pregnant. Open yourself to these good thoughts. Imagine these good thoughts passing right into your body, and if pregnant, into your baby too. Good thoughts are full of love. This love is powerful beyond measure. Allow these loving thoughts to connect with the spirit within. Feel this love growing stronger and stronger within you, as if a dimmer switch increases it more and more. This love is unconditional. It loves you regardless of who you are or what you have done. The nature of love is expansion. Feel the love within you expanding more and more and allow it to radiate out from you to all those in your family, friends, community, country, and to all women of the earth who are pregnant and giving birth. Remember, there is nothing that love can't heal. Love is the connection that brings us all together. There is nothing that love can't do. Love is much more powerful than fear. Be strong in your love. Hold onto love as the most precious gift that you have. A baby is a gift of love. You are love. Your child is love. Your baby is love. Love is in everyone. Think love, breathe love, be love, and all will be added unto you.

Birthing in the Spirit

In the past six years, I have had three miscarriages and three daughters. This stark contrast between life and death has deeply affected my birthing experiences going from devastation to abounding joy and incredible love.

With my first birth, I struggled with fear the entire pregnancy, desperate to know that she was okay and that my body would not fail me. Ultrasounds were my saving grace, along with many prayers. In labor, I was really fighting with my body, subconsciously doing everything to keep this baby inside, but with the loss of my mucous plug and then contractions, I was filled with fear. My mind connected these events with something bad…blood was bad, pain was bad. But I fought back and Eliana Grace was born after 46 hours of labor and two and a half hours of pushing. Her name means "God answers us."

After another miscarriage between Eliana and my second daughter, the joy of life overpowered my persisting fear. Labor with Michaela was six hours and less than 20 minutes pushing. Michaela Hope was born; her name means "Who but God could give us another baby?"

In my third birth experience, I was determined to give in to the pain and interpret each contraction as one "wave" closer to seeing my beautiful baby girl. I tried to make myself believe that the pain was good and God helped me to have the strength to overcome my fears. I gave birth to Brielle Faith (meaning "God is my strength") on Christmas Eve after four hours of labor and pushing for 15 minutes. She was almost 10 pounds and I was able to go through labor without any pain reducers or interventions.

Throughout it all, my belief and faith in Jesus Christ has carried me. Through the power of the Holy Spirit, I've been able to cling to a hope so lasting and sure that even in the darkest moments of my miscarriages, I knew beyond a doubt that God had wonderful plans for me.

—KARI ZIMAN. MOTHER AND TEACHER FROM ILL

CHAPTER 20

Detachment

*Above all, the conviction that you are not the body, but only a resident of the body,
has to grow in you. If you identify yourselves with the body you carry about
with you, you are inviting sorrow and suffering to overwhelm you
instead of the joy and peace waiting to bless you.*

SATHYA SAI BABA

Detachment is a concept little understood in the western world. It is a concept that, if understood, can be of immense value during birth, whether we are part of the birth team or the woman giving birth. Detachment does not mean complete separation or total non-involvement. It does not mean being uninterested, cold, dry, or unfeeling. Rather, it means having empathy, kindness, compassion, and unconditional love, but—and this is the most interesting part—being completely detached from the results of the action. In other words, it means whatever we do, not being affected by the outcome. It means that all our actions are being carried out with selfless compassion and not for self-interest or gain.

Detachment means being in the present, playing our role, engaging ourselves fully in our work, and carrying out our duties, but being unaffected by loss or gain, failure or success, slander or praise. A question I like to ask expectant parents is, "Can you love yourselves whatever your birth outcome may be?" It means *not* getting upset when things don't turn out the way we wanted them to.

Learning the concept of detachment is like being in the audience and watching ourselves on the stage of life at the same time. We are fully involved in the play, yet we are detached in the sense that we are watching it happen. It is very possible to be present in the physical body but watching it at the same time. A woman can be fully present in her labor, working through contractions, but at the same time be watching herself from a witness perspective.

We are all actors on the stage of life. To me, detachment feels like playing the game of life, singing the song of life, and meeting the challenges of life while being able to see the larger picture. A good analogy is that we are the movie being played out on the screen of life. Without the screen, there can be no movie. Yet while watching the movie, we often forget there is a screen. Becoming more aware that we are the movie on the screen helps to understand detachment, because it is just a movie. It is very possible to be aware of the movie and the screen at the same time.

I believe that the screen represents the unchanging reality that is in us and around us; there is nowhere that it is not. We cannot live without it, for then there would be no movie to play. We can

call it by any name and it will respond. When we are aware of its constant presence, we will never feel alone. It is a constant source of comfort and love and is just waiting for us to call out for it.

At the height of a long and difficult contraction, a woman who connects with her spirit can watch her body going through the contractions but at the same time be aware of the spirit's constant presence within, helping her with love and compassion and serving as her guide through labor. Whenever she calls, it will respond because it has been inside her and outside her all the while. Knowing this before and during labor can be a source of comfort and a resource for coping with the contractions.

The opposite of detachment is attachment. Attachment means being emotionally affected by the outcomes of our actions and events in life. Most of us become attached to material possessions, and when we lose them we feel sad. I lost the diamond in my engagement ring at the beach. I fought the inclination of attachment, since my husband had given it to me more than thirty years ago and there was sentimental value. But I also knew that worrying and becoming anxious about it would not bring it back, so why waste energy on that? Therefore, with some thought, I was able to find peace of mind.

Attachment in birth means not being able to let go of something in the past. Sometimes birth ends up differently than the way it was planned. A woman who panics may avoid a cesarean by having an epidural. In a very long labor, a little Pitocin may give a woman the strength she needs to birth her baby. Sometimes due to the situation the woman is in, she may agree to a cesarean versus delivering vaginally if the baby's health or life is at risk.

A woman who holds onto blame for anyone on the birth team—her husband, the medical system, or even herself—suffers from attachment. This is because the negative energy she is sending out will be reflected back to her, making her the victim. Attachment can be seen in a woman who has had a traumatic birth where she was not comfortable with the doctor or staff, but returns to the same hospital because that is what feels familiar. Still another example is a woman who is attached to the desire of having a water birth, but in labor discovers she needs to get out of the water to give birth. In such situations, if the woman can accept what happened and focus on seeing the good that can come out of it, she can begin to develop detachment. Attachment to events in life creates sorrow, whereas detachment gives us freedom and a feeling of lightness, as if a burden has been lifted off our shoulders.

It is also important for childbirth educators to feel detached from birth outcomes for women in their classes. A childbirth educator educates by providing choices through alternatives and options to help women have the births of their dreams. She encourages women to be active participants in decisions regarding their births and imparts a philosophy that is empowering. Beyond that, women need to take the information and integrate it into their own belief systems and levels of comfort, for ultimately, birthing parents will use the information as they like. Each woman knows what is best for her, and if she is provided with accurate, current information, she will make the best choices for herself. No one else can do that for her. She is the one who needs to feel safe.

Whether women have wonderful or difficult births, childbirth educators need to keep equanimity, not being overjoyed about one or dejected about the other. This is detachment. Praise goes a long way, empowering men and women to know that they have done the best they could; what more can they ask of themselves than that? Praise also helps to provide a good foundation for parenting. Guilt or anger for not birthing a certain way will only bring misery and regret, which are not healthy feelings. A childbirth educator who knows how to teach with the philosophy of educare will reach couples at deeper levels that will empower them to make changes in their own thoughts, and therefore their birth plans. Regardless of the birth outcome, each woman will apply this knowledge to her experience the best she can, knowing that at any given moment she has done the best that she could.

The concept of detachment is equally important for men in the birth process. The comfort and support of a loving husband or significant other is of immense value to a woman when pregnant, in labor, and during the years of parenting. Roles are constantly changing, and schedules require flexibility. There are sacrifices to make. Changing sleep schedules and fatigue compounded by the extra work of pregnancy, labor, birth, and parenting can raise tempers and escalate emotions. Sexual attraction can be at an all-time low. Practicing detachment can help men and women take a step back in the midst of chaos and look at the bigger picture of the miracle of growing and birthing a baby and raising it to become a responsible and mature adult.

Detachment is of immense value to a woman in labor. It means letting go of each contraction and welcoming the next. It means viewing the amazing work her body is doing, while at the same time working with contractions. It means "watching" herself in labor as if she is in the audience of the play of life whose part at that moment is labor. It is easy to do this when she has surrendered herself completely to the forces of labor and to the spirit.

When there is a very strong labor contraction, a woman who is working with her body goes into what seems like another dimension of reality. She is neither here nor there. She is oblivious to anyone around her and is not conscious of anything she has learned in books. She is connecting with her instinctive side. There is no sense of time. She is in touch with her spirit and is detached from the world. Her only thought is about birthing her baby, and all else fades into the distance. In this state, she is not affected by the outer world or by outcome because she is completely in the present and connecting to her inner self.

Women who have a positive outlook toward birth often describe labor as "a power within me" experience. They say, "I didn't know there could be such a strong force inside me," and are amazed by the experience. Those with a negative outlook say, "I was afraid if the contractions got any stronger I would lose control, and so I requested an epidural." They look at contractions as something to be feared and lose confidence in themselves to be able to work through them.

There are two choices here. One is to feel threatened by the contractions and the other is to be amazed, viewing them in a positive frame of mind as what is helping the baby to be born. In the first case, a woman is identifying with her body, perhaps feeling victimized and suffering. She may

have a more difficult time with labor. On the other hand, in the second case, she is identifying with the power inside that is deeper than form and that gives her strength and courage to do the work of labor. With an internal focus, riding each wave like a contraction all the way to shore, she will find resources within that she didn't know were there. She will be filled with awe and wonder and be empowered by the experience. She has the experience of doing the work of labor, but she is viewing it from the perspective of the spirit—involved but detached, watching the body do its work. She feels guided by a power greater than herself. When identifying with the spirit, she can love herself regardless of the outcome of the birth. This is detachment.

It is wise to detach from that which is constantly changing and instead attach to that which is permanent. Events in the world are in a continual state of flux, so it is not a good idea to be too attached to them because they will only bring sorrow and discontent. Attaching to the spirit, which is constant and unchanging, brings peace and contentment, and we will never have to detach from it. The spirit is always with us and can be considered our dearest friend who will never leave us. Attaching to the spirit automatically helps us to be in, but detach from, the movie of the world as seen through the limited view of the eyes and mind. This helps us to experience the oneness of all humanity.

There are practical ways to begin implementing the philosophy of detachment in childbirth.

1. ***Being the witness.*** Begin looking at your life in a new way by imagining yourself as an actress or actor in a movie, and you are watching it happen. Note how interesting it is—complete with times of happiness, sadness, conflict, resolution, eating, sleeping, pregnancy, giving birth, and parenting to name a few. Just watch it happening day in and day out.

2. ***Staying in the present moment.*** Stay in the present moment as much as possible. This decreases worry and anxiety and will help you to more fully appreciate the work you are doing. If pregnant, it will help to take each day one at a time, and in labor, one contraction at a time.

3. ***Keeping awareness in the heart.*** Carry out all actions without any desire for a reward in return. This means you are giving from your heart, which brings a feeling of freedom. You will increasingly be able to feel more detached from your actions, but at the same time will perform all actions with warmth, caring, compassion, and love. With the regular practice of this discipline, the consciousness can shine through you clear and pure. Expectant parents will be attracted to such a person for childbirth classes, doula work, and any member of the birth team.

4. ***Connecting with nature.*** Begin taking walks in nature and realize the beauty of God's creation around you. Do the trees want anything in return for providing shade? Does a flower want anything in return for sharing its fragrance? Just going out to view a sunset, or seeing a rainbow or waterfall, helps broaden the mind. Take a few minutes each day to stop and breathe slowly, appreciating the mystery of creation and the miracles around us every day.

5. ***Sensing the spirit's presence everywhere.*** Look for clues or "signs" of the spirit's presence in you and around you. This might be in a random act of kindness from someone, a smile on a newborn baby or child's face, a rainbow shining colors across the sky, or gazing at the stars at night. A pregnant woman watches her belly grow—this is a miracle. She is growing a baby inside! How does her body know what to do? This is a sign of the presence of the spirit.

6. ***Giving without desire for reward.*** At the moment of birth, a baby shares its love without any thought of reward in return. Begin to see the value of giving from the heart. What can you do today out of goodness itself without expecting something in return?

7. ***Meeting your goals.*** Be determined to meet your goals. Determination is necessary to train the mind because mental strength is needed to do the work we want to do. With determination, the mind can be trained to do anything. When we are consistent in our goal, it gains mental strength.

Detachment is not repression or denial. Repression and denial occur when fear causes us to separate ourselves from an event in our life. With true and unconditional detachment, there is no fear. Detachment is not a defense mechanism that hides feelings and fears from our conscious awareness. Detachment is the process of being able to be open to our feelings and fears, yet relating to them in a new way and being unaffected by the results. Detachment is the process of transcending the mind. It means being in the world but not letting the world be in us. It means doing our duty as best we can but not being attached to the results.

Remembering to connect to the spirit within in the midst of all difficulties is a challenge, because we can get so caught up in life that it is easy to forget to contemplate who we really are. Ego wants us to react, to return blow for blow, cheating for cheating, lie for lie, to hit back with all our might. But we can choose to tap into the power of love, not hitting back, not criticizing, developing a detached viewpoint, and letting go of any anger we may have toward others. They, too, were doing the best they could. If what happened was unfair or disrespectful, we need to forgive them.

Something as easy as looking up into the endless depth of the sky can help us to connect with something bigger than ourselves. Daily practice is required. Developing an attitude of detachment helps to preserve the heart. Says Ornish, "When the emotional heart and the spiritual heart begin to open, the physical heart often follows."[1] Remember that the love in us cannot be tarnished in any way. It is our eternal witness and is unconditional, loving us for who we are regardless of what we have done. We need to depend on it with our lives.

Beginning the practice of detachment little by little each day will prepare us for the day when we have to give up all we hold dear. Adding more to the things that bind us brings more attachment. Binding ourselves instead to the spirit and practicing its ways brings freedom.

Birthing in the Spirit

Before labor, I had thought that the labor pains would be in my stomach, but for me they were in my back, like a pinched nerve or something. There was tremendous pain through labor, but what I think is the miracle of birth is that as soon as I saw my baby's face, I didn't feel any pain. Seeing my baby made me forget about all the pain and I didn't feel anything at that point. All the other ladies I talk to have felt the same way. In the Indian culture it is believed that through the child's birth, God is giving the woman a second life. She goes through a lot of pain physically and mentally, but the reward is a gift for the woman that she is "born again" with the birth of her child.

—RANI BAI OTILINGAM, A MOTHER FROM INDIA

CHAPTER 21

Interconnection of the Senses, Elements, and Human Values

*All truths are easy to understand once they are discovered;
the point is to discover them.*

GALILEO

We take much in our existence for granted, moving through our daily lives not realizing how connected we are to everyone and everything around us and how this influences our lives. We are all familiar with the five elements of earth, water, fire, air, and ether, but have you ever wondered how they are connected to our five senses of seeing, hearing, touching, tasting, and smelling? The purpose of this chapter is to show the interconnectedness of the elements with the senses and with the values of truth, right action, peace, love, and nonviolence, and to describe how these can work to empower not only women in birth but all of us in our lives.

THE FIVE SENSES

It is only through our senses that we can experience the world around us. Each of our sense organs has the capacity to measure a certain type of experience. The eye can see but it cannot hear. The tongue can talk but it cannot see. The ear can hear but it cannot see or talk. Each has to accept its limitations and be content. Going beyond their limitations causes damage. Looking directly into the sun hurts the eyes. Listening to high, shrill sounds or very loud sounds damages the ears. We use all of our senses in life and in pregnancy, labor, and birth.

Misuse of the senses is a reason for ill health. The nose is used for breathing but people stuff it with tobacco and snuff. The tongue is used for talking and eating but people eat unhealthy foods and intoxicants are taken in. Overeating leads to adverse effects on the stomach and blood vessels,

which can impact the health of a fetus. Misuse of smell leads to desire and sensual craving, with the resulting development of products that damage the environment. Misuse of sight affects the eyes and leads to judging others, watching violence on television or elsewhere, living in the past or future, and constantly seeing faults in others. Misuse of touch leads to violence and ill feelings. The consequences of misuse of the senses are mental distress and physical disease. The senses are precious to us and we need to take good care of them.

Examining the sense organs first, we can realize that all of them are neutral. This means that they are, in and of themselves, neither good nor bad. The ears, eyes, nose, mouth, and hands are present on a body in which there is no longer any life force; however, none of them can function. Though they exist in the body, they do not work because the life force, the soul, has left. Therefore it is our own inner energy that causes the eyes, ears, and other sense organs to work, and what they see is a reflection of ourselves. It is we who see either good or bad—not the sense organ itself. A negative thought that enters the mind is a reflection of that person in some way. A positive thought that enters the mind is a reflection of that person too. We cannot blame the tongue for saying angry words. It only does what we tell it to do. I like to think of the body as a computer and our consciousness as the software. We enter our thoughts into the computer and it carries them out at our command. All is reaction, reflection, and resounding.

Hearing (sound)

Sound is everywhere. It is our primary form of communication and is filled with vibration. Even the slightest sound produces a disturbance in the air, creating vibration and then sound. A woman who vocalizes during labor moves the vibrations down deep into her pelvis to help her baby to be born. Letting air out through loose, puckered lips produces a sound that feels comforting at the height of strong labor contractions. Women often vocalize short mantras that give a spiritual strength to labor.

In his book *Stalking the Wild Pendulum,* Itzhak Bentov says, "We could actually associate our whole reality with sound of one kind or another because our reality is a vibratory reality and there is nothing static in it."[1] He goes on to express how even the sounds from our hearts all mingle with rhythmic electrical currents of our brains to form enormous interference patterns, spreading out and away from us. This explains how such energy fields intermingle and how the energy of one person who is near another person has an immediate effect. We "feel" the energy of another when we are near each other. A woman opening her body to give birth is vulnerable to the energy in the room. Whether she perceives it as safe or unsafe, fearful or loving, can make a tremendous difference in whether she opens herself to the experience of birth or becomes defensive and protective.

Seeing

The eyes see, but what force prompts them to see? The energy within is responsible for our ability to

see. The power of sight is more important than the eye itself, for there are those who have eyes but cannot see. The eyes see a vast expanse of space, but they cannot see the face to which they belong unless looking into a mirror. They cannot even see the entire body, as the back is beyond their view. In addition, they are neutral in and of themselves, meaning that they see neither good nor bad. They see only what you want them to see. We can choose to use the eyes to see good or bad or both. Choosing to see good things means holding the eyes in check, and doing so brings happiness. Any negativity that enters the body weakens the immune system because it results in a loss of energy.

I have spoken with doulas who express a feeling that they no longer want to accept clients who are planning to have medically managed births. What are these doulas seeing with their eyes and feeling with their hearts? They can choose to see a woman not birthing the way they think she should, or they can choose to see a woman who is doing the very best she can and offer her their love. This is what it means to see only what is good with our eyes.

Smell

The nose smells, but what allows it to smell? The olfactory nerves are prompted by the energy within. Smells help us to identify things in the material world like food, flowers, and babies. We back away from smells that are not pleasing. What smells good to one person may not smell good to another. My mother loved the smell of skunks. Respect for the sense organ of the nose means giving it only those smells that are pleasing. The smell of a newborn baby is very special.

Smells have strong recall ability. Remembering the smell of home-baked bread brings potent memories of one's childhood. Smells also alert us to be careful. A hospital has its own smell of antiseptics from cleaning and health regulations that is very different from the home. Women who are sensitive to hospital smells may choose to birth at home.

Babies who self-attach to their mother's breasts at birth are guided by smell, as the smell of the amniotic fluid in the womb is similar to the smell of colostrum. The baby gravitates toward that which is familiar. Smell is so sensitive that a woman should not use scented candles, massage oils, or aromatics so the newborn baby won't be confused with smells from its mother.

Touch

The skin is our largest sense organ and is associated with touch. What allows it to feel touch? It is the energy within that prompts the nerves that allow skin to feel anything. There are times when we find ourselves in situations where touch is healing, comforting, and loving. At other times touch can feel rough, painful, sore, and unsafe. This depends on the company we keep and our relationships with others.

Women in labor sometimes do not want to be touched, as they find it a distraction from the work of labor. Others find it comforting and useful. Deep pressure using the palm of the hand and letting sustained pressure from the shoulder move into the low sacrum area in the back often provides

relief for back labor. Some women may refuse touch or massage due to a history of sexual abuse. In such women, beginning with a foot massage can often help them be more receptive to massage on other parts of the body. Others find massage very helpful in being able to relax.

Firm holding is comforting for some women during very strong successive contractions. We tend to hunch our shoulders when holding tension, so kneading motions of the hands in shoulder massages are helpful in releasing the tension and relaxing them. Firm counterpressure may be preferred to moving touch to minimize distraction during a contraction.

Once the baby is born, infant massage establishes bonding between a mother and her baby. The massage can feel as good to the giver as to the recipient, especially when it is given with love. It is best to carry out during the quiet, alert time periods of the baby.

At any given moment there are thousands of particles of energy moving through space into and out of our bodies. The skin responds to this constant movement, though we can't see it happening. Touch is essential to our survival and hands can be considered the instruments given to us by God to do his work. We need to use them for good purposes, remembering the mottoes, "Help ever, hurt never" and "Love all, serve all."

Taste

The last sense organ is the tongue, which is associated with taste. The tongue only tastes what we put into the mouth. In and of itself it is neutral, neither good nor bad. The food we eat constitutes our moods and our health. During pregnancy, if taste has governed the eating of healthy foods, a woman will be healthier and have a better chance of growing and birthing a healthy baby. In labor, she will use her sense of taste to feel comforted when sipping juices, or in early labor, when eating light snacks.

THE FIVE ELEMENTS

The five senses are intricately connected with the elements, and therefore the body is very much connected to the elements. In fact, the body is a meeting place of all the five elements of earth, water, fire, air, and ether (space). The skin, organs, and blood vessels are composed of the food we eat, which comes from the first element, earth. More than 85 percent of the body is composed of the second element, water. That is why it is important to drink lots of water during the day. The inner current of electricity represents the third element, fire. Air, the fourth element, is breathed into and out of the body to keep us alive. The fifth element is ether or space, which is so pervasive that it is to be found everywhere, even between atoms. Let's take a closer look now at how the senses are connected to the elements.

Earth

Which senses do you think we can use to experience earth? We can see earth. We can touch earth. We can hear earth. We can taste earth. We can smell earth. The answer is all five. In addition, earth is very dense and moves rather slowly, as in a mudslide.

Water

Which senses do you think we can use to experience water? We can see water. We can taste water. We can hear water. We can touch water. But we cannot smell pure water. If you smell something in the water, it means something has been added such as chlorine, or perhaps some impurities. Pure water has no smell. We can only experience water with four of our senses. It is not as dense or heavy as earth and moves more quickly.

Water has the ability to store vibrations and act like a battery for consciousness. In fact, consciousness can affect the taste of water quite dramatically. In ancient times the Egyptians referred to the "Waters of Nu," or "Celestial Waters." The waters were charged with holy vibrations and the water was then drunk or bathed in to receive these vibrations during sacred ceremonies.

Water is a pleasing sensation for women in labor. In very active labor, a woman will want to drink only water as her body produces adrenaline in the final hours of labor. In the event of a longer labor, immersing in warm water feels soothing and relaxing. The buoyancy helps the birthing mother to move and change positions more easily. However, water can be so relaxing that a woman may instinctively feel the need to get up out of the water, even if she has planned a water birth; and at that moment, being exposed to the cooler air and an upright position, with pelvic shifting as she gets out of the pool, she may soon experience the fetal ejection reflex, with the baby being born soon afterwards. Therefore, water birth should not be a goal, but rather, an option that women choose if the moment is right. Other women often remain in the water to give birth.

Fire

Which of your five senses do you think you can use to experience fire? We can see fire. We can touch fire. We can hear fire. But fire has no smell and we cannot taste fire. We can only experience fire with three of our senses. Fire is lighter than water and moves even more quickly.

Air

Which of your five senses do you think you can use to experience air? We can touch air and hear air but we cannot see, taste, or smell air. We can only experience pure air with two of our senses, touch and sound. How do you know that air exists if it cannot be seen? It is because you can feel it and touch it. You also know that it is keeping you alive. So you have the experience that proves that air exists, even if you can't see it. Place your finger a few inches from your mouth and now blow on it. You can feel and hear the air as you make your own little wind. .

Ether (space)

Which of your five senses can you use to experience ether (space)? We cannot see, taste, smell, or touch ether or space, yet is so pervasive that it is everywhere. There is only one sense that we can use to experience ether—that of sound.

There are fascinating connections we can observe through these comparisons of the senses and elements; and as you will see, each one is very pertinent to a woman during pregnancy, labor, and birth.

1. The only sense that can be used to experience every element is that of sound.
2. The heavier the element, the more senses we can use to experience it. The lighter the element, the fewer senses we can use to experience it. We can use all our senses to experience earth, but only two to experience air, and one for space.
3. The heavier the element, the less pervasive it is. The lighter the element, the more pervasive it is.

Sound, then, must be very important to our existence, for it is the only sense that we can use to experience all of the five elements. When a woman in labor vocalizes through the contractions, she is using sound to help move her baby down through her body. It is as if she is giving her contractions a voice! Her ability to make primal moans or saying mantras during contractions will help her to relax in between them. She uses sound to communicate with her baby before and after it is born. Her baby uses sound to cry, expressing its needs. Women like to sing to their babies before and after they are born. Sound is so important that it becomes the link to expressing ourselves to others in whatever we are doing.

SENSES, ELEMENTS, AND VALUES

The senses and elements also have a relationship with the five values of truth, right action, peace, love, and nonviolence. Let's take water. Which of the values would you associate with water? Before reading on, try closing your eyes and see what comes to your mind. Many people install running waterfalls in their back- or front yard, and sometimes inside their houses as well. They take walks on the beach along the ocean, or sit and relax by a beautiful lake. Just hearing the water or being near it brings about a feeling of peace. Peace is the value we associate with water.

Which of the five values would you associate with earth? Take a moment and close your eyes again to see what comes to mind. Is it truth, right action, love, or nonviolence? Which association is the most apparent? It is right action. The earth carries out right action by giving us food with which to live. The earth provides us with plants and trees from which we are able to breathe and live. For that reason, the earth is often referred to as Mother Earth. I happen to love fruit. When I eat a section of a pear with some strawberries, I experience sheer delight that the earth could grow something so delicious!

Next is the element of fire. Which of the five values do you think is most closely associated with fire? Take a moment and close your eyes to see what comes to mind. Is it truth, love, or nonviolence, the three remaining primary values? The element of fire is associated with the value of truth, for it has the ability to burn away impurities. Figuratively, you can imagine burning away such tendencies as jealousy, envy, pride, or ego so that your inner light can shine full with love. Burning away such tendencies helps purify our actions.

The next element is air. Which of the five values do you think is most closely associated with air? Take a moment and close your eyes to see what comes to mind. There are only two primary values left—love and nonviolence. Which make the most sense to you? It is love. The air is a gift from God. It sustains our very existence and is full of love. This makes sense because we cannot live without air and we also cannot live without love. The two are very connected. In addition, both air and love are very pervasive, meaning they are everywhere. We all have love inside of us, waiting to be expressed. Just as a fish cannot live without water, so we cannot live without love. One who no longer feels loved, no longer wants to live. It is essential to our survival, just as is air.

Ether (space) is the last of the elements. It is associated with the value of nonviolence, the last of the primary human values. This envisions a broad perspective of seeing all as one, the unity in diversity, and experiencing the common bonds of humanity. Therefore, if we harm another, it is the same as harming ourselves. Below is a summary of the interconnectedness of the senses, elements, and values.

A summary of the relationship of senses, elements, and values

Values:	Truth	Right Action	Peace	Love	Nonviolence
Elements:	Fire	Earth	Water	Air	Ether (Space)
Senses:	No smell	All senses	No taste/smell	Touch/sound	Only sound

Love, the foundation of all values
Love as thought is Truth
Love as feeling is Peace
Love as understanding is Nonviolence
Love in action is Right Action

Now that we have an understanding of the interconnectedness of the senses, elements, and values, we can now apply it to the work of pregnancy, labor, birth, and life.

Water and peace: If I would like to experience more peace in my life, every time I drink a glass of water I can remember its association with peace. I can remind myself that the peace for which I am searching is already within me. Just the thought of peace begins to slow the rate of my breathing. As a woman in labor drinks water, or rests in a water pool or shower, she can think of the peace within

her. When she is breathing more slowly, she will be more relaxed and her work of labor will be more effective. Love as feeling is peace.

Air and love: As she breathes in air, feeling it move all the way down into her pelvis to breathe her baby out, she can be reminded of its association with love. There is nothing more powerful than a mother's love for her baby. Thinking love, breathing love, and pouring love—bringing love into every action—is a way to connect with the spirit and follow it as a guide for giving birth. It will also increase her levels of oxytocin, helping her calm and connection system to be strong throughout pregnancy, labor, birth, and on into the parenting years.

Earth and right action: When a pregnant woman eats food in the prenatal period and during labor, she can be grateful to the earth for giving it to her, nourishing her and her baby. The earth is performing right action by supporting the earth's population with nutritious foods. The woman can be reminded to eat healthfully. She may also remember to connect with nature by going for a walk in the woods, by a lake, or in the mountains, for in nature she can appreciate it with all of her five senses, which has a calming effect. This can help her center herself and quiet her mind in the midst of a constantly changing and chaotic world that she is likely to be experiencing through hormonal mood swings, a growing abdomen pregnant with a fetus, and prospects of what it will be like to become a mother, and perhaps mother more than one child. Love in action is right action.

Fire and truth: Perhaps she will light a candle for dinner. The flame can remind her of the sanctity and sacredness of birth. It can remind her to "burn away" her own impurities of ego, jealousy, anger, pride, attachment, and unlimited desires. Purifying ourselves brings us closer to our own truth. In the prenatal period, the woman can sit in front of the flame of a candle and do a light meditation, "bringing" the light inside herself so she can see good, do good, and be good. This brings good vibrations to her baby growing in her womb as well. In labor, she can remember her own truth that her body already knows how to give birth. She can choose to surrender to it and let it be her guide. Just as a thousand candles can be lit from one flame, so can she be an inspiration to all women giving birth by her example. For instead of coming to birth with fear, she comes to birth with trust and faith in her own ability to give birth. Love as thought is truth.

Ether (space) and nonviolence: Ether (space) is everywhere. This can remind the woman of how wise her body is for her organs to shift their space, allowing more room for the growing baby. It can remind her of the importance of moving around in labor. It can remind her of the need to keep her pelvis in a forward position, especially in the six to eight weeks before her due date. It can remind her of the fact that there is plenty of room inside her body to give birth, for what looks solid is in reality just space. Space is full of vibration, and vibration is only experienced by the sense of sound. Vibration is what helps a woman to conceive, sends eggs down to the uterus, and grows and births a baby. The wonder and awe of the human body can help her feel connected to all women who conceive and give birth. When all who are with her at her birth show respect, treating her as they themselves would want to be treated, there will be nonviolence. Love as understanding is nonviolence.

The five elements are perceptible only through our five senses, and they are interconnected with

the human values. Exploring this connection leads to a deeper understanding of ourselves and helps us to see the positive instead of the negative. It also gives us daily perspective into who we are and for what reason we are here on the earth. The relationship is so connected that what we see going on outside of ourselves is actually an image of what is on the inside. A woman who practices this philosophy—applying the interconnectedness of the senses, elements, and values—will enter labor with a completely different mind-set than one who doesn't, and it will provide her with insights into how she may give birth. She will also be grateful for the knowledge of how the elements can serve as a reminder of the human values within and the ability to then put them into practice in her life and her births.

Birthing in the Spirit

I chose to give birth with a midwife and without medication for two reasons; one, I am afraid of needles! Two, birth just seemed to me like a pivotal experience for women. When I thought about birth, it seemed as if it was something totally sacred and transformative. I wasn't educated like I am now, but intuitively birth seemed like a process which would unfold more smoothly if it wasn't interfered with.

I prepared for my birth in ways that might seem surprising. Every day I took time to meditate, pray, and bond with my baby. I had taken a picture of a rock off the coast of Oregon while visiting a friend there early in my pregnancy. The rock was huge and solid but in the middle the waves had carved a nice, round hole. If that rock can open to the water, I thought, surely my body can open to my baby. I expected birth to be painful but I didn't fear the pain. My girlfriends held a Mother's Blessing for me, in which we strung beads on a bracelet for me to wear during labor. For each bead they said a wish for me; strength during labor, peace, a healthy baby. I felt so loved. They put their hands on my belly, which they had painted, and chanted "Om." The energy and power in that room was palpable, and I carried it with me into my birth. My daughter was late (10 days), and my labor was long (40-plus hours), but I loved giving birth. I loved every minute of my labor, even the contractions, which did hurt. Still, in between the contractions, I felt amazing, so strong and so good. During transition I sat in the warm shower, alone. I could hear my midwife and husband talking together outside the bathroom. That part of my labor was a totally transcendent experience. I could hear the beautiful voices of my girlfriends chanting and felt almost as if I was floating above the shower. I felt so connected to this power that was both greater than myself and inside of me. It was incredible! Soon after that I was completely open; the pushing contractions hurt more than the others but in between, I swear, I have never felt so good in my entire life. When my daughter was born it was the biggest "high" ever; I felt so

much love for her and so much confidence in myself to mother her. Giving birth the way I did changed my life! I now know in ways that I couldn't have expressed before that the Universe is truly magical, and that we all come from and return to a place of love that is almost inexpressible. I wish every woman could experience birth as I did, feeling so loved and so powerful.

—KATHLEEN FURIN, CCE(BWI)

CHAPTER 22

Grieving and Healing

You came into my world all quiet peace and wonder,
Until that time, I only thought I had felt love.
A tiny precious infant whose sweetness drew me under
Then sent my spirit soaring high above.
First I gave you your life, then you gave me mine.
An unexpected gift of motherhood.
We two are gently wrapped in the sacred tie that binds,
For you opened up my heart when no one could.

JANIS CHRISSIKOS CCE (BWI)

The temple was crowded with her friends and family. Most people were wearing black. Their heads were lowered as the rabbi read words from the Torah. There was no music. It was a gray day outside, with air cold enough that we had to wear light jackets. I thought of little Camryn, passing on at only three years of age. She had been born with a condition called spinal muscular atrophy and had been in a wheelchair most of her life. Though she was completely dependent in all activities of daily living, her mind was bright and she could speak and carry on simple conversations. She always had a smile for us at the school where I work as a physical therapist. I had taught her aide how to do stretching exercises for her arms and legs and also how to establish more trunk control.

I was sitting on the long benches of the temple with many of my coworkers, including speech and occupational therapists as well as her special education teachers. Camryn was a special little girl who brought joy to the other children in her class, for they could help her do things sometimes. The mood was solemn. I thought to myself, *How odd. I would think Camryn would have wanted to be remembered as the joyful and playful little girl that she was.* I also thought, *She must feel so relieved to be free of her body that limited her in so many ways. Her spirit can now soar.* Just at that moment, in the middle of the temple, as if suspended in mid-air about halfway to the ceiling, I saw a blue streak of light. It hovered for a moment, rather playfully, and then with a sense of purpose took off through the open window. All around me heads were bowed in mourning. But I felt joy, for her spirit was now free.

After the ceremony we all lined up in our cars to go to the cemetery for the burial. The occupational therapist was in her car beside me. She had also been sitting next to me in the temple. I lowered my window and looked at her, hesitating a moment. Then I asked, "Did you see something in there?"

"Yes!" she replied. "Did you see the blue light? What was that?"

"I believe it was Camryn's spirit," I replied.

We were both silent, filled with awe and wonder at having witnessed the event. Later, I shared my experience with Camryn's parents and wrote a poem for them. Their grief and healing was softened by knowing that their little Camryn was okay.

We all want to avoid suffering because it can be devastating, penetrating, total, and profound, shaking us down to the core of our being. Suffering is a humbling experience, but there is good that comes out of it. Even if words sound empty and meaningless during times of loss, the experience of loss helps to shake our attachment to the outer world until we cry out for the inner strength to transcend it.

It is Charlie Brown who said, "Good grief!" Grief is very healing and good for the mind, body, and spirit. There are many times that a loss occurs during the time of pregnancy, labor, and delivery, and this will be followed by the stages of grieving. When people are aware of the stages of grieving, it will be easier for them to move toward resolution. When someone is in a state of grief, every aspect of daily living is deeply affected, including eating and sleeping patterns, mind confusion, and even health. An interactive discussion of the grieving process should be carried out in every childbirth education class, along with an opportunity to actually grieve a loss that needs healing. This has the potential to facilitate normal birthing, as a pregnant woman won't need to work out emotions from the loss during her labor. This happens especially when it occurred in a previous birth experience.

Losses that occur in and surrounding birth include stillbirth, having a handicapped child, and complications especially from a cesarean surgery or difficult birth. Sudden Infant Death Syndrome has been reduced dramatically by educating women to lay their babies on their backs instead of their stomachs, encouraging breastfeeding, and decreasing smoking in pregnancy. In rare circumstances, the mother can die. In fact, a fear men share if they feel safe enough is being afraid of losing their wives in birth.

Perceived losses include the loss of having a pregnant body, the loss of the birth experience of one's dreams, the loss of one's childhood, and the loss of realizing a significant other was not comfortable being at the birth and realizing he shouldn't be at a subsequent birth.

Miscarriage is another loss of childbirth. A woman at a workshop I was teaching said, "I'm a labor and delivery nurse and help drug addicts deliver their babies, but I've had eleven miscarriages and can't even hold on to one of my own!" No matter how long a pregnancy lasts, a miscarriage destroys hopes and dreams. Parents ache for their baby. Another woman I once met said, "I was a mess. I had to grieve for both babies before I could try again." Still another who suffered from a miscarriage said to me, "I experienced anxiety at every single milestone of my pregnancy." When a miscarriage occurs later in pregnancy, some women say they were never able to shake their fear. "It was only one month short of my due date and I still couldn't let down my guard," said a woman. Some women describe a sense of keeping themselves distant from their pregnancy after a miscarriage. "I didn't

tell people that I was pregnant for a long time," or "I didn't start to feel connected to my baby until it was over thirty-four weeks old."

More women than we realize have experienced sexual abuse or other trauma to the pelvic region, and they are often not conscious in that part of the body at the time of birth. It is possible for the consciousness to leave part of the body, for we know how to escape something that is painful. How can a woman be an active participant in giving birth when her consciousness is not present in her lower abdomen? In such cases, grieving the loss helps to bring awareness back into that area of the body, increasing the chances of the woman being able to work with her body to give birth. Take, for example, the story of a doula named Shellie who attended Sarah's birth:

> *Early aspects of her labor were going well, but then when the contractions became very strong, she stopped dilating. I don't know why. Sarah moved into various positions, rested in a water pool, and did all the right things I could think of. The baby appeared to be in a good position but there was no progress over several hours. Somehow I got the feeling that she wasn't connected to what was happening in her body. It was as if she couldn't work with her body anymore. We did all we could and then a cesarean was performed for failure to progress. The baby was fine and was in a good position. I was puzzled about her birth and was trying to figure out what makes some women work well with their bodies and some not. Later, I found out that Sarah had been violently gang-raped and was in therapy trying to recover, and this was the baby that was conceived. It was on hearing this that I realized her consciousness may not have been present in that part of her body. No wonder her labor wasn't progressing!*

Many people find it difficult to be with someone who is grieving because either they don't know what to say, or being with them may bring up issues in their own personal lives. Miscommunication is common. Take, for example, a woman who has suffered a miscarriage and is told at the hospital, or by well-meaning family or friends, "You'll get pregnant again!" or "I know just how you feel," or "It was probably for the best," or "A miscarriage isn't as bad as losing a child." These platitudes often make the woman feel worse.

A woman who is grieving may feel that no one can know the depth of her loss. If her baby died, she may find it difficult for a long time to be around families with children. She may even avoid going to church or temple or mosque for this reason. This further increases her loneliness. Some of the literature on grieving states an average time period for grieving to be approximately fourteen months to two years. Though such numbers may vary greatly, if it extends for many years, it becomes chronic, affecting our health adversely.

SOCIAL ASPECTS OF GRIEVING

There are both physical and social aspects to grieving. Socially, before birth, women and their pregnant bodies are the focus of much attention. There are celebrations such as baby showers or blessing ways. Men often treat their wives specially, perhaps bringing flowers or gifts. Women may find others, especially grandmothers, approaching them and giving words of advice. People may want to reach out and touch the pregnant belly.

After birth, the focus of attention is more on the baby. This may or may not be perceived as a loss for the woman, for she may feel proud to be the mother of her child. But now she is awakened throughout the night to feed her baby, resulting in interrupted and disturbed sleep patterns. Lack of good sleep can wreak havoc on the body, causing mood swings and even decreased clarity of vision. Tempers can get short and words of frustration can surface. A baby that keeps crying can lead to exasperation and frustration. Fathers often don't know how to handle such situations and relationships are tested. Sexual attraction may be at an all-time low, especially since the woman may feel spent from nursing and not want any further stimulation. The men can feel left out, with their wives needing to comfort and care for the baby and perhaps other children. This is the time of burnt dinners and fatigue unlike what a woman may have ever known before.

PHYSICAL ASPECTS OF GRIEVING

Physical symptoms of grieving are exhibited in terms of extreme behaviors. The grieving woman may eat too little or too much. She may sleep too little or too much. The mind can become easily confused with difficulty in decision making. The breath is shallow, with a higher-pitched and breathy voice that can be heard even in a phone call, letting you know she is grieving. If the grief is profound, she may lose the ability to talk at all, with her breath literally taken away. These conditions make a person prone to illness, as we need to have good sleep and to eat well in order to be healthy.

STAGES OF GRIEVING

There are five stages of grieving that are typically described in the literature. They may have varying titles but tend to follow the same progression. The first stage is always described as shock and disbelief. The fifth stage is always about resolution and acceptance. In between are the stages of anger, guilt, and what I like to call "expression of the depression." A person grieving may be in more than one stage at a time, or even move back and forth from one to another. Knowing about the stages of grieving is a source of comfort when actually experiencing them. When the world feels like it is turning upside-down, it is good to know that the emotions are normal and will pass if they are allowed to be fully expressed.

Shock and disbelief

"She just lost her baby and isn't even crying!" said a nurse after the stillbirth. In this stage, people are numb. They think that if they go to sleep, they'll wake up and find that it didn't really happen after all. It is a time when even though they may be told many things about what happened, little to none of it will register. The feeling of "It can't be real!" becomes more realistic in time. I lost my mother suddenly during heart surgery a year ago and found that just saying, "My mother died," helped me to realize that this was final and that it actually did happen.

Anger

It was pouring torrents of rain. The father pulled over to the side of the road and started yelling, "How could you do this to me! How could you come into the world and then leave me! What right do you have to do that! I was going to teach you how to play ball. Didn't you want to do that? I just don't understand what happened! I am so angry!" It had been several weeks since he had lost his son at birth. The rain seemed to match the anguish that he felt as he sobbed his own rainfall of tears. In this stage, when anger is allowed to be expressed, it can be short-lived.

I have had people in my classes who are in the angry stage of grieving. It becomes apparent right away just by their tone of voice, and it is important for others to realize this and not take it personally. It should be acknowledged right away. Remember that anger is one letter short of danger. Anger heats the blood, and the blood takes up to six weeks to become regulated to its normal temperature again. Anger appears strong but is actually very weak compared to the strength of pure love. Allowing any anger present to be expressed helps it to be short-lived.

Guilt

In the stage of guilt, the questions are "What if?" or "Why didn't you?" For example, a person might say, "If only I'd left the door five minutes later, I wouldn't have been in the car accident." "If only my childbirth educator had told me that, it wouldn't have happened." "If only I hadn't had the cesarean, I wouldn't have been separated from my baby." Guilt is closely associated with blame, as in, "If only my husband had protected me more, I wouldn't have had a cesarean." It is healthy for these feelings to be expressed even though they won't change what happened. It is the process of vocalizing them that leads to the stage of "expression of depression."

Expression of depression

This is the stage when people are ready to hear what happened at the time of the loss. When a woman is in this stage, she will want to talk a lot about what happened. She is ready to hear what caused the loss, even if the reason is unknown. She may have been told the reason initially but was too numb to hear it. Now she is ready to learn and understand, even if the reason it happened is unknown.

When people are in this stage of the grieving process, they are searching desperately for answers

to what happened. It is important to be a good listener and offer what information you may know. If it was a stillborn child, they may be ready to hear, "We don't know what causes this to happen." It is also common to repeat things over and over. Mary said of the birth of Joshua, "I knew there was something wrong even before he was born, but then I felt I was imagining things. Now he can't move his arms and legs well. Was it something I ate? Or the argument I had with my partner? Or there was the time when I got sick and had to take an antibiotic. I've been reading as much as I can about cerebral palsy. My birth was normal, so something must have happened while he was growing inside me. This isn't the way it was supposed to be . . ."

Acceptance and forgiveness

"Oh God, help me!" In this stage we are in closer touch with our own mortality and immortality, and people find themselves reaching out to God, or at least a higher power or purpose in life. It's as if connecting with something bigger than ourselves, perhaps a higher intelligence, can bring solace and help us feel okay again.

It is a time for a woman who has given birth to figure out exactly who she is angry with. It might be a doctor, a nurse, her significant other, the medical system, or herself. Without forgiveness there cannot be peace, so we must learn to forgive. Acceptance and forgiveness may not be easy, but holding long-term anger is worse for our health.

There are many ways to help someone process their grief. Being able to tell their story in a childbirth class, in the presence of those who show unconditional love and compassion for what happened, is very healing. Feeling safe to cry is healing. Many women are surprised that they have unresolved hurt feelings inside themselves. Having a chance to tell their story again the way they had wanted things to happen establishes a memory in the subconscious brain that is also healing. The instructor simply needs to be a good listener. It is not her role to counsel or try to fix the situation. She only needs to listen and the rest takes care of itself. She may recommend a woman go on for professional help if necessary.

Writing is another powerful and effective way to release emotions. A letter doesn't have to be sent; the process of writing itself is sufficient to heal. There was a good example of this in one of my classes. I was talking about how it is not our place to judge the magnitude of another person's loss, for how can we ever know how great or small that loss may be to that person? On the evening of the grieving class, a woman began speaking about her cesarean but appeared to have resolved it well, as her eyes did not water and she had a sense of peace about the birth. However, she proceeded to tell us, "And then they brought my baby to me…" and she began crying, saying, "And…and I didn't even know how to change his diaper! Here I have a baby and don't even know how to take care of him!"

Just then another woman in the class abruptly stood up and, looking like she was going to throw up, walked out the door of the room. I said to everyone, "It's okay; I'll go out to see if she needs help." But before I could go, she was back in the room and sat down.

I asked her, "Is there anything you would like to share with us?" She said no and mumbled something about comparing the loss of not knowing how to diaper a baby to that of losing a loved one. And then she abruptly stood up again and walked out the door of the room, again looking like she was going to throw up.

I again said to everyone, "Don't worry; she is doing what she needs to do and I'll go see if she is okay." But again, before I could go out, she came back in.

I asked, "Have you lost a loved one recently?"

She mumbled, "Yes."

"Would you like to tell us about it?"

"No" was the response. So I suggested that it would be helpful to at least write down what happened, and that if she did so, to keep writing until she felt a sense of peace about what happened. I reiterated that it is not our place to judge another's loss, but we can acknowledge a loss with compassion. The class was then over.

All that week I was wondering how she was doing but knew she would call me if she needed to. The next week I almost didn't recognize her as she walked into the class. Prior to that she had always been tight-lipped with limited smiles and rather abrupt body motions. But this night she had a big smile across her face and such a soft look that everyone was amazed.

She couldn't wait to tell me something. She said, "You won't believe what happened! I went home and wrote and wrote and cried and cried, and I kept writing as you said until I felt better, and now I feel so good!"

We were all very happy to see this wonderful change and didn't need to know what it was about. It was just important that it happened.

An example of how grief attaches itself to various parts of the body was evident in Janice's story. It was the evening of grieving and healing in my classes. In the classes we discuss various aspects of grieving and healing, and then participants are given the opportunity to actually grieve a loss. Janice volunteered and began talking about the cesarean she had had, and then she continued, "And now they are putting in the IV in my right arm. Oh my God, my arm is going numb!"

The entire class moved from their chairs to come closer to her. She continued to describe what was happening as she was prepped for the cesarean and the operation was performed. She cried and others cried, as parts of her experience were also their own experience. Others shed tears out of compassion alone. There was a feeling of deep intimacy present, with all there feeling the good coming from Janice's birth story.

At the end of her grieving, we stayed an hour until the feeling came back into her arm. She felt lighter, as if she had "shed 30 pounds!" This is always the experience of those who allow themselves to grieve a loss. It is as if a tremendous burden has been lifted that they didn't know was there before.

A man in class grieved the blame he was feeling from his wife for not stopping or protecting her from the sequence of events that led to a cesarean. Men are taught to keep their emotions in check,

so I am very moved in my childbirth classes when a man feels safe to let go and cry. Grieving is of immense value to the entire class. I believe that the inertia created by emotions being held inside the body leads to tension, and if the tension is not released, over a period of time it can become disease, or disease. Charlie Brown is right. Grieving is good because it releases anguish and sorrow.

CHAOS, REORGANIZATION, REFINEMENT

I like to describe what I call three rules of the universe: chaos, reorganization, and refinement. Using the analogy of a volcano, at first there is complete chaos and destruction when it erupts. The terrain is so changed that it may barely be recognizable. In time, there is reorganization as plants, flowers, and trees begin to grow again, attracting birds, insects, and animals. Then eventually there is refinement as the landscape begins to look normal with forests growing once again.

The human body is not any different. Trauma is the equivalent of chaos. We are confused and vulnerable and don't know what to do. How many of you have left your body while sitting in the dentist's chair? A woman who has suffered from sexual abuse, an abortion, or miscarriage may have "left" her lower body and will not bring her consciousness back in until she feels safe. It is possible and easy to be conscious in part of your body and not in another part.

I have worked with clients in the techniques of myofascial release and external uterine massage. As they allow their consciousness to re-enter, there can be shaking, confusion, and fear as they work to become conscious again in that part of their body. As reorganization occurs, they gradually begin to experience sensation and consciousness. Eventually, with refinement, they begin to accept that part of their body again. It is always good to follow this process with affirmations or positive thought patterns and/or healing exercises such as writing or doing the Figure 8 exercise (see next page).

It is our natural state to be happy, and so one who holds onto grief chronically will not be healthy. Grief is a relentless emotion that will keep surfacing throughout life until it is released. Pent-up grief might result in a person becoming angry about a small thing that then gets blown up out of proportion. Though we will never forget the loss, we *can* come to a place where there is acceptance of what happened.

A loss cannot be undone. A woman who has lost a baby will always be a mother. It is healthy for her to hold her baby if it has died, and to give it a name, because we can't grieve a cloud. She may choose to save a lock of hair in a locket, take pictures for memories, and have a burial ceremony to bring closure to this difficult time in her life.

When suffering a loss, we ultimately need to move on beyond what happened and let life get back to normal. I heard a teenager who lost his mother in 9/11 say, "I can't be unhappy forever!" We need to make peace with what happened, forgiving anyone or anything that needs to be forgiven. Reaching out to the spirit that is beyond relationships, pleasure or pain, the world of the senses,

and the mind brings comfort and healing. The spirit transcends duality and transforms pain and nothingness into love so we can move on in life.

The Figure 8 Exercise is a powerful way to heal losses.[1] A loss is usually associated with a feeling of anger or blame toward someone or something. When this happens, there is an energetic attachment to that person or thing that is connected into our own bodies. In order to heal, that attachment needs to be broken. It is important to first identify where you feel that attachment is in your body. It could be attached to your heart, your head, your throat, your solar plexus, or your back, to name a few possibilities.

THE FIGURE 8 EXERCISE

While standing, extend your arms straight out to your sides at shoulder level. In your mind's eye, make a circle on the ground that has a diameter of your stretched arms. When that is finished, make another imaginary circle in front of yours that touches only where the two circles meet. Place yourself in your circle, and then place the person from whom you want to separate in the other circle. This could be a person, an emotion, or even a system such as the medical system. In your mind's eye again, begin tracing the circle in front of you in a clockwise direction, continuing around to your circle in a counter-clockwise direction, and back up to the other circle. Keep tracing this over and over again with your finger, a crayon, or even a blue neon light. Do this every day for two weeks, for five minutes each.

If you want to just separate from the person or object in the other circle, you can end the exercise here. I used this exercise to let go of any subconscious control I may have had with my own children when they graduated from high school. Knowing that there is such a tendency for parents to control their children and continue managing their lives even when they are grown up, I wanted to loosen the attachment so they could have "wings to fly" and would not be bound by my desires. The love I have for them both is very deep and we are very close. In fact, we are best friends. I believe this exercise helped that to happen.

If you want to cut the ties completely, determine where the energetic ties of this person or object are connected to your body. When you are ready to cut the ties, decide what equipment you need to energetically cut the ties. In your mind's eye you can use something very strong, like scissors, a knife, fire, or even a chainsaw. When you are ready, go ahead and cut the tie in whatever way you need to. Make sure it is cut completely. Now, where the tie was connected to you there will be a gaping hole. Send golden, healing light into the hole where the negative energy was attached. Keep sending this loving energy until your wound is healed and you feel whole again. Next, again in your mind's eye, take off all your clothes and wash them so they can be clean and pure before putting them on again. Or, you can just throw them away and put on new clean clothes. You can go through this process of cutting the ties as often as you need to.

I do not believe in coincidence and do believe that everything happens for a reason. You can

thank this person or object for coming to teach you what you need to know. See the good that came out of the experience by examining how you, yourself, have changed, perhaps becoming wiser and stronger. Always be grateful to the spirit, whatever experience it offers you.

Birthing in the Spirit

Writhing in an attempt to work my way out, I have to take pause to catch my breath, to rest my tiring body, and to devise a plan that will get me through. Will I get through? When will I be able to see? When will I be able to breathe fresh air? And I pause again. Oh! This is terribly frustrating! But I'm going to get out! After one more long pause I reset my determination. I work it out and feel the top of my head poke through. Feeling the air on my forehead and the tightness around my eyes, I push my chin up enough to be able to open my eyes—it seems so much brighter than I remember, so I close them. I catch my breath, again. Realizing that my work is not over, I go for my final push—and my nose, mouth, and chin are free!! I did it. Me. In one fell swoop, all of the angst of the previous day's realization got swept away and I felt reborn. Brand new. The room was brighter, I was exhausted, my skin was nakedly sensitive, and then I became aware of how vulnerable I felt. So I wept. And I wept. And as I wept more, I felt kind hands upon me. Not moving, just holding me there as if to say, "You're safe. Be still and take what you need." I did just that. The next day I grieved, and healed. The sun came out and everything was brilliant. I continue to heal. I continue to grieve and I continue to grow. I can only imagine what my next birth-giving experience will be like, now that I have been introduced to Birth Works®.

—BARI HENDERSON, FOLLOWING THE TURTLENECK EXERCISE AT A BIRTH WORKS® INTERNATIONAL
CHILDBIRTH EDUCATION WORKSHOP

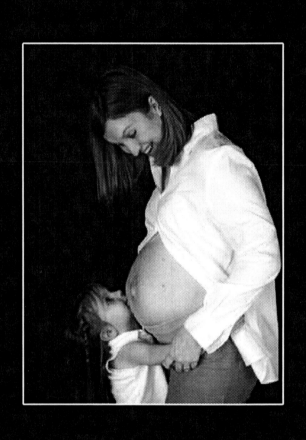

CHAPTER 23

Our Mothers and Our Health

A child asked God, "They tell me you are sending me to earth tomorrow,
but how am I going to live there being so small and helpless?"
"Your angel will be waiting for you and will take care of you."
The child further inquired, "But tell me, here in heaven I don't have
to do anything but sing and smile to be happy."
God said, "Your angel will sing for you and will also smile for you.
And you will feel your angel's love and be very happy."
Again the child asked, "And how am I going to be able to understand
when people talk to me if I don't know the language?"
God said, "Your angel will tell you the most beautiful and sweet words you will ever hear,
and with much patience and care, your angel will teach you how to speak."
"And what am I going to do when I want to talk to you?"
God said, "Your angel will place your hands together and
will teach you how to pray."
"Who will protect me?"
God said, "Your angel will defend you even if it means risking its life."
"But I will always be sad because I will not see you anymore."
God said, "Your angel will always talk to you about me and will teach you
the way to come back to me, even though I will always be next to you."
At that moment, there was much peace in heaven but voices from Earth could be heard
and the child hurriedly asked, "God, if I am to leave now, please tell me my angel's name."

"You will simply call her 'Mom.'"

ANONYMOUS

E very religion teaches us about the importance of honoring our mothers and our
fathers. Some mothers and fathers are simply wonderful and others may suffer
from alcoholism, be mentally unstable, manipulative, or controlling. Some may
have given a child up for adoption. Regardless of these, all parents deserve the love of

their children, for if it weren't for them, we wouldn't be here. We must learn to see through any perceived negativity and be grateful to them for bringing us into the world. Our mothers are special because we grow inside of them and they give birth to us, but without our fathers, our mothers would not be able to conceive us. That is why we need to be grateful to both our mothers and our fathers. They are our angels.

When in the womb, we were at one time intimately connected with our mothers on a cellular level. She knew us from the moment we made our first kicks inside of her. As a fetus, we could hear blood rushing through the vessels, hear her voice, feel her love, and sense her fear. We could hear her singing, laughing, crying, and could sense all her moods. Many mothers like to read to their babies in the womb. Babies also have an affinity for the foods of their culture.

At the moment of birth, as a mother looks into her baby's eyes for the first time, she may say or think, "I've been waiting so long to see you!" The baby's eyes are mysterious, wise, completely innocent, and full of love. Many women who are spiritually inclined believe babies come directly from the spirit world. They want to ask questions such as, "What was it like out there before you came into me?" "Did you choose me as your mother?" "Were you in the light that people talk about?" "How did you come into me?" Others simply take it for granted and don't attempt to think about such questions.

No one loves a child as much as its mother and thus a mother's prayers for her child are very powerful. Our mothers want us to love them the rest of their lives, and having a good relationship with them is a gift to be cherished and preserved. Grandparents in Native American tribes are entrusted with the role of teaching their grandchildren values. This helps to ensure relationships of mutual respect between mothers and their daughters and sons.

By mid-life, our parents may be facing health problems, financial difficulties, or may be unsure of how they want to spend the rest of their lives. If they have teenagers, both of them may be going through difficult transitions in life. When children leave home to live on their own, parents need to know that they are still important to them. Their grown children may now have their own families with children to take care of and nurture. Many women make these transitions in life smoothly, but others may find their relationship with their mothers challenged, resulting in confrontation, hurt feelings, and a distancing between them.

But a creeping awareness surfaces in some pregnant women who do not have good relationships with their mothers. Here they are, about to have a baby and wanting their baby to love them, but they themselves have become estranged from their own mothers. They may think, *My mother must have felt this love towards me when I was born, but look at us now. Everything she does annoys me and we hardly talk anymore.* So the love she wants from her own child, she herself is not able to give to her own mother. And what if her own child grows up and in time learns to feel that way toward herself?

Other women have wonderful relationships with their mothers and feel very close to them, seeing their mothers as their best friend. I was fortunate to be one of them. Their children are more likely

to keep close relationships with their own mothers through life. Life is not easy, and many obstacles are sure to surface along the way. But the bond of a healthy mother-daughter relationship brings courage, support, and encouragement that can overcome and work through any obstacle. The bond between them is unlike that of any other and therefore is a special friendship.

I'll never forget back-to-back Birth Works® childbirth educator and doula workshops I once taught. A woman who attended both workshops came with her two children and then her mother arrived to take care of the children. When they met, there was no sign of warmth between them—no hugs, the mother's attempted smile was tight, and the daughter was nervous. At the workshop we talked about the value of a good mother-daughter relationship. This woman related that her mother's marriage was a "convenience" marriage at this point, and that her mother and father didn't love each other any more. So her mother was feeling lonely in her own marriage. When her mother came to the daughter's house, she rearranged things, just trying to be helpful, but this upset the daughter and so their relationship had become distant as well.

In such circumstances it is often the daughter or son who needs to take the initiative and approach their mother or father to heal the relationship. We must work to help our parents feel happy by paying loving attention and bestowing affectionate care on them, even if this is not reciprocated. Though this may feel challenging, we have much to lose by not trying, for our own children are watching us carefully and we are role models for them. We have to remember that there is nothing that love can't heal.

At the workshop I suggested that she initiate physical contact such as a hug the next time she saw her mother. Her mother was lonely, and perhaps a simple hug could open up their relationship. The daughter who attended the workshops took our discussions to heart and decided to act on them. After the first workshop, she approached her mother and reached out to give her a hug. She said her mother stiffened at first, not knowing what to do. But then gradually an amazing thing happened. Her mother started to initiate hugging her daughter. Now the mother and daughter are communicating on a more intimate basis and are becoming friends again. The hug was a small step that had tremendous impact, likely to impact generations to come.

As we grow older, we often seek information from our mothers about how we were born. My mother lived in a generation when women were made to lie on their backs and often were restrained. All my life I only heard negative things about birth from her. Her first comments to me when I was designing the Birth Works® program were, "Why would you want to encourage women to go natural? I wish someone would have given me a shot to make the pain go away." She later grew to understand that birth is an opportunity to develop confidence and self-esteem, and instead said, "I wish someone could have been there with me to help me through labor."

Some women who have good relationships with their mothers invite them to be at their births. This can increase the bond of love between them even further and make the grandparent bond special. Some women feel they could never do this, feeling that it would interfere with their ability to labor. For my mother, it was a gift to be invited to my sister's birth of her first child. My dad also

happened to be there. My mother had had six children but was not able to see any of us being born. They both saw their grandchild being born and it was the first birth they had ever seen.

My mother was also present at another sister's birth. She was laboring beautifully but my mother kept saying, "Give her something to help her!" Actually, it was my mother who needed medicine to calm her down. But later she would be heard saying this was such a beautiful birth. Being present at both of these births was very healing for her. Inviting our mothers to our births is a personal choice and very often can form a bond of friendship and admiration, especially since they are then seeing their grandchildren being born. It can also heal mother-daughter relationships that have been difficult.

Some mothers for various reasons are not able to talk about their birth experiences, perhaps because they were too traumatic. In addition, with fewer births happening at home, knowledge about birth is not being passed down to daughters and sons as it was in the past. When the daughters become pregnant, they must rely on what they learn in childbirth classes, movies of births, and information from their friends and family. Births portrayed in the media are often highly dramatized, traumatic, life threatening and also simplistic, depicting birth as one push and the baby is out. I will always be grateful to my youngest sister, who invited my children to one of her births. They saw her breathe her baby out on her hands and knees and now have a memory of birth that is normal and natural.

Whatever the situation is between a mother and her daughter and son, feeling love for our mothers and fathers is essential to our own health. This was demonstrated by two very important prospective studies that were conducted at Harvard and Johns Hopkins over fifty years ago, and which are described in Dr. Dean Ornish's book *Love and Survival*.[1]

In the Harvard Mastery of Stress Study [2,3], 126 healthy male students randomly selected from Harvard classes of 1952 to 1954 were asked to describe their relationship to their mother and to their father as being very close, warm and friendly, tolerant, or strained and cold. Thirty-five years later, medical records were obtained and it was discovered that 91 percent of the participants who did not have a warm or friendly relationship with their mothers had serious diagnosed diseases in mid-life (including coronary artery disease, high blood pressure, duodenal ulcer, and alcoholism), as compared to only 45 percent who described a warm relationship with their mothers. It was also discovered that the effects were additive. All (100 percent) of those who described relationships low in warmth and closeness with both parents had diseases diagnosed in mid-life. The researchers wrote, "The perception of love itself…may turn out to be a core biopsychosocial-spiritual buffer, reducing the negative impact of stressors and pathogens and promoting immune function and healing."

In addition, the Harvard Mastery of Stress Study counted the number of positive and negative words that the participants used to describe both their mother and their father. They found that the number of positive descriptions were a significant predictor of their future health and illness in mid-life. "The authors found that 95 percent of subjects who used few positive words and also rated their parents low in parental caring, had diseases diagnosed in midlife, whereas only 29 percent

of subjects who used many positive words and also rated their parents high in parental caring had diagnosed diseases in mid-life."[4] Although Ornish was quick to point out that saying negative words does not cause illness, still the words we use reflect our perceptions of love and relationship, and this in turn has a deep impact on our health and survival.[5] The results show how important relationships between mothers and fathers and their children are in terms of their own long-term health and well-being.

The Johns Hopkins study found similar results. More than 1,100 male medical students in the 1940s participated in the study that was designed to determine if the quality of human relationships might be a factor in the development of cancer. "Medical students who subsequently developed cancer were more likely to have described a lack of closeness with their parents than their healthy classmates when they were tested up to fifty years earlier. It was found that the predictive value of this test did not diminish over time and was not explained by other known risk factors such as smoking, drinking, or radiation exposure.... The best predictor of who would get cancer decades later was the closeness of father-son relationships earlier in life."[6,7] In both of these studies there were only male participants because back then, there were very few females in college. I believe the results would be the same for women, especially since it is the mother who gives birth to her children.

Birth offers a wonderful opportunity to bring new mothers and fathers closer to their parents who have become grandparents. Babies have an amazing ability to heal relationships that are not healthy. The time of birth offers the opportunity to look at our own relationships with our mothers and fathers, seek forgiveness, and allow healing to take place. Not to do so may adversely affect our own health.

Parents need to be encouraged to see the good aspects of their mothers and fathers because choosing to see good is essential to our health. If a woman's mother is an alcoholic or is mentally ill, she can still love her simply for bringing her into the world. If a woman was adopted, she can still choose to feel love towards her mother even if she doesn't know where she is. No matter how our mothers feel toward us, we can choose to love them. We can't change someone else, but we can change ourselves. Holding onto negative feelings only brings negative energy back to us, and this can cause disease. There is nothing to gain by doing this. Our mothers won't be here forever, and when they are no longer here one day, those daughters and sons who took the first step of healing their relationship with her will be so glad they did.

I lost my mother suddenly in August of 2005. She didn't make it out of elective heart surgery to repair an aneurysm. My world suddenly turned upside-down and I felt a great void. She was my best friend and understood me like nobody else could. She was eighty-three years old. I have dedicated this book to her not only because she brought me into the world, but also because I know she would have been very happy about my writing the book. The week before her surgery, we took long walks along the ocean and had a chance to talk about everything. She always worried about things, and we could talk about anything together.

She was scared of the surgery. She knew that if something happened to her, we would take good

care of my dad. She believed that after death, people live on in the memories of those who knew them. But I said, "Just wait. You'll see that the mind and spirit continue after death because they don't need form to exist." She smiled and continued walking. Every night since she died, I pray for her safety and well-being in whatever dimension she has gone to.

One year after her death, she gave me an indication that she was all right in a visitation that seemed like a dream but wasn't a dream. She was smiling, and her face was soft and free of any worry. Upon seeing her, the thought flashed through me, *You're not supposed to be here.* So I touched her leg to see if she was real, and I felt skin, muscle, and bone. I looked up at her and she smiled at me, conveying a nonverbal message that I understood as saying that indeed, the mind and spirit do continue after the form goes. Now her smile will always be with me and I'm grateful. The ways of the spirit are mysterious and wonderful.

Birthing in the Spirit

It is birth that ties us all together. We are all born. Giving birth connects us in spirit with all mothers who have given birth before us, and all mothers who will give birth after us. The love that a mother has for her child is universal; it spans all cultures and all time frames. The true spiritual awakening that happens when a couple has a child is the realization that over the course of your child's lifetime, he or she will touch the lives of other people, sometimes in ways that you will never know about; and in this way, because the two of you came together and loved each other, the world is forever changed.

—MINDY TROGE, CHILDBIRTH EDUCATOR AND POSTPARTUM DOULA

CHAPTER 24

LOVE:
The Foundation of All Human Values

When you come to the edge of all the light you know, and are about to step off into the darkness of the unknown, faith is knowing one of two things will happen: There will be something solid to stand on, or you will be taught how to fly.

JONATHAN LIVINGSTON SEAGULL

"I am not aware of any other factor in medicine—not diet, not smoking, not exercise, not stress, not genetics, not drugs, not surgery—that has a greater impact on our quality of life, incidence of illness, and premature death from all causes," writes Dr. Dean Ornish, referring to the healing power of love and intimacy.[1] Love is the undercurrent of all the human values. When love illumines thought, truth is revealed. When love motivates action, it is transformed into right action. When love saturates feelings, it becomes calm and serene and ensures peace. Love comes as understanding and when there is nonviolence.

The power of love is such that it can move us to tears of joy. I cried tears of joy all the way home from the hospital after giving birth to my daughter. I couldn't believe I was a mother and I was totally unprepared for the magnitude of the experience. Two years later when my son was born, I wondered if I would have as much love. The amazing thing was that I did; in fact, the love just kept getting deeper and deeper. I know I would have felt the same if I had had more children. This is the nature of love—it flows and flows from the heart (consciousness), just like an endless spring bringing water up from the earth. Love gives freely of itself and can never be depleted.

In the English language there is only one word for love, and it can refer to everything from loving your car to loving your children and loving God. Other languages such as Greek have separate words for the various meanings of love. *Eros* refers to a passionate love with sensual desire and longing. *Philia* refers to a dispassionate, virtuous love such as one's loyalty to friends, family, and community.

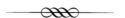

Agape comes from the word *agapo,* which is the verb "I love." It refers to a general affection or concern rather than the physical attraction suggested by *eros.* Finally there is *storge,* which refers to a natural affection like that of children for their parents.[2]

Deepak Chopra in his book *The Path of Love* describes the difference between definitions of love and its limitations in the English language: "Our materialistic worldview has reduced love to a haphazard flow of hormones coupled to psychological fantasies. The spiritual truth is very different. Once the walls fall down, we discover that our real problem is that there is too much love around us, not too little. Love is eternal and unbounded; it is only we who take tiny sips from its infinite ocean."[3]

LOVE AS THOUGHT IS TRUTH

When women believe in the truth that the knowledge about how to give birth exists within every woman, and that love exists within us all, they will be more easily guided by the spirit when giving birth. Pure and simple, I believe the presence of love during pregnancy, labor, and birth is the most powerful and important concept to understand about childbirth, for it impacts everything from the body's ability to produce abundant oxytocin to helping a woman feel safe so she can open herself to give birth. All childbirth education should be focused on how to ensure the presence of love during this peak experience in life.

A number of excellent books have been written addressing the topic of love. Michel Odent has described the importance of love in birth in his book *The Scientification of Love.*[4] Dr. Kirsten Uvnas Moberg from Sweden has described in great detail how oxytocin works physiologically as the hormone of love in her book *The Oxytocin Factor.*[5] Deepak Chopra in his book *The Path of Love* shows us how we can fulfill our heart's desire by rediscovering a powerful source of love in spirituality.[6] *Rediscovering Birth* by Sheila Kitzinger[7] and *Ina May Gaskin's Guide to Childbirth* by Ina May Gaskin[8] also address the importance of love and spirit in birth. I believe that when pregnancy, labor, and birth are planned around the importance of integrating the mind, body, and spirit and realizing the importance of the love in terms of physiology, the way in which women are giving birth today will be transformed completely. This transformation can come more quickly than we think.

Without love, any action is cold, dry, uninviting, harsh, and meaningless. Love has everything to do with feeling good, comfortable, confident, and safe. We cannot exist in the world without love. It is so essential to our survival that it can be likened to a fish swimming in water. The water is above it, below it, beside it, and inside it. There is no place that the water is not. If you take the water away, the fish will die. In the same way, love is above us, below us, beside us, and inside us. We are so dependent on love that without it, life loses meaning and we may want to stop living. It is the feeling of love that helps a woman in labor to feel safe. This feeling is so powerful that it can carry her through any contraction.

Every human being yearns to be loved. When deprived of love, loneliness sets in and people lose

their sense of meaning in life. Because love is part of our true nature, we are lost when we don't feel loved. It is love that makes life worth living and brings beauty into our lives, making us feel good. It is love that a baby and mother pour into each other at birth. It is love that helps us to forgive and that connects us with a power greater than ourselves, providing comfort. Love is everything.

LOVE AS FEELING IS PEACE

When we feel loved, we feel nurtured through and through. Words cannot quite express how good love feels, but when we feel loved, we experience peace. When love flows from the heart consciousness, a feeling of peace permeates the body, resulting in decreased pulse and breathing rates, making us feel very relaxed and very good. Chopra states, "There is a center in the body where love and spirit are joined, and that center is the heart (consciousness). It is your heart that aches or swells with love, that feels compassion and trust, or that seems empty or full."[9] If the heart consciousness is clouded with negative qualities, making it feel barren and polluted, how can it feel love? Where there is love, there can be no fear, no anxiety, no doubt, and no disharmony. When we are afflicted with disharmony, we can be sure that our love is restricted and we are not feeling peaceful. Peace deepens with the practice of equanimity, accepting the ups and downs of life with a steady mind.

LOVE AS UNDERSTANDING IS NONVIOLENCE

The eyes are like the lens of a camera and the world is like a mirror. It is as if the mind is constantly taking pictures and recording them in the brain so that we see whatever objects are kept in front of us. When we change the way we look at things, the things we look at change.[10] The difference between having clarity of vision or being confused lies in whether our vision is narrow-minded or open-minded, fearful or loving. An open-minded person is more understanding because he sees the "bigger picture." It is by seeing the bigger picture that a woman understands what she may want to change in a subsequent birth from what happened in her first birth. To feel more respected, she may decide to change the doctor, the hospital, or decide this time to hire a midwife or doula.

Understanding means welcoming the difficulties of life and having faith that whatever happens is for our own good. When a woman's labor is not progressing, when a baby is crying with colic, when he is a defiant two-year-old, when she doesn't want to eat, when he doesn't want to go to bed, when she is fighting, when he is having a tantrum, when she says you don't understand, when he needs to be disciplined—in all of these situations and more—the question is, "Can we accept all of these situations with understanding and love?" In all these scenarios and more, being able to respond with understanding and love softens the energies and maintains a nurturing relationship between a mother and father and their children.

A woman who has had what she perceives as a traumatic birth experience and who feels anger toward those responsible for it needs to realize that understanding is the key to resolution and peace. Hospitals are businesses, and they are used to doing things a certain way. These habits and

routines are entrenched in the system and are hard to change. With understanding, she can forgive those who upset her, and even forgive entire corporations or herself if need be. Without forgiveness, we become the victims and suffer.

If you don't believe in coincidence, then it is easy to believe that we each have a role to play in this game of life, and every moment is perfect and meant to be. This philosophy helps to keep a steady mind and fill all actions with love.

LOVE IN ACTION IS RIGHT ACTION

Any action performed with love is right action. This assumes that a sense of discrimination and responsibility are present. Such action is performed without expecting any reward in return and is offered unconditionally from the heart. Putting it into practice more consistently in our daily lives is the challenge. This is the love of a mother toward her child, or of people helping others who are disabled and suffering. When performing such actions, we will find that they are governed by human values. We are born into society, and so being able to give selflessly back to society is a wonderful thing. Those who can be with a woman in birth, helping the baby's first experience in the world to be one that feels loving and safe, are serving humanity. Helping a woman to have a birth that is a peak experience of wonder and awe in her life is one example of love in action.

MAGNETISM

Magnetic energy pervades the entire universe. Magnetism is the cause of attraction between human beings, birds, animals, and even insects. There are many examples of this. Green pasture attracts a cow, so green grass is like a magnet for the cow. A flower and its nectar attract the honeybee. A mother attracts her child. People use magnetic power in their everyday relationships with each other when they feel an attraction that makes them reach out to touch another. Magnetic power is present in the human body deep into the cellular level.

Attraction is a primary characteristic of love. The more pure the love, the stronger is its magnetic attraction. It is what draws things together and makes one yearn for another, as two lovers long for each other, children are drawn to their parents and grandparents, and humans love God. Love for love's sake alone is unsullied, pure, and pristine. It is kind, compassionate, and selfless. It is a love that feels safe, nurturing, protected, peaceful, warm, kind, understanding, and accepting. It is unity and not duality. No matter how much love is drawn from this pure love, it is ever full and cannot be depleted in any way.

LOVE AND FAITH IN BIRTH

There are few experiences in life that can bring us as close to experiencing pure love of the spirit as birth can. The intensity and yearning with which a woman in labor cries out to the spirit during

the height of a strong contraction draws the spirit close to her. The powerful forces that build inside the body as the uterus contracts are unique in birth. Feeling this power instead of fearing it allows a woman to say, "I am powerful beyond my wildest imagination!" and "Having done that, I can do anything!" This burst of confidence serves as the foundation upon which she will build her skills for parenting. She has felt the power of love in her body through the contractions and it has transformed her. She then looks into her baby's eyes for the first time and forgets everything else. Such is the transforming power of love.

When we live in a philosophy of love, we will find people coming into our lives at the right moment when we need them. This is because when we are living in love, we are closer to the spirit. A pregnant woman will use the knowledge she has learned to plan her birth and then will have faith that what she needs will be given unto her. The magnetism of love works in mysterious ways, but once we surrender to the path of love, we will behold amazing things happening in our lives and our births. This requires faith.

Where there is faith, there is love. Where there is love, there is peace. Faith, love, and peace are very connected. Faith helps us feel more secure in expressing love, and love helps us to have faith. From the time we wake until we go to sleep, everything we do is based on faith. We have faith that people driving in their cars will stay in the correct lanes. We have faith that an airline pilot will take us to our destination. A baby has faith that its mother will take care of it and feed it. Women have faith that their uterus knows how to grow a baby. Women have faith in their birth team.

But our faith is often tested. People have faith in God and then are shaken when misfortune and tragedy hits them even though they've said their prayers. For example, a baby may be born with a complication in spite of prayers being made for a healthy baby, or a woman may suffer from infertility even though she has prayed earnestly for a baby. When such misfortunes happen a loss will be grieved, but in the end, having faith helps us to find peace through forgiveness.

THINKING ENERGETICALLY

Since emotions cannot be seen but are only felt, we need to understand their energy. Here are two exercises that I do in my childbirth classes to help birthing parents experience the energies of love versus fear/anger. We then discuss how they impact birth.

1. *Feeling love/fear energies.* Have two people sit facing each other about three feet apart. One is instructed to close her eyes. The other person chooses either fear/anger or love and then energetically pours that on the other person for about three minutes. The receiver has to guess which one it is. At first, I tried having them choose fear, anger, and love as three options, but it soon became clear that the energies of fear and anger were too similar to each other to be discerned. The vibrations from fear/anger versus love were relatively easy to detect. I believe we practice this subconsciously in our daily lives. All day long we are involved with communicating with others, and we are very good at sensing moods. In

childbirth classes participants quickly realize the significance of this concept in birth and choose their birth team more carefully. Women in labor need and deserve an atmosphere that feels safe, kind, and loving.

2. ***Determining your energy field.*** Our energy fields commonly project about five feet away from the body. More evolved souls will have energy fields projecting much further. To find out how far your energy field extends, try the following exercise. Take two wire hangers and unbend them to form the letter "L." Give them to a friend and instruct this person to hold one hanger in each hand, with the bottom of the "L" pointed in your direction. Standing approximately eight feet away, have the person with the hangers walk very slowly straight toward you without moving her hands. The ends of the hanger will begin to deflect and move out to the sides when they come in contact with your energy field. Seeing is believing for anyone skeptical of the presence of energy fields.

OXYTOCIN AND LOVE

When the birth team shows kindness, respect, compassion, and love toward a woman in labor, their love connects with the love in her, empowering her for the work of labor and birth. Remember the characteristic of love is that of magnetic attraction. As Dr. Moberg describes in her book *The Oxytocin Factor,* oxytocin is involved in the core of the workings of all major metabolic systems in the body. Just by reading the following list of its extensive roles, we can realize not only the extent to which love exists within us, but also its powerful abilities. [11]

Oxytocin:
1. Stimulates production of prolactin, a hormone that increases milk production.
2. Acts as a thermostat, shifting warmth from one part of the body to another. Warms the front torso by dilating blood vessels on the skin, providing warmth for a mother nursing her baby.
3. Stimulates the uterus to contract and expel the fetus.
4. Has an anti-anxiety effect, inducing calmness by reducing blood pressure and stress hormones.
5. Prompts maternal behavior.
6. Has a positive effect on social memory, i.e., helping to recognize someone met before, particularly helping a mother recognize and prefer her young over others.
7. Reduces anxiety and increases curiosity (when present in small amounts) but reduces curiosity when present in larger amounts.
8. Helps to alleviate pain.
9. Reduces stress and improves learning ability.
10. Stimulates the secretion of gastric juices and the release of digestive hormones.

11. Influences the activity of the Vagus nerve in the parasympathetic nervous system, either promoting or inhibiting storage of nourishment in the body.
12. Helps maintain the body's fluid balance.
13. Stimulates the extraction of sodium by the kidneys and promotes urination.
14. Stimulates growth through the transformation of food.
15. Helps to heal wounds.
16. Heals and rejuvenates mucous membranes and produces anti-inflammatory reactions.
17. Stimulates the release of eggs from the ovaries and the production of sperm in the testicles, thereby helping to increase fertility.
18. Has effects on appetite, thirst, and strengthening of the immune system.

Moberg states in her book, "The body's innate system of checks and balances is complex; oxytocin is constantly present and working in many different ways. The effects of this coordinated system are connected like the threads in a marvelous web."[12] Oxytocin appears to be the means through which love works in the body, and wherever it is present it is trying to help the body in some way. Just as a flower serves as a means through which fragrance can flow, so oxytocin and its receptors serve as a means through which love can flow in the body.

LOVE AS A POWERFUL FORCE

I believe that the true power of love is not fully understood by most of us, including myself. However, as I practice human values in my life, I am more aware of the power of love than I used to be. During a discussion about love and anger at a conference I attended, I realized that people believed that the only way to make change was to be angry. They perceived love as being weak, gentle, soft, kind, and not capable of effecting change. Initially anger may look strong, but it is actually the energy that is weaker. It wreaks havoc on the body by raising blood pressure, the pulse rate, and the rate of breathing. It causes the release of catecholamines such as adrenaline and cortisol. These decrease digestive function and the production of oxytocin. When people are angry, listening skills are decreased and there can easily be miscommunication or no communication. The body is guarded and in a defensive mode in which the ability to learn is affected adversely. Over a period of time, if there is an imbalance in the body's two systems that govern fear-based responses versus those of love, with the fear-based system dominating, the result can be illness.

On the other hand, the power of love is healing. It slows down our breathing and pulse rates, helping us to relax and feel more at peace, which brings a feeling of safety and opens channels of communication. Love allows the calm and connection system of the body to manifest, restoring homeostasis. When the body is in balance, we feel peaceful. Love is more powerful than fear. As our connection to the love within increases, our experiences in life will be more profound and beautiful.

Attempts to seek this love within are made by those who meditate and try to steady the mind. Though this brings positive effects such as relaxing the body and the mind, it is mostly only concentration. True meditation occurs when we don't realize we are meditating, as in connecting with the spirit of love throughout the day wherever we are and in everything we are doing. This is the practice of constant integrated awareness (CIA). True meditation occurs when we practice a spiritual love so automatically, seeing it in everyone and everything, that we don't even realize it but we *are* it.

I had one such experience about six years ago that was transforming in nature. I was at a spiritual retreat, walking down a path in the middle of the day. A woman with whom I was walking excitedly handed me some headphones with special music saying, "You've got to hear this!" I put them on my ears and the next thing I knew, I was drawn out of my body into a bright light. I was conscious that I was one with the light and felt myself having the colors of the sun; in fact, it felt like I *was* the sun. While in this light I looked out on the path, where about 200 people were walking toward the cafeteria. I was aware that there was normal color with green grass, the red cafeteria building, and cars parked in the parking lot, but the strange thing was that none of the people had forms. All I saw was the shadow of their spirit souls.

My immediate thought was expansive, sensing that all that happens on the earth is actually small in nature, so we shouldn't get so upset when things happen. "It's just small stuff." And then I was back in my body, continuing to walk down the path. I was left to wonder about what happened, and over the years have come to realize the experience taught me much about detachment and love.

The ways of the spirit are mysterious, but living in the spirit—living in its love—is what gives life meaning. It is how the body functions, how women conceive, grow a baby, give birth, breastfeed, and hopefully raise their children. It is what connects us to all other women who have given birth, and to all beings and creatures of the earth.

I am fascinated by an experiment on heart disease at Ohio University in the 1970s that had very unexpected results. The experiment demonstrated the power of love. In this experiment rabbits were genetically bred to develop heart disease, and in addition, were fed a toxic, high-cholesterol diet in order to block their arteries, duplicating the negative effect that such a diet has on human arteries. Consistent results began to appear in all the rabbit groups except for one, which strangely displayed 60 percent fewer symptoms. Nothing in the rabbits' physiology could account for their high tolerance to the diet, until it was discovered by accident that the student who was in charge of feeding these particular rabbits liked to fondle and pet them. He would hold each rabbit lovingly for a few minutes before feeding it; astonishingly, this alone seemed to enable the animals to overcome the toxic diet. Repeat experiments, in which one group of rabbits was treated neutrally while the others were loved, had similar results.[13] In this experiment the power of love transformed the toxic food so it wouldn't have harmful effects on the rabbits.

In Kahlil Gibran's book *The Prophet,* he states, "And think not you can direct the course of love, for love, if it finds you worthy, directs your course."[14] He goes on to say, "When love beckons to you, follow him, though his ways are hard and steep. And when his wings enfold you, yield to him."[15] Instead of being afraid of the power of love, we need to make more of an effort to understand this principle of love. Only love can remove all the bitter feelings and enhance the sweetness of life.

The speed of light can be measured, but not the speed of love. Because love is everywhere, it is wherever you wish it to be in the blink of an eye. Know that if your baby is in the neonatal intensive care unit, you can send love to him or her in a second because when we think love, it is there instantly. If your loved one is on a trip halfway around the world, just think love and it is with him immediately. If you are a working mother and miss your children, think love and it is with them. Love is constant and gives of itself, not expecting anything in return. It is changeless and is the eternal witness to all that is happening. It is unaffected by criticism, blame, guilt, or failure. Nothing can taint or tarnish such love. This love is within us all. There is nothing that cannot be accomplished with such love. Let your life be filled with love. Live in love. Birth with love. Be love. Learn to see through the eyes of love, hear through the ears of love, and cultivate feelings of love.

A way to become more aware of the love within is to remember the three C's: conscious, conscience, and consciousness. These sound similar but actually vary in their meaning. Their interconnectedness can be understood in the statement "Use your conscience to be conscious of your consciousness." The consciousness is our inner voice, our heart center. I believe it is always directing us to conduct our lives in such ways as to bring happiness to others.

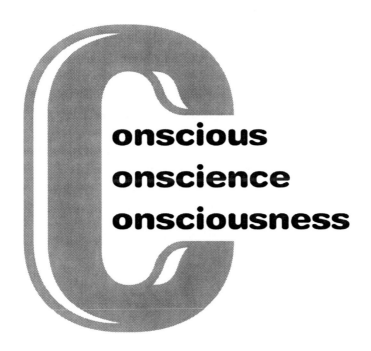

Conscious
Conscience
Consciousness

To connect with the love within you, here is a short multi-sensory visualization.

MULTI-SENSORY VISUALIZATION

So just now, allow yourself to sit back and close your eyes, becoming conscious of your breathing. Breathing helps us to feel connected with the plants and trees of the earth that give us oxygen to breathe. See if you can feel connected to all beings who also breathe air in and out to stay alive. Imagine yourself breathing in love with each inhale and out with each exhale, saying to yourself, "I breathe in love and I breathe out love. I am love. All is love." Feel this love going through your entire body with each breath. There is no place that it is not. Love hormones are working in every cell of your body, helping your body to do its work. See if you can feel your heart center opening as it gives and receives love. Allow each breath to open your heart a little more so the feeling of love can expand outward. As love flows from your heart consciousness to every part of your being, see if you can feel your body relaxing more and more with each breath...relaxing into the good feeling that comes with feeling loved, with being love. Love is your constant companion and your best friend. With this love, you are never alone.

You are a being of love and your cells are yearning to feel this love. Where there is love, there cannot be fear, so breathe out any fears on the next breath. Love is more powerful than fear. Love helps the eyes to see that which is good, the ears to hear that which is good, the tongue to say that which is good, and the hands to do that which is good. Now, see if you can intensify the love that is within you, making it stronger and stronger until it radiates out from your very being. As love has no form, it passes through form easily. Feel it expanding beyond the body to your family and friends in the community. Expand it even more to include all of the Americas and the Western hemisphere. And now feel it touching all those suffering around the world. Allow this love to connect you with all women who have ever given birth. Feel more and more love. Feel it expanding out to the stars and distant galaxies and all dimensions of existence. Love is in you, above you, behind you, and around you. Feeling this, allow yourself to go even more deeply into relaxation, slowing the breath even more. The body repairs tissue best when we are in deep relaxation. Feeling loved helps us to relax even more with each breath. Allow this feeling of love to stay with you as long as you wish, and know that it is always within you, just waiting to be expressed. When you are ready, become more aware of your breathing, move your fingers and toes, and gradually open your eyes to come back.

Birthing in the Spirit

As a midwife, I have always regarded birth as sacred. I have always kept in mind the spirit that was coming through as I attended women in birth. And what is so wonderful is that spirit

can be communicated with on a level where words do not exist, so it has always been possible for me to know how these beings were doing in the absence of technology or even in spite of it.

While birthing my own son, my connection with his spirit was so strong; although it was a long birth, I knew he was fine. It's obvious we were connected physically, but the spiritual connection was so intense and so pure, unlike anything I had ever experienced before. It was like a beautiful dance breathing him down and out while he did his part moving down and flexing his head. I told him what he needed to do and the birth unfolded in utter perfection of that communication. In that moment you could see the magical circle of two people existing only for each other.

—KRISTINE LAURIA, CCE (BWI) AND MIDWIFE

CHAPTER 25

Love Is a Verb

*I expect to pass through life but once. If, therefore, there be any kindness
I can show, or any good thing I can do to any fellow being,
let me do it now, as I shall not pass this way again.*

WILLIAM PENN

The CD was playing a prayer called the Gayatri Mantra for the Indian woman whose birth I was attending. This particular mantra is a prayer for protection, and its holy vibrations filled the labor room where she was laboring. Her husband and I supported her on either side as she moved her pelvis in sweeping, circular motions. The mantra was repeated over and over again, bringing a sacred feeling to her labor. Her husband chanted mantras along with the tape, with his voice increasing in strength as her contractions intensified. She went deeply into another dimension through the sound. When fully dilated, she wanted to remain upright but her doctor insisted on her lying down to give birth. Perhaps being in a better position by following her own instincts could have made her birth easier, as she wouldn't have had to push against gravity.

In another labor, a woman brought Tibetan bells. Each time a contraction came, she had her husband ring the bells. It immediately created a sacred atmosphere, causing those present to stop talking. It had the effect of bringing people back to the importance of the moment, the work she was doing to ride the contractions, and the intense focus and concentration that was required as the creative forces were at work. The ring of the bell had wonderful lingering effects that lasted through much of each contraction.

Singing with the mantra and ringing Tibetan bells are forms of prayer. Prayer that is deep and genuine can serve as a natural antidote to pain without negative side effects. It encourages movement into the inner world of consciousness where the woman can connect directly with her spirit guiding her through the birth. Prayer carries an energy that results in action. Since prayers are usually filled with compassion and love, we can say that love is a verb.

Every breath can be a prayer. In this way the awareness of love can be present upon waking and sleeping, during prayers before meals, and even during other daily activities. One who prays will never feel alone. Prayer comforts and strengthens us. When prayer becomes an active part of daily life, it brings the spirit closer to us, offering us guidance, strength, protection, and wisdom.

Becoming more focused on making contact with the love consciousness on a regular basis begins

with thinking about all the actions performed on a given day. We like to be busy and fill our days with actions, which all have verbs. When we view love as a verb, every action performed throughout the day that is done with the thought of love becomes sacred action. This ranges from talking with a friend, driving to work, smiling at a coworker on the job or a child at home, to activities of daily living such as taking a shower, cutting vegetables for dinner, taking a coat off, or blinking our eyes. The fun part is then figuring out how each of these actions can remind us about love and other human values and also rid us of such negative qualities as jealousy, anger, and pride.

For example, "talk" is a verb, and with love awareness we can remember the importance of speaking only what is true, avoiding gossip, and practicing the value of silence. "Drive" is a verb, and with love awareness we can imagine ourselves making the wheel "turn" toward love and driving on the royal highway of love. "Smile" is a verb, and with love awareness we are reminded to convey kindness during conversations with others. "Shower" is a verb, and with love awareness we can feel ourselves letting go to the warmth of the water and being showered with peace.

Verbs can also remind us to lessen negative qualities. For example, "cut" is a verb, and while cutting vegetables we can pray to cut away the ego. "Take" is a verb, and when taking off a jacket we could think of taking off jealousy. "Blink" is a verb, and blinking our eyes can remind us of blinking away sorrow. Seeing love as a verb in these ways is a practical way to bring more kindness, compassion, and love into our lives, which leads to transformation.

Here are some other verbs, with ideas on how to turn them into ways of improving and transforming ourselves:

- Breathe out tension in the body
- Turn away anger
- Walk toward right action
- Jump for joy
- Pluck away doubts
- Sing for joy
- Tap into the spirit
- Listen for truth
- Brush away the ego
- Run away from pride
- Squeeze out excessive desires

When you think of an association with values or with eliminating negative traits, see how this would relate to pregnancy, labor, and birth. For example, from the list above, breathing out tension from the body helps a woman in labor to relax, thereby making her contractions more effective in dilating the cervix. Turning away from anger results in a greater production of oxytocin and a greater ability to relax and feel safe. Walking toward right action means basing your plans about birth on the truth that your body already knows how to give birth. Jumping for joy can be associated

with remembering the importance of having good thoughts, which in turn help the body to produce hormones of joy.

Now that you have the idea, see if you can think of more ideas for the following verbs you might use in your daily life: swim, yield, yawn, garden, shout, move, dress, mix, go, do, chew, learn, read, live, wash, rub, cut, and dry. For example, *yield* to the power within, *ride* contractions like waves, *exercise* good thoughts, *move* or *change* into different positions, *shift* weight on a birthing ball, *rub* love into your belly and to your baby inside, *climb* the steps of cervical dilation in labor, *send* messages of love to your baby, and *gaze* into the wisdom of your baby's eyes. Perhaps you can think about how these and other verbs can do the same: sit, eat, drink, think, massage, sleep, roll, open, relax, swallow, drink, watch, smile. It is fun putting this philosophy into practice, and doing so will start making wonderful changes in your life that will carry over into your birth(s).

"Contract" is a verb, and behind every labor contraction is a force of immense power. This creative force is instinctive and works through a woman's body, knowing exactly how to birth a baby. The ovary didn't have to learn how to let go of an egg, and the fallopian tubes didn't have to learn how to pass the egg down into the uterus. The uterus didn't have to take any lessons to know how to implant the embryo into its walls and develop blood vessels for it to obtain food. The uterus didn't have to take any lessons to know how to contract to move the fetus down through the pelvis to be born. And all these actions are verbs. Since oxytocin is present, the actions are associated with love. Love is a verb.

Of what value is any knowledge unless it is put into practice? When we take something we have learned and put it into practice, it is called practical knowledge. I believe most people are trying to better themselves in some way through the practice of moral virtues and human values. We don't feel good when we get angry, so we try to exercise more control in stressful situations. We don't feel good when we eat foods we know aren't healthy, so we try to eat better—especially when pregnant— knowing the food is helping to grow a baby. When we don't feel in shape, we try to exercise more. When we are short and impatient with our children, perhaps because we are tired, we try to make it up to them. We have good intentions but get caught up in activities of the day and forget about what really matters, which is being kind and compassionate with each other and learning to see the good in things that happen to us.

THE FIVE D'S

Another way of practicing love as a verb is to incorporate the philosophy of the five D's into our daily lives. As I describe the five D's, look for verbs you would associate with childbirth and see how they can help you to remember to put love into practice. For example, in just the first paragraph alone, I see the verbs *connect* (associate with connecting to the higher consciousness), *work* (doing the work of labor), and *carry* (carry away pride or carry to transformation). Just for fun, you might want to underline the verbs you see as you read and make the associations.

The five D's stand for duty, devotion, discipline, determination, and discrimination. All five are so closely connected that one doesn't work or make sense without the other. This is a wonderful guide in carrying out any activity, and although I will relate it to birth, it can be a model for any activity in life.

Duty

Only women have been given the precious gift and ability to be able to conceive, grow, and birth a baby. If women did not carry out this duty, we would not have people on the earth. When we see a woman who is pregnant, we are touched by the awe, wonder, and mystery that accompany the bringing of another soul into the world. She is responsible for growing families and caring for the young. Women are natural nurturers and have been prepared for this job by being born female. If a woman chooses to conceive, then it is her duty to do the best she can to grow a healthy baby by eating healthy foods, getting good sleep, exercising, managing her daily activities to keep a balance in her life, and choosing to see only that which is good by decreasing negative thoughts. It is her duty to birth as naturally as possible, using medical procedures only when medically indicated, as they contain an element of risk for both herself and her baby.

Devotion

The major role that the body's natural oxytocin plays in birth encourages the idea that birth is an experience of love. Love is associated with spirituality. Thus, birth is a spiritual experience simply because it is largely an act of love on the part of the body physiology and the indwelling spirit. All women deserve to have beautiful births filled with love. Births with or without medical interventions can be full of devotion. In fact, in a time of crisis, the soul may call out to the spirit with even greater yearning.

Devotion means carrying out all activities with kindness, compassion, respect, humility, and love. Everything loses value when there is no devotion. When a duty is carried out without devotion, it has no "heart." Devotion is love that connects us to others and sanctifies all our actions. Love melts hearts and draws us closer together. When we have true devotion, we realize that love is in our hearts, permeating all our actions.

A pregnant woman feels devotion toward her baby even before it is born, talking to it, singing to it, reading to it, sending it endearing messages and even prayers. She continues to send her love during labor, and after birth this continues through skin-to-skin contact, cuddling, holding, and giving her life-giving breast milk. When she births with love and devotion, the experience is intimate and full of compassion, with the opportunity to experience bliss.

Discipline

Discipline in pregnancy means that a woman accepts responsibility to take care of her body and her

baby the best that she can to ensure good health for both. A lack of discipline would be reflected by eating too much or too little, eating the wrong kinds of foods for good health, sleeping too much or too little, and being overly anxious, worried, or angry. In other words, when there is an imbalance, there is a lack of discipline and we suffer. Discipline requires focus, knowledge, and good planning to achieve the birth of her dreams.

Choosing to see the positive aspects of life and not dwelling on the negative, a pregnant woman—or anyone for that matter—will feel happier and her joy will be her baby's joy. It will also help her to practice more discipline in her life. If you are pregnant now, think about the last few days. Have your thoughts been joyful? Have your actions been helpful to others? Are you taking care of yourself in terms of nutrition, sleep, and good thoughts? Are you getting good exercise? Even in the last weeks of pregnancy, walking and swimming are excellent forms of exercise.

Other ways to practice discipline include seeking faults first in ourselves and working to correct them instead of finding faults in others. Discipline means working on steadying the mind by keeping excessive desires in check. A pregnant woman can ask herself the question, "Can I remain calm, unruffled, poised, and balanced, keeping my equanimity in whatever I do and whatever my birth outcome?" Calmness of the senses, passions, emotions, feelings, and impulses exemplifies true discipline and brings a feeling of peace. At a time of great upheavals in her life, a pregnant woman will benefit greatly by keeping such a balance, as it helps her to keep things in perspective. When feeling moody she can think, *My hormones are working!* When worries and fears surface she can think, *I am focusing on the present and breathing slowly and deeply.* Discipline also means ensuring unity of thought, word, and deed so that what she says (based on truth) is what she does.

Determination

Winston Churchill's famous statement exemplifies the importance of determination. In a speech containing only six words, he said, "Never, never, never, never give up!" and he then sat down. This speech will never be forgotten. In pregnancy, labor, and birth, a determined woman will not give up on her dreams or on making plans for what is important to her. It also means she will not be rigid and will be open to changes that need to occur based on unforeseen circumstances.

In labor, she needs to be determined to work through contractions one by one, not giving up on them no matter how much they hurt or how tired she is. She can gain strength by knowing that the spirit is working within her and that it is powerful. She will realize that she can do much more than she thinks she can and will respect her body for the important work it is doing. Without determination we often fall short of our goals. Thus, determination is required to carry out any duty to completion.

To ensure that only good vibrations enter her body, a pregnant woman needs to avoid watching violence on the television or in movies. There is so much violence in the world today that it permeates much of what we hear in life. But good thoughts can only come from watching and

hearing good things. Violence brings fear, and this produces stress hormones in her body. Her baby then experiences and learns fear.

A woman who continues to smoke or drink alcohol during her pregnancy may know that it is not healthy for her baby, but may lack the determination and willpower to stop. Group support can be invaluable to her, as well as keeping company with those who don't smoke or drink.

After birth, determination will carry her through the work of taking care of her baby and perhaps other children at home, even while her sleep schedule is having to adapt to that of her baby. She needs to be determined to get sleep whenever she can so her energy stays strong. Carrying out actions that are heartfelt makes the job of parenting easier.

Discrimination

Discrimination is a function of the intellect that controls the mind. It means knowing right from wrong and is based on both knowledge and common sense. When women ask themselves, "Should I or shouldn't I?" they can then go inward and wait for the answer. This may come in an urge or by an impression. Without discrimination there may be wrong actions and resulting feelings of guilt.

Reaching discriminatory knowledge means going inward. If a woman's focus is continually outside herself, she may find herself struggling with decisions. Seeking discriminatory knowledge means accessing the conscience. It is one thing to be aware of what the conscience is saying and another thing to act on it. Unless what is learned is put into practice, it is useless.

Deciding whether to give birth at home, the hospital, or a birthing center requires that a woman use discrimination to determine where she feels safe. Discrimination lets a woman in labor know when something doesn't seem right and that she should ask for help. Discrimination is working when a woman is so exhausted from a long labor and from having tried everything from warm water immersion to positioning, that she knows it is okay to ask for help from a drug or medical procedure. Discrimination helps a woman decide what exactly is important to her when giving birth and helps her to make birthing plans. Discrimination is constantly at work in our lives and our births, and when there is devotion, it is heard more clearly as the inner voice.

UNCONDITIONAL LOVE

Unconditional love means loving only for the sake of love, without any conditions. Mothers and fathers who love their children unconditionally bring up confident and secure children. It is my experience from teaching childbirth education workshops over the last twenty years that many women are searching for unconditional love.

The Love Circle Exercise gives women an opportunity to feel unconditional love and is an experience many never forget.

Love Circle Exercise

Have people sit in a circle and then ask one to be the volunteer. Explain to her that everyone in the circle will "pour" their love on her energetically. Describe love as a verb that has action and that, though it can't be seen, can be felt. Tell the woman who has volunteered that she can keep her eyes open or closed—whichever feels right—and that as she feels the love coming toward her, she should allow it to flow back out to everyone in the circle. Play soft music during the exercise, which lasts just a couple of minutes.

In that short time women consistently say that they felt tingling sensations and/or "waves" of energy, and sometimes light, coming toward them. They feel "full" with this energy of love and want to let it flow back out to others. They often shed tears of joy. Some say that it is the first time they have felt being loved unconditionally.

An interesting side effect of this exercise was brought home to me at a workshop where thirty women were gathered. Doing this same exercise at the workshop, we all poured our love on a woman who had volunteered. Amazingly, the woman *behind* her reported afterward that her feet had been cold, but now they felt warm from the heat she felt coming toward the woman. Love is a verb, and its energy is warm!

I believe that love is the "glue" that connects us with each other and all of humanity. I believe that thoughts of love are like little prayers that bring us closer to the transcendent and allow us to communicate with something bigger than ourselves. Just as a flower is a vehicle through which fragrance is expressed, so the body is a vehicle through which love is expressed. When all actions are permeated with love, they are sanctified and we can sense ourselves as instruments of the spirit.

If you are curious and decide to work toward reaching a higher level of your full human potential, then begin by thinking about love as a verb and make it a part of your conscious awareness in daily life. This practice will carry over into your births and be well established in your psyche when you need it. The only way to experience this is to go through it. I have full confidence that you will find it a fascinating journey of transformation. And, with love as our best friend, we are never alone . . .

Footprints in the Sand

One night I dreamed I was walking along the beach with the Lord.
Many scenes from my life flashed across the sky.
In each scene I noticed footprints in the sand.
Sometimes there were two sets of footprints, other times there was one only.

This bothered me because I noticed that during the low periods of my life, when I was suffering
from anguish, sorrow or defeat, I could see only one set of footprints.

So I said to the Lord,

"You promised me, Lord, that if I followed you, you would walk with me always. But I have noticed that during the most trying periods of my life,
There has only been one set of footprints in the sand.
Why, when I needed you most, have you not been there for me?"

The Lord replied,

"The years when you have seen only one set of footprints,
My child, is when I carried you."

—MARY STEVENSON, 1936

Birthing in the Spirit

We adopted a cat from the Society for the Prevention of Cruelty to Animals and one day it showed up on the doorstep with a kitten it its mouth. She dropped it off at my feet and left. Ten minutes later she came back with another kitten and dropped it off at my feet and left again. I waited, but finally she came back and stayed with her two kittens. I knew something was bothering her and believed that she was looking for another kitten but couldn't find it. Maybe it didn't survive. When my second daughter was born, she had to be hospitalized for an ABO blood incompatibility. I told the nurses that I was breastfeeding her. They took her from me and I waited patiently. After a half hour I started asking where she was. They told me that they were working on her. They said I should wait, but I couldn't. I started walking around looking for her. I heard a baby crying and searched, but couldn't find her. Finally, someone told me she was down in intensive care. I ran down, only to find that the nurse was pinching her feet, trying to wake her up so that they could feed her sugar water. I was mad and came into the room and took her. They said I couldn't have her, but I said I was going to nurse her. The doctor came in and told the nurses it was okay for me to be with her. They then put me and my baby in a room and let me stay with her by her incubator. I had to keep a blindfold on her eyes to protect them from the bilirubin lights, but I was allowed to take her out to feed her, and I was allowed to stroke her back and arms and could talk and sing to her.

—HEIDI KUCERA, A MOTHER IN CALIFORNIA

CHAPTER 26

Respecting the Unity in Diversity

If we hope to create a nonviolent world where respect and kindness replace fear and hatred, we must begin with how we treat each other at the beginning of life. For that is where our deepest patterns are set. From these roots grow fear and alienation—or love and trust.

SUZANNE ARMS, JOURNALIST AND FOUNDER OF BIRTHING THE FUTURE

One of my favorite books is *The Home Planet* by Kevin W. Kelley. There are many large pictures of the earth from outer space with quotations from the astronauts during various parts of their mission. The planet is so piercingly beautiful when viewed at a distance that the quotes reflect the emotions, mystery, and deep respect the astronauts feel for our very existence. We are one people on one earth. The astronauts are transformed by their experience in outer space and feel heartfelt wonder. One astronaut quoted in the book, Russell L. Schweickart, said:

We are all different people. We come from different cultures. And even within the same culture we have vastly different experiences and origins. It is therefore not unexpected that we would express our feelings and impressions of our home planet in unique ways. And yet it is the golden thread that runs through all these expressions of individual experience that is the magic of life. We spend a great deal of time identifying and emphasizing the differences between things in our professional roles, including ourselves. And yet it is our common human experience, our shared fear, hope, joy, and love, that link us as human beings beyond all differences.[1]

Astronaut Sultan Bin Salman al-Saud from the kingdom of Saudi Arabia said, "The first day or so we all pointed to our countries. The third or fourth day we were pointing to our continents. By the fifth day, we were aware of only one Earth."[2] Astronaut Aleksandr Aleksandrov from the former USSR commented after seeing snow on the earth from outer space, "I have never visited America, but I imagined that the arrival of autumn and winter is the same there as in other places, and the process of getting ready for them is the same. And then it struck me that we are all children of our Earth. It does not matter what country you look at. We are all Earth's children, and we should treat her as our Mother."[3] The astronauts' deepened respect for the earth makes them wonder why we can't live in peace, and why there is so much violence. When there is love and respect, there is

nonviolence. Whenever I find myself starting to think small, I pull out this book to help expand my thinking.

NONVIOLENCE

When we think of ourselves beyond ourselves, we are able to respect the unity in diversity. Seeing ourselves as many people on one earth means our very survival is dependent on how well we take care of the earth.

Nonviolence means more than not causing physical harm: it includes not inflicting harm even by a word, look, or gesture. Nonviolence is present when we refrain from doing to another what we don't want to have done to ourselves. This is a principle shared in all religions and is expressed as "Do unto others as you would have them do unto you."

There is much violence in the world today, and it often starts in the home. It has penetrated all aspects of society, including birth. In its more subtle aspects it can be expressed and perceived as disrespect. Women have been known to say, "He broke my waters in labor without telling me," or "She thrust her hand up into my uterus right after my son was born vaginally to check the scar from my previous cesarean without telling me. It was so excruciating that I couldn't smile at my newborn son." Newborn babies are often suctioned deeply with a bulb syringe, and although intentions are good, the baby experiences trauma and, in some instances, harm to its trigeminal or fifth cranial nerve responsible for sensation in the face. Ignoring pleas for help when a cesarean is being performed and the epidural did not take effect is violence.

There are shades of violence that range from saying harmful words to another to eating excessively and harming the body. Speaking too much, working too much, and harping on the faults of others are to be avoided, for they result in wasting energy, causing harm to ourselves. Children are often abused and the elderly are often not respected. Restraint must be practiced in all the areas of eating, sleeping, talking, working, birthing, and any actions of daily life. Tolerance, fortitude, and equanimity are needed to bring more respect to all of these.

UNITY IN DIVERSITY

In this cosmic university, we are all students. I love holding a prism in the light of my kitchen window, and I delight in watching the spectrum of beautiful colors that dance around the walls. In the same way, nature often shows us a beautiful rainbow across the sky. On such an occasion, people can't help but stop their cars to take a moment out of their busy day and experience the awe and wonder of nature. The prism and the rainbow teach us the lesson that out of one comes many. This is unity in diversity.

The white light contains all colors, but we can't see them until the wavelengths are separated into the colors of the rainbow. In the same way, people are like the colors of the rainbow, unique in their

own way—being from different cultures with different beliefs, customs, and appearances—but we all share the same human values of love, kindness, joy, sorrow, respect, and compassion. Respecting these differences yet sensing the unity of values we share together can help us move past the narrow vision of the "individual" and into a broader vision of the universal. With advanced technology the world has become "smaller" in that we can know what is happening in many other countries almost immediately. Increasingly people are realizing that the more the global community works together, the safer the earth will be. How healthy pregnant women are and how they give birth has much to do with this, for these children are the future leaders of our world.

To have the vision of unity in diversity, we must think expansion, not contraction. Each of us needs to become aware that we are a part of the one truth that encompasses everything in the universe and that we are all very connected with each other. When the heart is righteous, one has character. If one has character, there is harmony in the home. This leads to order in the nation and ultimately peace in the world.

We can find many examples of unity in diversity in nature. Rivers are many but water is one. Lamps are many but light is one. Bulbs are many but electric current is one. Stars are many but sky is one. Jewelry is many but gold is one. Religions are many but the message is one. Nations are many but earth is one. Beings are many but breath is one. Women are many but birth is one. Though we look different from each other and have different beliefs, we can choose to look for the underlying unity that exists.

All women are born with the potential to give birth (unity), but the way in which they give birth (diversity) varies tremendously from country to country depending on the ratio of midwives and obstetricians. Where there are more obstetricians, midwives often lose their autonomy and rates of cesareans rise quickly.[4] Countries such as Brazil, South Korea, Taiwan, China, Turkey, Southern Italy, Greece, and the US have higher cesarean rates than a country such as the Netherlands, which has a higher ratio of midwives than obstetricians.

When we allow differences to enter our minds, not recognizing unity, we develop feelings of guilt, blame, judgment, and failure. These make us feel distraught and lower our confidence in ourselves. Differences represent duality, the opposite of unity. Choosing to see differences means separating ourselves from others, creating a competitive edge where one woman feels superior to another because of the choices she makes. Such choices include birthing naturally or by cesarean, working with contractions or having an epidural, breastfeeding versus bottle feeding, or staying at home to raise a child or going back to work. If natural is the ideal, every other choice represents a failure to some women. These issues become socially charged with an "I'm right and you're wrong" attitude. Some even equate certain decisions with "loving your kid less" if the mother doesn't choose the natural way to birth and breastfeed, or choose to stay at home.

A healthy attitude is necessary to respect the unity in diversity, and it means choosing to seek the unity and see only what is good. This requires becoming more aware of our thoughts. Seeking unity in birth, we can say that most women who conceive—regardless of their race, creed, or culture—will

grow a baby. All babies swim in their little amniotic oceans. All pregnant women grow a placenta that in turn feeds and nourishes their babies. All women are born with the knowledge about how to give birth. Looking for unity brings us together; looking for differences separates.

When a woman who has given birth feels judged about her experience, she can easily feel depressed, saying to herself, "I'm a failure." I personally do not believe there is failure in childbirth. I believe every woman is doing the very best she can at that moment in time, and this needs to be respected. Respect means helping each other to feel good regardless of what has happened. As students in the cosmic university, we need to work toward unity rather than separation. Love is strong; anger is weak. Acceptance strengthens; judgment weakens. A woman in birth who experiences love and acceptance is ready to embrace the world.

SELFLESS SERVICE

One who sees unity in diversity is more likely to perform selfless service. Service in its spiritual sense is any work carried out from the heart that is without desire for reward in return and without ulterior motives or judgment, thereby rendering it selfless. Selfless service is an important component of nonviolence, for seeing an aspect of ourselves in others means that harming them would be as if we were harming ourselves. It means filling all actions from the heart consciousness and having mutual respect for each person. Carrying out selfless service is a good way to begin cultivating and respecting the common bond of humanity.

Do you remember a time, maybe just yesterday, when someone helped you in a random act of kindness or when you helped someone else? Maybe it was as simple as allowing a space for a car to pull in front of you and the driver waving thanks, or holding a door open for someone. Maybe it was a smile to someone having difficulty, or giving a gift. When we help others, we not only feel good but also know ourselves better, for we feel the kinship we have with each other. Respecting this kinship is what leads to selfless service.

Having been born into society, it is our duty to give something back to it by helping others and making it a better place in which to live. Just as a single flower can't make a bouquet and a single tree can't make a forest, so a single person can't make a society. An individual's spiritual success, his beneficiary nature, and his virtues, when pooled with those of many others, become the wealth of society, the common property of all. "Love all, serve all" is the motto by which we can all live.

In order to have a pure heart when serving selflessly, we must first examine our motives, skills, intention, and qualifications. We can ask ourselves, "What is the purpose for which I am doing this?" It may be to earn a living, but hopefully the primary motive is the compassion and help we can offer to others. Instead of craving a name or fame, crave instead the joy that shines in the faces of those being served. Establish a heart-to-heart connection with them. Selfless work purifies us, and work that is done with love becomes the highest service.

REACHING FOR IDEALS

Lewis Mehl Madronna, MD, once said, "If a woman is going for normal birth, she may end up with interventions. If she is going for self-esteem, she may end up with a normal birth." His point is that it is healthy for us as human beings to set high ideals for ourselves, and building self-esteem and self-confidence is what can help us to have the birth of our dreams. It is not enough to aspire to just normal or natural birth. If we aspire for self-esteem and self-confidence, there is a greater probability of normal birth.

Learning to see unity in diversity is a lofty goal, but it is certainly reachable. It requires a change of perspective in life, a change in how we relate to others, and more awareness of our thoughts. Here are some ways you can start:

1. Become more aware of how important it is to see love as the foundation for all human values, and work from that viewpoint.
2. Start watching your thoughts more carefully to determine if there is love in them, or criticism and judgment. If there is criticism or judgment, learn to be silent until words of kindness flow.
3. Turn to nature and see what it can teach you. What is the unity that it expresses? All trees have roots. All plants need sunshine and water. All birds sing.
4. Learn to transfer the practice of seeing what unites, instead of what separates, into daily life. Choose to see similarities instead of differences.
5. Begin seeing a part of yourself in others, knowing that we all experience happiness, sorrow, pleasure, and pain.
6. Start writing poetry. It connects us with that which is creative and inspirational. Make your life an inspiration.
7. Begin carrying out more random acts of kindness for others.
8. Find a way to do selfless service to make others happy.
9. Practice humility, a feeling of equality where you do not see yourself as better than another. Humility is a hallmark of respect and can be felt in words filled with compassion. Communication between birthing parents and their caregivers during the time of pregnancy, labor, and birth needs to be open, honest, and respectful.
10. Believe that love resides within you and let your life be its message.

To love and respect others, we must first love and respect ourselves. This means seeing yourself as your own best friend. This is not cause for an ego trip but is genuine love for the sake of love, without ego. Feeling this love helps us feel the love in all, for love is a reflection of the spirit. Get the flower and you have its beauty and fragrance. In color, see harmony. In light, see joy. In outward form and in the depths of things, behold the love within you. If you are pregnant, have courage, trust, and faith to birth in the spirit and feel your connection with all women who have ever given birth.

The word *religion* comes from the Latin root *religare (rel-i-garay)* and means to bring together to make whole. Notes come together to make a beautiful song, or colors are put together to make a beautiful painting. Life is more beautiful when we sense the many as one. This is unity, not duality; it is one, not two. The spirit is one and reflects the many. It joins us together and helps us to see the unity in diversity.

As women, we will be stronger when we move into birth with the confidence that comes from respecting the unity in diversity. In time, our lives will be our message, and this message will touch the hearts of many. A woman who believes it is best to stay home with her children will be able to respect the woman who chooses to go back to work, and vice versa. A woman who gives birth naturally will not think less of a woman who has an epidural or cesarean. We will be able to love all and serve all unconditionally. When two people face each other and connect with the spirit, each enters the eye of the other, and they are different in name and form only. It is said that we can't know everyone in the world, but if we know the spirit in ourselves, we will know everyone.

Birthing in the Spirit

Standing on the edge,
I am overtaken by fear.
Fear of the darkness,
Fear of the unknown.
And yet, standing here,
In this awesome place,
I can find that which is most Holy.
Standing here, in this place of unknown,
I can begin to see
Why I was brought into this world.
I can see myself becoming the woman
That I was created to be.

MIRIAM MASLIN, HOLISTIC BIRTH SUPPORT AND
COUNSELOR FROM JERUSALEM, ISRAEL

THE PROMISE OF BIRTH

CHAPTER 27

Birth Times

That instant of birth, with what respect it should be treated! What a fragile, fleeting moment it is.
The child is between two worlds. At a gateway. He hesitates. Don't push him, don't hurry him!
Let him take his time. Let this little being in. Let him do it in his own way, making the change from
foetus to newborn child.... It is true that each child arrives with his own personality....
In spite of everything, birth is only an instant. To be sure. But a privileged instant.

FREDERICK LEBOYER IN *BIRTH WITHOUT VIOLENCE*

We are changing the times of birth. More women are choosing cesareans as a way of giving birth than ever before, and this—along with increases in induction rates, epidural anesthesia rates, and drugs to speed up labor—is changing the times that babies were meant to be born. In addition, the number of women requesting primary elective cesarean is increasing. I believe that there is more structure to our existence than we realize and that interfering with the time of birth, the time when a soul is supposed to be born, has repercussions that go beyond our understanding; but intuitively, I also feel it. Something is very wrong.

In *The Mystery of Time*, John Langone quotes Longfellow: "What is time?" he asked. "The shadow on the dial, the striking of the clock, the running of the sand, day and night, summer and winter months, years, centuries—these are but the arbitrary and outward signs, the measure of time, not time itself. Time is the life of the soul." For Aristotle, time's passage is "the number of movements in respect of the before and after, and is continuous."[1]

Natural rhythms of the earth take us from day to night and back to day. They bring in changes of seasons and the rise and fall of ocean tides, all of which are fairly predictable within certain time frames. We are also governed by our biological rhythms. There are rhythms within virtually everything in our lives, synchronized within a twenty-four-hour day and night cycle and with effects from the moon and sun. Scientists believe that precise time-keeping mechanisms are actually buried in our cells, with each being capable of driving or coordinating a rhythm and regulating processes within every life form.[2]

A study showing how precise the timing of our very existence is was carried out by Harvard University researchers in 1999. They determined that our internal clocks run precisely on a daily cycle of twenty-four hours, eleven minutes. To arrive at this conclusion, they had twenty-four men and women, young and old, go to bed four hours later each day, making their day twenty-eight hours long. This cycle distributed their light exposure, sleep and wakefulness, work, and play evenly

around the biological clock. The subjects now experienced a six-day week, and instead of getting light exposure at the same time each clock day, light and dark occurred at different times each day. This revamped schedule freed internal clocks from the sleep-wake cycle, enabling them to tick at their natural pace. Amazingly, despite six-day weeks, body temperatures and hormone secretions went through seven cycles every week, and no matter when the subjects retired or woke, no matter what they did while awake, their body temperatures and hormones continued to rise and fall on an average cycle of twenty-four hours and eleven minutes. The conclusion was that the human circadian pacemaker is as stable and precise a mechanism in measuring time as that of other mammals, some of whom seem to have even more finely tuned biological clocks and instinctive time senses than humans.[3]

Biological rhythms are entrained by light and also by gravitational effects, again showing our connection to the universe in which we live. Live oysters open and close their valves in rhythm with the tides, which are in phase with the moon. When these oysters are moved a thousand miles westward, away from the ocean in tight, opaque containers filled with seawater, within two weeks they start shifting their rhythm to one that coincides with the passage of the moon in their new location.[4] Animals and birds are more strongly tied to light-dark cycles than humans because we live under the influence of artificial sources of light. Migrations of birds are influenced by an inner timing mechanism that alerts them to seasonal weather changes. If you have seen the movie *Winged Migration,* one of my favorites, you will know that such migrations are essential for their survival.

All people have a built-in diurnal rhythm of approximately the same length. Biological clocks signal some animals to be awake in the day, and others at night. Internal clocks in humans and animals time our metabolic systems, brain waves, blood pressure, heartbeat, digestion, and in women, menstrual cycles. The timing of women's menstrual cycles, which occur on the average of every twenty-eight days, is not a coincidence and is correlated with the phases of the moon. Biological clocks also control our sleep-wake cycles, pulse hormones into our bloodstreams, and keep our reproductive rhythms rolling. However, our chaotic work schedules, jet lag, and social schedules cause us to deviate from our biological clocks and this results in fatigue and the accumulation of sleep debt. In our fast-paced lifestyles, there is tremendous pressure to achieve, and we are flooded with enormous amounts of information. Many families work long hours or two jobs just to make ends meet. Our stress-related fight or flight system is on such chronic overload that we overcome it with coffee and other caffeinated drinks. This puts much stress on the body.

All elements of the earth are contained in the human body. In fact, we are 80 percent saltwater, and so the waning and waxing of the moon affects us just like it does the ocean. There is a superstition about "full-moon nights," in which people will attribute something that happens to them that night to the full moon. I believe that if phases of the moon control the tides, they certainly have an effect on the body, which is mostly water.

Mammals give birth after certain periods of gestation. In humans, gestation is about forty weeks and is based on the phases of the moon, which gives a two-week leeway, making anytime between

thirty-eight and forty-two weeks normal. Normal blood pressure is 120/80, and deviating too much from this can reflect illness. Our normal pulse rate is about sixty beats a minute, and there is even a separate craniosacral rhythm of about twelve beats a minute. You can feel this rhythm by placing your hands on someone's head and literally feel it expanding and contracting. We breathe rhythmically in and out of our lungs about 23,000 times each day.

We may think that many things happen by chance, but actually everything happens in its own time for its own reason. The earth rotates around the sun, specific phases of the moon can be mapped out well in advance, and we can even predict when to see Venus setting near the sun at certain times of the year. These timings and rhythms of the earth and all who live on it are very important. Long ago I came to the conclusion that there is no such thing as coincidence, and I have a strong hunch that the natural timing of when a baby is meant to be born is of great significance.

I came across a book called *Birth Times* written by Michel Gauquelin, a trained psychologist.[5] The subtitle is *A Scientific Investigation of the Secrets of Astrology*. I found myself fascinated by the book. As you read through his findings, I ask you to do so with the spirit of inquiry, to see if it resonates with your own consciousness. I personally do not know much about astrology, but I do have complicit trust in the planet, the galaxy we live in, and the universe, and believe it is more mathematical than we realize. Since timing is so precise in our existence, I believe there must be a connection to our birth times. I also believe that the individual soul who is without form has to come from somewhere. Where that is remains a mystery, but it must be in other dimensions of reality that we do not know.

Astronomer Bart J. Bok wrote, "Why should the precise moment of birth be the critical instant in a person's life? Is the instant of conception not basically a more drastic event than the precise moment when the umbilical cord is severed?"[6] We do not know the answer to his question, but changing the time of birth will affect the total gestational period. Many things have existed for thousands of years before they were discovered to be true. For example, gravity has always been a part of the earth, even before Newton "discovered" it. A baby has always known how to initiate labor, but this was not recognized to be true until the twentieth century. The precise timing of birth may be more crucial to our growth and development than we realize.

Dr. Gauquelin began his research by raising two questions—the first being, "Is life made up of a succession of haphazard events, or is there a more or less unconscious thread running through and directing our efforts to some sort of specific aim?" and the second being, "If the foetus should leave its mother's womb in its own time, is it a serious interference to make it be born at another moment?"[7] He also believed that the planets have an effect on us; otherwise, we would not see them. He laboriously studied thousands of birth times to see what correlations there were between the rising and setting of various planets and the times people were born.

His research was methodical, and he began by obtaining the exact hours of birth for people in various professions. His approach was strictly scientific, drawing conclusions that sometimes deviated from his assumptions. The first birth time he received was that of Louis Braille, inventor of

the reading system for the blind. Soon thereafter he obtained the birth times of 576 French doctors from 1820 to 1939. Gauquelin wrote, "The specific hour of birth is of crucial significance. It is this which fixes the position of the planets in their daily movement, what astrologers call their position in the 'houses.'"

He worked out by hand the position of the planets at the hour of birth of each doctor and made a statistical compilation of his findings. He wrote, "Suddenly, I was presented with an extraordinary fact. My doctors were not born under the same skies as the common run of humanity. They had chosen to come into the world much more often during roughly the two hours following the rise and culmination of two planets, Mars and Saturn. Moreover, they tended to 'avoid' being born following the rise and culmination of the planet Jupiter."[8] Gauquelin then obtained hundreds of birth times of non-doctors to see if they were also born under the culmination of Mars and Saturn. They were not.

To further test his results, he went through the experiment again, using another group of doctors and seeing if they had birth time links to Mars, Jupiter, and Saturn. Once again, "my doctors 'chose' the rise and culmination of Mars and Saturn and 'avoided' being born when Jupiter was moving through those sectors of the sky."[9] His research was already showing that at the moment of birth, each body in the solar system was housed in one of the sectors of the celestial wheel, and that this placement had significant outcome.

He went on to see if there were any other planetary influences with other professions. "The planet Mars, when positioned at birth in the sectors following its rise and culmination, favoured the success of sports champions and exceptional military leaders; Jupiter, in the same sectors, featured most frequently at the birth of actors and politicians. Where scientists were concerned…it was Saturn which was dominant; on the other hand, artists—painters and musicians—presented an entirely opposite picture, since they 'avoided' being born when that planet occupied the key sectors of rise and culmination."[10] Gauquelin went on to carry out thirteen repetitions of his French observations using European data, and in every case the results observed correlated with his French research. The same was true for birth times in the US. All birth times studied in each case were of people outstanding in their fields of study. Interestingly, he found nothing abnormal in the control groups of people unknown in their fields of study.[11]

Gauquelin went on to conduct experiments on how laws of heredity might influence times we are born. After extensive research examining over 60,000 births, he found that "children have a tendency to be born when a planet has just risen or culminated, if that same planet was in the same regions of the sky at the birth of their parents."[12] The effects were found to be true for the most massive planets closest to us in the solar system—i.e., the Moon, Venus, Mars, Jupiter, and Saturn—and no hereditary similarity was observed for the planets further away from us—i.e., Uranus, Neptune, Pluto, and Mercury. The results did not depend on sex. If both parents of the child were born at the rise or culmination of the same planet, the tendency in the child was doubled.[13] He went on to say that "my most interesting discovery was the way in which all planetary effects

on heredity disappeared in children whose births did not occur naturally, that is, whenever there was surgical intervention (a caesarean), or whenever the birth was stimulated or accelerated by the administration of drugs."[14]

Gauquelin next researched character traits, defining, for example, champions as being "iron-willed," actors as being "outgoing," scientists as "introspective," and writers as "sensitive." He found that "at the birth of 'iron-willed' champions, Mars was twice as often present in the key sectors of rise and culmination as at the birth of 'weak-willed' champions. 'Outgoing' actors came into the world with Jupiter in the key sectors much more often than actors who appear less expansive. 'Introspective' scientists were born in greater numbers at the rise or culmination of Saturn, unlike the 'anti-scientists.' And 'sensitive' writers were born when the Moon was on the rise or at its culmination."[15] He then wanted to determine if, in addition to "iron-willed" sporting champions, "iron-willed actors, scientists, and writers would also be born under Mars, which would explain a planetary type. He found that "persons with an 'iron will'" often had a tendency to be born under Mars, the "expansives" under Jupiter, the "introspectives" under Saturn, and poetic temperaments under the Moon.[16]

What is most important is that through all his research Gauquelin was finding consistent patterns of groups of people born with certain character traits and in certain professions within key times of planet positions. He also cautioned that planetary types do not explain the entire personality of an individual, with education and environmental factors also playing key roles.

In 1979, the work of Gauquelin *et al* was published in *The British Journal of Social and Clinical Psychology*.[17] His conclusion was that in all cases, using categories as defined by collaborator Hans Eysenck in 1975, "the 'introverts' were born far more often than chance would allow with Saturn in the key sectors of rise and culmination; the 'extroverts' chose to come into the world when Jupiter or Mars were in those zones of the sky. By contrast, the 'introverts' 'avoided' being born when Jupiter or Mars were at the rise or culminating, and the 'extroverts' 'avoided' being born when Saturn was going through those zones of the sky.[18] He found that the 'tough'-minded people were born much more often under Jupiter and Mars than under Saturn, and vice versa.

Attempts of Gauquelin to determine the planetary effects for ordinary people were unsuccessful for a variety of reasons, one being the limitations of self-reporting in questionnaires. Gauquelin cautioned against predicting the future temperament and behavior of the newborn child based on his planetary heredity. "I believe that planetary effects must always be considered along with the role played by hereditary factors, education, social position, and chance in the make-up of the individual."[19]

Paradoxically, early research showed the least results were for the Sun itself. Gauquelin proposed this may be due to the fact that the Sun is a star and not a planet. Even though the influence of the Sun on the earth is very powerful, its astrological role in his research did not show itself to be very significant.[20] However, believing the sun must have some effects, later research showed that "it can now be said that the planetary sensitivity of the child at birth appears to show itself more easily

in a disturbed geomagnetic environment." His hypothesis was that the "sun acts as the motor and the solar field as the medium. The Moon and the closest and most massive planets would cause a disturbance in this field and the stronger it was, the more intensely it would be felt by the child at its birth....In short, the foetus would only be sensitive to the same planets as the retina."[21]

In addition, when researching effects of the zodiac, which typically gives character traits for horoscopes, Dr. Gauquelin consistently found them unfavorable to astrological findings, with chance ruling everywhere.[22] I am not personally a believer in the scientific authenticity of horoscopes, but do have to say that, being a Libra, I have always felt most comfortable when I am balanced, and I always seem to try and keep things balanced like the Libra scales.

BEING OPEN TO NEW PERSPECTIVES

History has shown that original theories are often not accepted by others at the time because people are too entrenched in old ways of thinking and have a hard time opening themselves to the credibility of new theories. More than 2,000 years ago Hippocrates asserted, "When the time is ripe, the child moves, breaks the membranes holding it in and leaves its mother's womb."[23] Back then he was derided, for the uterus was perceived as a "mausoleum entombing the foetus within it, a fortress impregnable to anything other than sperm. There was no internal or external stimulation of any kind until, at the end of the nine months, life suddenly burst out."[24] Around 1975, the reverse theory began to take hold and gained widespread acceptance: "It is the foetus which tells the mother when to expel it."[25]

Research by Dr. G. C. Liggins, professor of gynecology and obstetrics at the Auckland University in New Zealand, worked with sheep, and he wrote, "What we show first is that if you destroy the foetal pituitary and remove its adrenal glands which direct the hypothalamus, labour in the sheep does not occur and the pregnancy will continue for months after term."[26] He maintained that the fetal organs transmit information to the hypothalamus, which results in prostaglandin release into the uterine tissue, which triggers contraction and the onset of labour."[27] The current medical view is that "when the brain of the baby reaches a certain state of maturity, it releases a substance that begins a chain reaction finally leading to delivery."[28]

Chronobiologists, those who study rhythms, have found that it is much better not to meddle with the biological clock of the child and to let it be born according to its natural rhythm, i.e., at night or in the early hours of the morning.[29] But for the doctor's convenience, and increasingly for women wanting to plan when their child will be born, there has been a tremendous change to day-time deliveries. It is paradoxical that doctors would accept the idea that babies initiate their own times for birth, yet they readily interfere with the timing of birth by performing such procedures as inductions.

In natural childbirth the mother plays an active part in bringing her child into the world, but today doctors are reducing the mother to a passive object in the hands of technology with all of its

surgical, electronic, and medical resources. During electronic fetal monitoring, the doctor does not simply decide when to trigger labor but controls it from beginning to end. In effect, it is childbirth by computer—a far cry from the mother's active participation in delivery. It is an era where birth has become "patients in hospital" rather than human beings going through normal physiological developments.

CURRENT INTERFERENCES IN BIRTH TIMES

What are the ways in which birth times are interfered with in today's birthing practices? First, there is amniotomy, or artificially breaking the amniotic sac called the "bag of waters," which typically shortens labor by one to two hours. This was first carried out in 1810 by Thomas C. James, professor of obstetrics at the University of Pennsylvania in Philadelphia. According to Gauquelin, even in this short time frame, in terms of the planetary effect, "There is no longer perfect synchronization between the parents' generation and the child's. For example, if the parents were born with Mars in the key sectors of rise or culmination, their child will have a tendency to be born with Mars slightly before those key sectors."[30]

The use of forceps is another form of intervention, designed to assist in getting the baby's head out from its mother's womb. Gauquelin determined that "planetary synchronization between births of parents and children in key sectors was even less clearly marked than in the case of artificial rupture of the membranes. Although the planetary effect on heredity did not completely disappear, it was drastically reduced in the children."[31]

The administration of synthetic oxytocin, more commonly called Pitocin or simply "Pit," also obscures the role of the fetus and interferes with timing of the delivery. Hormonal function established over thousands of years is confused and overwhelmed by the introduction of such drugs into the mother's bloodstream. A huge pharmaceutical industry has been developed to promote drugs during deliveries, and the industry is thriving. Even a mother's own rhythmic production of oxytocin is affected if she has a cesarean section.

Pitocin allowed elective induction of labor to quickly become a trend starting in the 1960s, and in the last decade has increased dramatically due to the availability of Cytotec, a much less expensive drug than Pitocin. Cytotec was originally approved to treat peptic ulcers and has never been approved by the Food and Drug Administration for use in obstetrics. Induction meant that children could now be born within office hours and during weekdays. This has changed the birth times of both the normal hour of birth and the actual day.

All of these interventions that alter the timing of birth may be significant, as Gauquelin's research shows. In a time when there is birth by appointment and cesarean on demand, it is a concern that his findings showed that "when children are born by Caesarean, the planetary effect on heredity disappears entirely."[32] This means that some connection that was supposed to be present is lost. How significant that is, we simply don't know. Doctors say, "If the mother demands it [the cesarean], we

cannot see any reason to refuse."[33] Professor Claude Sureau, past head of the Baudelocque maternity hospital in Paris, gives the obstetrician's point of view: "At the beginning, I was hesitant about opening the stomachs of these pregnant women but, literally pressured from one side by my patients and from the other by the anesthetists, I did so and I must say, if the mother demands it, I don't see any reason to refuse."[34] This is the pressure doctors often feel that makes them do things they never thought they would do.

As humans, we are often shortsighted and unaware of long-term effects. As more education and primal health research has developed, a movement has grown up to counter obstetrical technology and managed births, returning to natural birth. The people in this movement are also concerned about the pollution of the environment, synthetic foods, and abuse of medicines. They believe nature should be allowed to follow her course, but also accept technology when it is truly medically necessary. R. D. Laing expresses their feelings about birth:

To be born is a momentous event in our life cycle. In recent years, hundreds of thousands of people have been going through experiences as adults which they themselves feel to be related to their actual birth experience. Traces of the experience of being born seem to occur in dreams, myths, fantasies, physical events, or to be acted out in different ways. The preference for unnatural childbirth practices, which seems to be spreading across the world, despite countermovements to tune into the natural process, has led birth, in many places, to be a major psychobiological disaster zone, in which almost everything is done the exact opposite way from how it would happen if allowed to.[35]

Frederick Leboyer, a French doctor, published his well-known book *Birth Without Violence* in 1982, advocating that babies be born in quiet, dark environments and bathed in water right away so that their transition into the world would be as gentle as possible. Interestingly, the fundamental assumption underlying his belief can be traced back to Paracelsus, the famous physician, alchemist, and astrologer of the early Renaissance, born in Switzerland in 1493. Leboyer believed strongly that the instant of birth was of great importance and that this should not be rushed, letting the baby come into the world in his own way.[36]

Dr. Michel Odent's dramatic change from an obstetrician who performed all the medical interventions and cesareans to one who promoted gentle birth was based on Leboyer's work and philosophy. Odent to this day brings his message of love and respect for the baby in the primal period to countries around the world and is effectively helping to change current birthing practices, lowering cesarean rates and helping birth to be reborn.

G.I. Kloosterman, professor of obstetrics at the University of Amsterdam, states: "Childbirth in itself is a natural phenomenon and in the large majority of cases needs no interference whatsoever— only close observation, moral support and protection against human meddling. A healthy woman who delivers spontaneously performs a job that cannot be improved upon."[37]

As of this writing, a report of the latest research of the dangers of routine medical intervention in birth was published in *The New York Times* in March of 2007. Researchers at Yale and in Sweden are

showing a disruption of fetal brain development in lab animals after ultrasounds and a Minnesota study of autopsied brains of autistic children found a similar pattern of abnormal nerve-cell migration. Even though we have thought ultrasound to be relatively safe as a procedure, preliminary scientific data is suggesting that it may cause significant changes in the fetal brain's ability to organize itself, possibly resulting in autistic spectrum disorders.[38]

I sincerely hope that the mechanization of childbirth is a passing fad and that the pendulum will soon begin to swing the other way as birthing parents become more educated about their full human potential, developing more trust and faith in their bodies, and realizing both the short and long-term effects of current birthing practices. I know that some good will come out of this electronic era, in that we will have improved our ability to care for premature and compromised babies. But gradually I believe we will move into what Michel Odent calls the "Post-electronic" era, where more women give birth as nature intended with less fear and more joy; there will then be less interference in birth times.

I have presented a theory by Gauquelin that is based on significant research and findings. However, when researching planetary dimensions, there is still much we don't know. One of the reasons I find his research to be fascinating and unique is because after the 1950s and 1960s, and especially into the 1980's, there are so many medical births that we may no longer be able to obtain a significant number of birth times that occurred naturally in order for further research to be carried out.

No matter what the research, the idea that birth times are significant and to be respected comes to me instinctively and intuitively. This is summed up in what a young woman said to me recently, "I trust natural. I trust God. He must know more than we do!" I agree.

Wake up my dearest friend

Wake up my dearest friend!
Life is waiting for you now.
You've been sleeping all too long.
Wake up! Wake up!
Wake up my dearest friend.
Take a look around yourself.
The energy of love is everywhere.
Choose to see it now.
Wake up! Wake up!

FROM *GINNUNGAGAP*, A MUSICAL FROM DENMARK,
DRAWING INSPIRATION FROM NORSE MYTHOLOGY

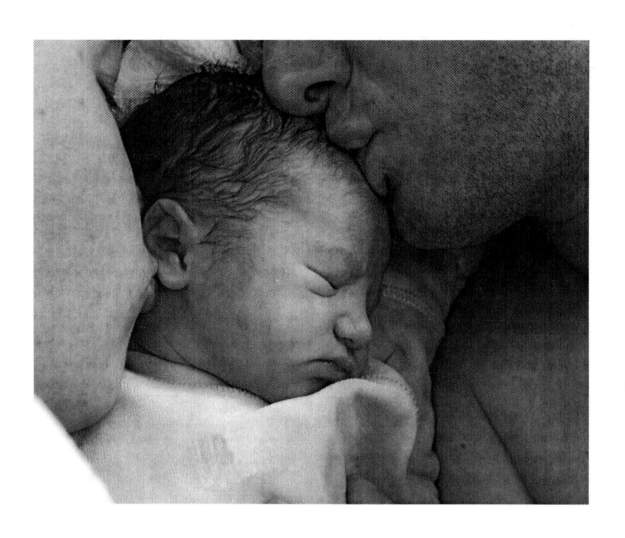

CHAPTER 28

The Full Potential of Birth

Birth as a process is so saturated with overwhelming emotion and rushes of intense feeling that most women experience ecstasy at some point along the way. A woman laboring with an epidural may not be transported from her usual consciousness, but watch the ecstasy catch up with her as she births her baby and melts into joy and love and motherhood. You may see it in the father too. If watched from afar, you may see ecstasy drench all three of them as the world disappears and they become new. There is as much room to involve ecstasy in the moments of a medicated labor as there are in our daily lives. It is good practice to find peace in our every day moments— to learn to respond to the world with a "yes."

SHANNON WILLIAMS

When a woman believes that her body knows how to give birth and is familiar with the inward journey of connecting with her spirit, she will experience peace knowing that whatever the outcome, she did the very best that she could. It is the process that is important. However, when hormones are allowed to function in their full capacity, not being influenced by drugs or anesthesia, the full potential of birth is more likely to be experienced.

I believe that one of the most powerful films of the twentieth century was *Star Wars*. Even though it was not a film about childbirth, it has much to teach us about birth. In the film, Darth Vader represents the evil empire. He looks menacing, powerful, and fearful with his black mask, but in the end when he removes it, what do we see? We see a strange and pitiful sort of undifferentiated face. He dies when the mask is removed. His power looked strong, but it was weak and could not be sustained against the power of good represented in Luke Skywalker. Darth Vader was never able to develop his own humanity. He was like a robot, not able to live on his own terms but rather only in terms of an imposed system.

We are in a similar situation with birth. The financial, economic, and political pressures are powerful systems. Movies show women in birth lying flat on their backs with legs wide open, surrounded by people watching the electronic fetal monitor, telling them when a contraction is starting because they can no longer feel it themselves as they are anesthetized by an epidural from

the waist down. An intravenous needle is in their arms just in case they hemorrhage, and there are bright lights. An oxygen mask is on her face even though she is a healthy woman. People have their hands on the baby's head, trying to help pull him out. Birth has been reduced to a medical event where the woman's birth is being managed and the baby is being delivered.

The question is, are we as women going to allow the system to flatten us out and deny us the full potential of birth? When a woman *gives* birth, she becomes empowered. She feels strong and ready to be a mother. She feels that if she can give birth, she can do anything! Being confident and reaching the full potential of birth means holding onto ideals based on truth and, like Luke Skywalker, rejecting the imposed system's impersonal claims upon us.

A favorite moment of mine in *Star Wars* is when Obi-Wan Kenobi says to Luke Skywalker in the climactic moment of the last fight, "Feel the force!" Luke turns off his computer at the crux of the battle, turns off his machine, and allows himself to be guided by the force. When Luke does this, he achieves success and the audience I was in broke out into spontaneous applause.

A woman at the height of labor needs to do just what Luke Skywalker did. She needs to turn off her rational brain, be assured privacy, and be left undisturbed in dim lights. Decreasing stimulation of the neocortex, or thinking brain, is a way for her to go deep within to her inner being where she can "feel the force," connect with the spirit, follow her intuition, and trust her feelings.

Star Wars asks us the question, "Are you going to be a person guided by your inner knowing, in tune with your consciousness, or are you going to follow routines of the "system" as if on an auto-pilot that requires little work or thinking, doing what you are told without questioning?" I love the part of *Star Wars* where Luke Skywalker makes his way past the Darth Vader guards by telling them what to think. They are so robotic that they have no ability to think for themselves; they merely comply without the ability to question. How many women are like this today, not able to express their needs, perhaps paralyzed" by fear? Living in the world, not in tune with our spirit, turns us into computers. When we practice human values, we become composers.

When Obi-Wan Kenobi says, "May the force be with you," he is speaking about our electromagnetic power and not that of programmed machines. We are full of electromagnetic power. This power gives women the strength to give birth. It is our intuition. It is our conscience. It is organized and directive. It can be trusted and will always lead us in the right direction. A fraction of it can be felt in the powerful contractions that can place women in a state of awe of the force within their own bodies.

We each have our own journeys in birth and parenting. We can choose to follow our bliss and realize our full potential as human beings, or we can allow ourselves to drown in fear. If we think, "Oh, I can't do that!" then the dragon of fear is locking us in. We must slay the dragon. This is a journey into selflessness, a journey into the spirit. The world without spirit is a wasteland. Anything that is alive has validity. The thing to do is to make it come alive. The only way to do that is to find out where the life is and become alive ourselves We must find our bliss and have the courage to follow it. It is the experience that counts.

Preparations for birthing in the spirit

How can a pregnant woman prepare for birthing in the spirit? She can begin by practicing seeing good in everyone and everything. She can eat healthy foods and make sure that all her senses of seeing, hearing, tasting, smelling, and touching are being used only for good things. She can pray or meditate to keep in touch with her higher self and connect with the spirit with love. She can believe that love is her form and truth is her breath. She can realize that the knowledge about how to give birth is already inside of her. She can pray for its guidance during labor and in all decision making. She can choose to love her enemies because the power of love changes hearts. Just as clouds block rays of the sun, so animal qualities of greed, jealousy, anger, and pride block love from the heart. The heart is the center of love. If the door of the heart is closed, love cannot flow. She can work hard to stop anger and refrain from criticizing or harming anyone. She can put into practice unity of thought, word, and deed that will also make her a good parent. She can say to herself, "Whatever happens to me in my life is good for me and is life's teacher."

Love is like a magnet when kept clean and free of any impurities. If there is rust on the magnet—representing jealousy, anger, and pride—it loses some of its power. The more we can rid ourselves of such impurities, the stronger our love can shine and the greater will be its quality of attraction. It will pull toward it any entity, irrespective of capacity, power, or strength. Such is the magnetic attraction of love.

We have many duties to perform in the world. Doing them without love is deplorable. Doing them with love is desirable. Feel the spiritual love that binds us together as one and transform that love into service. Transform the service into devotion. See anger as your enemy and patience as your shield of protection. Make happiness your heaven. Become who you are and have a peak birth experience that will empower you for a lifetime.

As you read the following stories of women's births, see if you can identify ways in which the human values worked through their births. See if you can identify the women putting into practice the concepts of seeing, hearing, and doing only that which is good. The hospital, home, or birthing center can all become sacred spaces for a woman giving birth when she has connected to her spirit and feels safe and when human values are put into practice by the birth team. The location no longer matters. It is being able to birth in the spirit that matters.

Barbara:

I felt "gassy" before going to bed, but woke up in the middle of the night with contractions. I took a long, hot shower washing my belly and telling my baby I couldn't wait to see it. The contractions were mild but rhythmic. I kept my midwives posted. It was a beautiful spring day and even though the contractions were becoming more intense, we went out for a walk in the flower garden. I imagined my cervix opening like the flowers in bloom.

The midwives came and soon afterwards I heard a "pop" as warm water gushed down my

leg. Excitement and anticipation increased as my body gave me more signs that birth was near. Lying on my side, the contractions became stronger and almost unbearable so I stood up again and walked which helped me to work with them better. The hall in my home was just big enough to walk up and down with stops to sit on the toilet. I wrapped my arms around my husband's waist during each contraction. Sometimes we would sway side to side as in a slow dance.

The power I felt was overwhelming. Power is the best word I can find to describe my labor. Moaning helped to push the energy down through my uterus and out through my legs. I could feel the waves come and go. I went into warm water as the contractions came now in waves one on top of the other. For the two minutes in between I could actually have a peaceful sleep. How peaceful that time was when I was so inside myself. It was an elevated state of consciousness, one of the most spiritual experiences I've had. The undeniable urge to push came and when it was over I went back into the bed.

My mother was in charge of handing hot compresses and olive oil to my birth doula Amy, who placed them on my perineum. My husband John was beside me and I could feel his love. With each push I let out a yell that could surely be heard all over the neighborhood. I was so powerful. It felt so good as it was the energy release I needed to get the head out. The burning of my perineum stretching was intense as the baby's head crowned. Suddenly, my beautiful daughter slithered her way out and was on my belly. I was oblivious to the bustling going on around me with the birthing of the placenta.

I had lost some blood and had a small tear and so felt a little weak, but I had full faith in the people around me. What affected me the most about this birth was the realization of how powerful my body is. Before my daughter was born, I could say that I knew my body was powerful and perfect to birth a child, but it wasn't until I actually experienced it that I knew the overwhelming nature of it. I've always been a feminist, but now am much more in love with the fact that I am a woman and have the special ability and power to bring forth life.

Stephanie:

I have never felt so close to God than during the two times that I have given birth to my children. My daughter Hannah was born by cesarean section. That was probably one of the most spiritual times of my entire life. My husband had given me a beautiful blessing before the operation in which he told me that the baby and I would be safe and healthy and that we would live. I had pre-eclampsia. He told me that I would have a healthy body and I would heal from the surgery, and that I would have many more children that were waiting to join our family. He also said that I would have peace. Though I was quite ill at the time and the epidural anesthesia failed for my cesarean, I felt my great-grandmother and many of my ancestors who have gone

before me putting their arms around me and surrounding me with love. I have never felt so close to heaven. I left my body to escape the surgery and struggled for a moment about returning. I was surrounded by a big bright light that was filled with so much love. It was difficult to ignore that. I knew that my baby needed me so my decision to come back was not a difficult one. I will never forget feeling the spirit so strongly during a time in my life that could have been very scary. I fully believe that our family members who have gone before us and our future children are all in the spirit watching over us as guardian angels and are eager and excited about the birth of a baby. To them, it is a joyous event and one that is filled with joy and love. It is a time when birth and death are so close and the veil between earth life and the spirit world are so closely connected.

During my son Michael's birth, I was filled with the spirit and given another wonderful blessing by my husband in order to help me decide what kind of birth I should have. I felt directed by the spirit to have a homebirth instead of a repeat cesarean section. This was the choice that resonated with my very being. Having a homebirth VBAC was the right thing to do and I felt at one with all the women of the earth as I pushed my son into this world. As he slid out, his whole being took on an aura of other-worldliness. He was truly in two worlds at once and I was at peace. It was an incredible moment and I thought of my guardian angels watching over us. I knew that they were there and smiling down on us. My mother attended Michael's birth as well and she and I bonded on a different level as she watched her daughter birth her grandson.

Birthing in the spirit to me means that we birth in a spiritual plane that many people are unaware of or are not looking for. When you look for that spiritual connection in birth, you will find it. It is there more strongly than at any time in our lives except death. You will always find it through another person or through your own spirit or the spirits of all women of the earth.

Julia:

When I had my second son, Christopher, I experienced almost the perfect birth. I felt stunted because they wouldn't let me out of bed until his heart rate slowed down and they had me on an IV. But once the doctor came and told me I could move about, I didn't move off the bed because I was really almost ready for him to be born and I had no desire to move at all. When I was pushing and he was moving through the birth canal, physically it was almost completely ecstatic. Then I felt the wonder that comes during climax in making love. This wonder was like all my senses—physical, mental, emotional, and spiritual—were being overwhelmed at once. As he was born, my husband "caught" him and laid him on my tummy. I was practically unaware of who was doing this because I was so consumed by all the feelings I was having.

After he was on my tummy, I was living on another plane, emotionally, mentally, and spiritually.

Here was my child and we were on this plane together, physically united in a new way, body to body, but spiritually we were still one. I felt like I was flying in another dimension with him. He urinated on me, and I was ecstatic because his body was doing what it was supposed to. I didn't care about being messy, the physical was unimportant in that moment. What overruled all was just being with him and seeing him and touching him with my hands. And no one interfered with that process. No one took him away to weigh him or suction him or clean him up. We were all goopy and messy together and everything was exactly as it was supposed to be. I suppose people were cleaning him off while he was on my tummy, but I was very unaware of that. No one swaddled him and put a blanket between us. It was skin to skin; there was no one else in the universe in that moment that I could take in with any consciousness. After a long time, they took him off for around five minutes to weigh him, but then he was back in my arms and it didn't seem like any time had passed at all. It was one of the most beautiful moments in my life. I see that moment as though a great light was shining on us, but it was a comfortable light that just enveloped us with love. And we were all together, Christopher and I and this light. The people in the room were background noise, dim at best, and really not distracting at all. It was a moment in my life that I am very grateful could happen the way that it did. I am also grateful that the hospital staff allowed us this privileged time and didn't disturb it.

Adriane:

My labor started at 2:00 A.M., eleven days past my "due date." Before going to bed I lost my mucous plug and had been having lower back cramping all day but nothing serious. After cleaning my kitchen floor (on my hands and knees), I set up the birthing tub (the kind with a built-in heater) and then headed to bed to try to get a good night of sleep. I woke to strong, regular contractions and I had to get out of bed and walk around to cope with them. They still were not very intense. I filled my birthing tub to pass the time and keep busy since I could not go back to sleep. I had some toast with fruit preserves to make sure I would have some energy. I finally was able to sleep for about an hour around 5:00 A.M.

The rest of the morning I just spent my time doing things around the house and walking up and down the stairs. My three-year-old daughter went to preschool, so it was just my husband, me, and my 18-month-old daughter. Around 11:30, things started getting more intense so that I didn't feel like doing anything except concentrating on what my body was doing, so I called my midwife. From that point on I was either walking around, leaning against my birth ball, in the shower standing or on my hands and knees, or on my hands and knees on the staircase.

My midwife arrived around 12:45 and I wanted to get into the water between 1 and 2 P.M. My husband picked up our daughter from preschool. Before she had left for preschool that morning,

she looked at the tub in the kitchen and got very excited and said, "Baby is going to come out of your belly today!" I had spent the past few months talking to her about it and showing her videos of home water births so she would know what to expect. She helped my husband rub my back and offered me sips of Gatorade; it was too cute!

I spent the whole time in the tub on my knees, leaning against the side of the tub, making low noises, and self-affirmations. My water broke at 4:00 P.M. and at that point I knew things were going to happen quickly because it was such a huge release of pressure. I knew the baby would be able to move down my birth canal. Things were getting very intense and I kept telling myself to "just let it hurt more" so I could just completely surrender to the amazing power of my body. As the baby moved down, the pressure got so intense I knew things would be over very soon.

Twenty minutes later the baby's head emerged and my midwife checked for a nuchal cord, then the rest of the baby slipped out. There was no tearing! I reached down and picked up my son out of the water. Noah Samson Burns was born at 4:20 P.M. and weighed a whopping 10 lbs. 4 oz. and was 21 inches long. He is a quiet and peaceful baby and such a good nurser! After the cord stopped pulsating, the midwife helped my three year old cut the cord. My daughter talks about it every day and I'm so happy that the gift of a normal birth has been imprinted in her memory forever. My labor went perfectly and I couldn't have pictured it any better.

The forward leaning positions that we talked about at the Birth Works workshop were certainly the best way for my big baby to come out and they just happened to be the positions that my body preferred during labor. During the last 20 minutes, I did consciously lift one leg up to create more space for the baby to come out. My birth experience was phenomenal and it totally made up for my previous two experiences. I had the right belief of birth being a completely normal experience and I now feel so much more confident in teaching the Birth Works philosophies since I have experienced it myself.

Pam:

I look at my husband who trusted me enough to step outside his comfort zone and support me in my homebirth. I leave my watery haven and lie on the bed, half dozing, panting gently through the waves. The midwife arrives and I practically leap back into the tub. I begin pushing in earnest now, able to give myself up to the sensations of labor and turn off my practical, analytical mind. It is indescribably powerful to feel my baby move down, to feel the burning that signals impending transition from womb to arms. And as my baby slithers from my body in one huge movement, I am exultant, triumphant, ecstatic... victorious.

To listen to our souls, we need to trust the more indirect side of ourselves. Doing so brings us closer to our full human potential and to the powerful experience that birth offers. Doing so is a choice. It is a choice about living life as the status quo or taking the initiative to make changes that we believe will make us better people. Often, these changes mean taking risks, having courage, and choosing to end old habits and developing new, healthier ones. It means following your conscience, even if what it says is contrary to what others around you are saying. But if you feel what your conscience is saying resonates with you, learn to trust it and follow it as your guide regardless of what anyone else is saying or thinking. I believe those are the moments you will always remember.

Birthing in the Spirit

At 42 years of age, I had already given birth to five children, three vaginally and two by cesarean, and was now in labor with my sixth at home with midwives. Contractions were progressing nicely and I looked forward to their coming and going. They were strong and I melted into them and went deep inside to hear what else I could do. It takes time to become familiar with the range of feelings during labor and perhaps that's why labor happens over time instead of in an instant. We can focus on how much it hurts, or we can be awed by the strength that surges through us. It's a choice. The fact is, to have children, one must go through labor of one sort or another—even cesareans have their difficult trials. What I learned in this birth is that we can appreciate the forces going on within us or we can fight them. We can work with them and use them for a higher purpose, or we can drug ourselves, run away, and let someone else deal with it. Giving birth is a microcosm of life. Just as in life we are often presented with opportunities, it's our choice to make the time and take advantage of them or not. Birth offers us the opportunity to strengthen our belief and trust in God. It offers us the opportunity to show how much we trust in Him that for example, we wish the process on others. He entrusted women with the challenge of birth. He trusts we will keep giving birth and bringing forth generation after generation.

—MIREL ORLOFSKY, CCE (BWI)

CHAPTER 29

Parenting

A person's wealth can be measured by the love of their children.

ANONYMOUS

G iving birth is one of the most beautiful experiences of a woman's life and offers the potential for tremendous personal growth. A good birth experience brings confidence and strength to a woman for her entire life and serves as a good foundation for parenting. Take for example the experience of Wendy. Wendy had a history of low self-confidence and self-esteem that affected her in school and in the job market. She met a wonderful man, married him, and they lived in an apartment in New York City. When pregnant, she went two weeks past her due date and was no longer allowed to give birth at the birthing center. After one meeting with the doctor at the back-up hospital, she knew she could not go there. So, at two and a half weeks past her due date, she found herself sitting in her apartment with no place to go for birth and no one to be with her.

She contacted me and I was able to find a wonderful midwife who was willing to accept her as a client. I also gave her the basics of Birth Works® training. She went into labor shortly thereafter. She had had no ultrasounds or medical procedures. She gave birth on hands and knees on the hospital bed without drugs or any procedures. The midwife used a fetascope to listen to the baby's heart rate. Wendy went on to give birth three more times with similar beautiful birth experiences. As the children grew and she had a chance to talk to more mothers, she realized not many women had had such beautiful births as her. To this day, she is a wonderful mother for her children.

Wendy's births were a turning point for her in her life and empowered her for the work of parenting. It was not only a transforming experience for her, but it also brought four children into the world with gentle births full of love and respect. Her children in turn have love and respect for their parents.

Love and respect for parents is universal and cross cultural, in all lands and all continents. We are born of parents and learn our first lessons from them. It is said that if you want to know whether or not to marry a man, look at his father. A man should look at his prospective wife's mother. We carry many traits from them whether we like it or not.

Parenting a child or children is one of the most important jobs that men and women will ever have, for they are entrusted with raising a confident and secure child who will be an asset to society as an adult. There are many books written about parenting and new parents are often confused as

to the right or wrong things to do when raising children. When presented with a problem, they are likely to revert back to the way in which they were parented by their mother and father, for what is experienced is familiar.

The primary emphasis in most schools is to provide an academic education, with a lesser emphasis on teaching values. But there is a difference in approach between teaching values versus believing they are already inside us and simply needing to be expressed. In this chapter, I will share with you some insights and information I have about good parenting skills based on values that I hope can help you become a better parent.

LEARNING BY IMITATION

There can be no stronger message about good parenting than realizing that we learn by experience and imitation. We are programmed to imitate and copy what we see, and this begins the moment we are born. Newborn babies intently study the faces of others and try to stick their tongue out, imitating their mother or father doing the same. As adults, we still carry facial expressions and body gestures from our parents. Even if a woman doesn't look like her mother, she will often act like her in mannerisms or expressions. This is true for men as well with their fathers or mothers.

EARLY LIFE EXPERIENCES

As a mother is the child's first teacher, she must understand that her behaviors and responses to situations are all being imitated by her child. In the womb, the baby "feels" her mother's emotions and hears her voice. She can also hear music being played in the room. A fetus is so connected to her mother on a cellular basis that she senses her moods and is already familiar with her food tastes by the time she is born. It should not be surprising then that a newborn baby already knows much about her mother just after she is born. When pregnant women are happy and thinking good thoughts, their children are more likely to be born with the same tendencies, because this is what they have experienced in the womb. These first experiences are powerful and have an effect on the baby through life into adulthood.

One way to have more positive thoughts is to avoiding watching or reading about violence during pregnancy and parenting after birth. Suppose a pregnant woman is fighting with her husband while pregnant. The fetus hears and feels this fighting. So now he is familiar with the feeling of fighting. As he grows, he has a fight with another child. Where do you think he learned to do this? His first experiences in the womb are the most powerful and a tendency toward violence has already been planted in his psyche. This may also have been reinforced by continued fighting of the parents after he was born. [1]

From the moment of birth, babies need as much closeness and intimacy as possible, for this gives a sense of safety and security. Crying and physical gestures are the baby's first means of

communication until the ability to speak words is developed. In the first days of life, crying helps a newborn to fully aerate his lungs. Babies cry to let us know when they are hungry, tired, or ill. When hungry, they can also be observed making gestures such as "rooting" with their mouths toward the breast for breastfeeding. Breastfeeding provides intimacy along with optimal nutrition for the baby, and babies often fall asleep on the breast. Holding and snuggling the baby, either sitting or walking around and patting her on the back, can help to calm her down. After 12 weeks, a baby begins to coo and make other kinds of sounds.

Babies often cry due to intestinal discomforts caused by a little gas perhaps preceding a bowel movement. You can help to relieve this by placing one hand lightly on top of his belly and one under his back. Hold them there for about five minutes, and feel warmth coming from one of your hands through the baby to your other hand underneath. Allow the baby's energy to move your hands very slowly, keeping contact with the soft skin while sending love through your hands.

When babies cry they are comforted by what feels safe and familiar. While in the womb, a baby hears the constant low hum of the sound of blood passing through major blood vessels of his mother's body. How interesting that the sound of the blood rushing through the mother's vessels sounds in some ways similar to a vacuum cleaner or the low hum of a car engine! Many mothers know that just turning on their vacuum cleaner, hair dryer, or going out for a car ride helps to calm their babies These have a calming effect because they are familiar sounds. Going for a walk in nature also has a calming effect on both the mother and baby. A change in environment may be just what is needed, and what better place to go than nature where all the human values can be found.

A mother is the child's first and most important teacher in life, and this begins in the womb. Babies are much wiser than we realize. This was shown in experiments by Dr. Anthony DeCasper with one- to two-day old infants.[2] At this age, mouth control is already very developed. He was able to demonstrate through a nipple in the mouth that an infant could quickly learn to control its environment by sucking at higher rates to a woman's voice or lower rates to a man's voice. Furthermore, these young infants were shown to have an immediate preference for their mother's own voice over that of other women, and by one week after birth, 80 percent showed a preference for their father's own voice over that of other men. The immediate preference for their mother's voice must be due to a fetus hearing her voice throughout pregnancy. In further experiments, it was determined that a fetus whose mother read the story *The Cat in the Hat* and the poem *The King, the Mice and the Cheese* during the last six and a half weeks of pregnancy was able to use sucking rates at three days of age to receive the story they wanted to hear.[3] You will be filled with wonder at the amazing talents of the newborn in one of my favorite books, *Your Amazing Newborn,* by Marshal and Phyllis Klaus.

Parents continue to be teachers for their children as they grow and become young adults, and during this time the children are observing them carefully. The mother is usually the baby's primary caretaker and he looks to her for food, sustenance, and nurturing. While parenting, we need to be more aware of what our children are learning from us. It works both ways. I often look at my

children as an extension of myself and learn about myself from them. If a child sees her mother smiling and singing, she feels that herself. If she sees and hears her complaining a lot, frowning, and stressed out, that that is what the child is learning. Young children are so innocent that sometimes it is simply a smile to their mother that can help the mother to relax and regain her composure.

Our children observe how we act and behave in certain situations. Are we telling the truth? Do we lose control of ourselves in stressful situations? Do we have a more positive or more negative outlook in life? Do we go to the church, mosque, temple, or synagogue? We are their role models for the day when they become parents. What children see in us as good, they will choose to keep when they themselves become parents. What they don't like, they will choose not to use. I started doing this when I was a young child. I remember one time, I must have been only about three or four years old, when my mother held my head under the bathtub faucet to wash soap out of my hair and I couldn't coordinate my breathing to get enough air. There were six children in my family and I can't imagine the stress she was under getting us all ready for bed. But at that moment, I resolved that someday when I was a mother I would never do that to my kids, and I never did.

TOUCHING

Touch is highly developed in newborns and they need lots of it. Gentle infant massage can soothe a crying baby. Massage is known to affect the baby physiologically by increasing its production of growth hormones and aiding the immune system. Massage relaxes the baby, helping him to sleep, and this gives the mother a chance for much needed sleep too. It is especially helpful for premature infants, actually resulting in weight gain so important to their survival. I massaged my children for many years just before bedtime. I don't believe we ever get too old for touching. My 85-year-old father goes for a weekly massage, and in spite of some short-term memory loss, he never forgets his appointment!

Holding the baby close to his mother's heart is soothing because he feels comforted by his mother's warmth and loving energy. Carrying a baby around in a car seat cannot give these comforting effects. Instead, using infant-carrying slings or front carriers helps a mother to be more in tune with her baby's signals and needs, giving him more security and eventual trust in the world. When held close to her body, he hears the familiar sound of her heartbeat from when he was in her womb. What is familiar feels safe. The closer he is held to his mother, the more responsive the mother will be to his needs and the more comfort he will feel. On my trip through developing countries of the world, I always saw women carrying their babies with them in slings or wraps and I also saw them nursing children well over three years old. This was so common that when I had my babies it felt natural to do the same

Depending on each woman's own personal circumstances, having a baby and caring for the baby (or babies in the case of twins/triplets) can be a very trying experience that continues as they grow older. Sleep schedules have changed and there are more mouths to feed, more clothes to clean,

and more issues to deal with, such as ear infections. Some parents think it will become easier as the children grow older, but they then enter the stage of chauffeuring children to activities such as sporting events and clubs or plays in which they have a role. It is hard to find a time when the whole family can sit and have a meal together.

A HAPPY HOME IS A GOOD HOME

Through all the ups and downs of parenting, if parents accept their responsibilities cheerfully and work to keep things in balance by making good choices, they will "juggle" schedules and events remembering that they are nurturing a family. They will seek ways to bring healthy learning experiences to their children so they can feel loved in whatever they do, and however good they are at what they do. A home where there is respect is a happy and good home. Really, it is love that matters. Stress interferes with the ability to feel love, so parents need to recognize this and work to make changes.

When you feel stressed during parenting or otherwise, take a step back for a moment and try the following suggestions to get back into balance again. Just following one or more of these suggestions can help put things back into perspective in a short time.

1. Become aware of your breathing. Maybe the baby is sick, or the third grader didn't get his homework in on time, or the teenager didn't get to play in a game or didn't get a part in the play, or finances are tight, or your husband or significant other has come home exhausted and there's been an argument between you both. At these times, become aware of your breathing. Work to slow it down.

2. Get a cup of tea or coffee, a glass of water, or whatever feels calming to you.

3. Go for a walk in nature. It will have a calming influence.

4. Work to put into practice the detachment concept, being a witness to what is happening so you can see it from another perspective.

5. Try to understand what is behind the actions of others. For example, if your husband or significant other has had little sleep the night before followed by a full day's work, patience may be short and critical words said. Remember that love as understanding is nonviolence. Work to see what is behind the words and actions.

6. Check your own words and actions and keep them positive. It will have a calming influence on you and the family.

7. Singing has a soothing effect on the brain and can dissipate stressful situations, especially in young children. Many children learn how to do things through song as melody and rhythm engage both sides of the brain. I used to make up songs about anything and everything with my children. We sang in the car. I sang them to sleep at night. We sang goofy songs where they would laugh, such as "Down by the bay, where the elephants go, back to my home, I dare not go, for if I do, my mother will say, 'Did you ever see a fish, wearing a dish, down

by the bay.'" And we would take turns making up silly verses. Young children who know how to talk like to sing opera. We did this especially in car trips where every word in the conversation was sung.

8. Reaffirm to yourself that you are a good mother and that you love your children and your family. Be an example to them of how it is possible to deal with stressful situations with equanimity. They won't forget it.

FAMILY INTIMACY

A family that has fun together and that communicates with love and respect is likely to have a feeling of intimacy. This is "fertile soil" for raising good children. There are a number of ways to bring more intimacy into the family.

1. Have family meetings. Once a week, it is healthy to all sit down together and express feelings, make decisions, and bring up issues that need to be discussed. It is a wonderful way for children to begin problem solving and to accept more responsibility.

2. Find times to just sit together and talk without having any agenda. My mother said that as she was growing up, she, her sister Mutz, and her Mama and Papa would sit out on the porch in the evenings talking into the early evening as the sky became dark. As she described this to me I felt an intimacy that was very special for her. That was before the time of television. Today, we are more likely to watch a movie together instead of just talking together. Maybe the time we say "No," to the television and "Yes," to being together, talking, or going for a walk will be what we remember most about growing up in the family.

3. Make time in your busy schedule to do something special with each child individually. A good time for this is on a birthday, or just picking a special day. Children will remember spending special time together with their parents all their lives.

CHANGING ROLES OF MEN AND WOMEN

Compounding the work of raising children is the fact that the intact nuclear family as we knew it even 50 years ago is changing. My aunt who is now in her late seventies was one of few women who went to college in her time. Most women stayed home with their children. Their job was to care for the children, clean, and cook. One time on the TV program *60 Minutes*, Andy Rooney went back through magazines to see which year they last showed a woman wearing an apron. I believe he said it was 1954.

Much has changed since then. Men and women are playing dual roles. Many women are working in outside jobs and professions and at the same time coming home to be mothers to their children and run the household, chauffer children to many activities, and cook and clean. A quick meal is often needed and fast-food chains are more popular than ever, serving foods high in sugar and

unhealthy saturated fats. The added income is helpful, and in single-parent families is essential, but the additional work responsibilities bring more stress. One study looked at how men felt about these changes. It found that fathers felt having to help with housework depressed marital equality, whereas wives felt it helped to improve marital equality.[4] Being a female, I'm not surprised.

Many fathers take off from work to take their children to doctor's visits, volunteer in the classroom, help to cook meals, take their children to sports practices and games, and help their children with their homework. Parenting has very much become a joint venture. But there are also many single moms and dads who try to work and parent alone, which can be very stressful.

As male and female roles have changed over the last 30 to 40 years, the nuclear family has been affected in some good ways and in other not so good ways. Some men, like my own brother-in-law, are stay-at-home dads, with their wives providing the primary income for the family. They are a healthy family. However, when both parents are working, someone else must help take care of their children. Daycare centers have become a big business. There are critics on both sides of the debate about whether one of the parents should stay home with their children or go back to work. Since the first five years lay the foundation for the rest of our lives, it is best that one of the parents stays home with their children at least during this time. But if this is not possible for financial or other reasons, the good thing to know is that children are amazingly resilient and adapt well to new situations. Whatever is going on in their parents' lives, the most significant predictor on how it affects the children in the short term seems to be the attitude of the parents.

WORKING MOTHERS

A woman can be a good mother while working on the job. She can think about ways to find work closer to home or in the home with flexible hours, or might even find a part-time job so she can spend more time with her family. Some careers are more demanding than others and women need to consider this before accepting a job, or returning to a job they had before the birth, so they don't allow too much stress to enter family life.

It is said that when a mother is happy, the whole family is happy. The mother as nurturer plays a central role in the family. If she plans to return to work at a new job, other things for her to consider before accepting it are the pension, benefits, insurance, 401Ks, IRAs and any other perks offered. A woman who feels the money would be good but that the additional responsibility would be too much for her and the family needs to consider what sacrifices she can make to keep things more in balance. Maybe it is a less expensive vacation, or making do with the car she has, or not putting in a swimming pool. When children know that they, and not money, are the priority in their parents' lives, they won't forget it.

For example, when my children were born, my husband and I had just returned from our world trip with our bank balance close to zero. We decided to take out loans to get him through medical school. I decided to stay home with the children because I knew I would never have this chance

again and I wanted to experience it fully. I have never regretted my decision and the loans were eventually paid off. When my children were in their early teens, they began to realize the sacrifice we had made and they said to us, "You made us a priority in your lives and sacrificed much for us; we will always take care of you." I was touched in my heart in a very deep way.

EFFECTS OF DIVORCE

However, there do seem to be long-term effects of parental separation from their children, as was shown in a study on "offspring divorce." When children did not live with either of their parents while growing up, they were found to have an increased incidence of divorce in their own lives as adults.[5] However, whenever there is a divorce, children usually spend part of the time with their mother and part of the time with their father, having two homes. Children grow up perceiving this simply as a way of life, and again the most important aspect is the attitude of the parents. If parents criticize each other in front of their children, the children feel torn about which parent to love more. When the parents are supportive and are seen to be friends with each other by their children, the children adapt and have fun wherever they go. Unfortunately, in today's world they don't find themselves alone and can relate with many of their school friends going through the same thing.

Many times, one parent (often the father, but not always) completely abandons the parental role and disappears. This is difficult not only for the remaining parent but especially for the children. As the children grow, they wonder why their mother or father deserted them and they may have feelings of abandonment.

An overall current projection by the National Center for Health Statistics is that about 40 percent of men and women who marry get separated or divorced within 15 years, with the average length of marriage being eight years. The study is based on the National Survey of Family Growth, a nationally representative sample of women age 15 to 44 in 1995.[6] About 10 percent of marriages seem to end up in divorce in the first five years, another 10 percent within ten years (cumulative 20 percent), reaching the 30 percent level after 18 years of marriage and the 40 percent level at 50 years of marriage.[7] The stresses of modern-day life often take parents to the brink of incompatibility and the situation worsens quickly if the child has a developmental difficulty.

OVEREXTENDED CHILDREN

We live in a day and age when parents feel pressured to give their children as many experiences in life as possible. Thus, they sign up their children for numerous activities with the expectation that they will excel in each one. It is hard for a parent not to compare his or her child with others in the class, and children feel these subtle pressures. With my own piano students, it is not uncommon for their piano lesson to be the third activity of the day. So the children have a full day of school, some with before and after school daycare starting at 6:30 A.M. and ending at 5:30 P.M., then a sport, next dance

or gymnastics, then a spiritual lesson through their place of worship, and they still have homework to do. One girl I used to teach just shut down completely and wouldn't do anything. The parents had no choice but to pull her out of all the activities. Even when my children were young, I signed my son up for soccer in second grade, believing that unless he had a lot of solid team experience in his early years, he wouldn't be able to compete to be on the team in high school. In those years we spent hours and hours at soccer games and tournaments.

I remember growing up in a small town in Pennsylvania called Huntingdon where we lived in the countryside. My days were spent walking amongst the flower gardens, riding my horse, having a campout with a friend up on the mountain, or helping my mother by picking green beans in the garden or arranging gladiola flowers. I realize now how lucky I was to have time to just "be" without the pressures of many organized group activities. Girl Scouts and piano lessons once a week were my only scheduled activities outside of school.

FEAR- VERSUS LOVE-BASED PARENTING

When communicating with our children (or anyone), our tone of voice is important. A consistent negative tone induces fear-based parenting with feelings of disrespect. A consistent positive tone induces love-based parenting and respect.

As parents, we need to become more aware of what we say and how we say it. So many parents are frustrated, saying, "My child won't listen to me!" One way to approach this problem is to become more aware of how we are talking to our children. For example, what if the mother or father is stressed, and in a typical day the child hears, "Don't run around!" or "Stop playing with your food," or "Stop whining!" or "You didn't do your homework yet!" What does the child hear? Negative, negative, negative. No wonder he isn't listening. What if instead the mother or father would say, "Could you please sit down for awhile?" or "Is your stomach full?" or "What is it that you need?" or "When are you planning to do your homework?" Now instead of hearing "Don't," "Stop," "Didn't," the child is hearing, "Please," "What is it?" and "When are you planning?"

When a child continually hears negative words in a commanding and criticizing tone of voice, he is likely to stop listening. He simply shuts it out because there is implied threat, fear, and failure. This is not empowering. Having the patience to say things more positively brings a feeling of safety and encourages more cooperation.

If we are judging and criticizing others, they will learn to do the same. Take a moment to look at yourself. Do you tend to have a negative outlook on life, always worrying about everything? Or do you tend to have a positive outlook on life, not afraid to meet life's challenges guided by your spirit? Whichever way you tend to be, this is what your children are learning and it is what they will bring to their adult lives. I love the following well-known poem about how children learn:

If a child lives with criticism, he learns to condemn.

If a child lives with hostility, he learns to fight.
If a child lives with ridicule, he learns to be shy.
If a child lives with shame, he learns to feel guilty.
If a child lives with tolerance, he learns to be patient.
If a child lives with encouragement, he learns confidence.
If a child lives with praise, he learns to appreciate.
If a child lives with fairness, he learns justice.
If a child lives with security, he learns to have faith.
If a child lives with approval, he learns to like himself.
If a child lives with acceptance, he learns to find love in the world.

—Dorothy Law Nolte

When parents love their children, the children will grow up feeling safe. They can feel love as praise and love as discipline. Boundaries are important, but if we carry out acts of violence through words or physical means, the children learn to do the same. It amazes me when I see mothers hitting their children to show them what it feels like when they hit others. And what do the children experience? They see their mother hitting so it must be okay to hit. Mothers are their primary role models. If they see their mothers becoming anxious and agitated about the little things in life, they will learn to do the same. All is reaction, reflection, and resound.

Some books dictate that holding babies too much spoils them. In fact, babies who are held constantly, especially in the first year of life, are more stable and confident as adults because in the early weeks of life their needs of feeling safe and secure were met. I don't believe a baby can be spoiled in the first year of life. There are many things parents have to sacrifice in their lives during these early years, but learning to do so joyfully is what raises healthy children. Our children were always welcome in our bed and eventually they simply grew out of it.

Have fun with your children. Believe me, someday they will be on their own, leading their own lives, and all the years with them will feel like they passed in the blink of an eye. These are special times you will never have again with your child. Be aware of how precious they are and enjoy them fully.

There are important stages of child-parent relationships that can serve as guidelines to raising children healthy in the mind, body, and spirit. I am describing a primary focus for each, but certainly there is overlap in all stages. Love is the foundation in all the stages for love as thought is truth, love as feeling is peace, love as understanding is nonviolence, and love in action is right action.

Birth to age 5: LOVE

From birth to five years old, love is the predominant factor needed for children. This is the time to really love, love, love your children. No matter what they do—if they are crying, moody, sick, fighting, or not listening—love them anyway. At this age, their minds are easily imprinted with experiences in life. If they experience love, then that will serve as the foundation. If love is missing at this time of life, they will learn not to have trust and faith in others and will grow into insecure adults. When a baby experiences respect from its earliest memories, it will enter the world a more confident person, able to grow into a mature adult who is not afraid of meeting challenges and overcoming them. He may seek positions of leadership and be a role model to others. The world desperately needs people like this now.

Ages 6 to 11: DISCIPLINE

Six to 11 is the age of discipline. Children need to be punished not only for safety reasons but also so they know their boundaries and limits. I believe in disciplining with love and brought up my children that way. This is a concept expressed as "Love and Law." I personally do not believe in spanking and never spanked my children. If I am to be a role model for them, and they see me hitting, then they will think it is okay to hit too. I cannot imagine hitting someone I love and my love for my children is so deep. Instead, they took "time out" in a chair and weren't allowed to get out of the chair until they told me what they did that was wrong. This was so effective that one day I saw my son sitting in the chair without my telling him to go there. I asked him why he was sitting there, and he proceeded to tell me what he did that was wrong.

0-5 years
LOVE

6-11 years
DISCIPLINE

12-16 years
CHARACTER

Human Values

17 years and on
FRIEND

STAGES OF PARENT-CHILD RELATIONSHIPS

Children need to know right from wrong. When they do something wrong, they need to receive punishment of some sort, but I believe this punishment should never inflict physical harm. I used to say to my children, "It's because I love you so much that I'm punishing you so you will grow up knowing right from wrong." When much love is shown, the child's punishment may even be feeling very badly about having disappointed his parents. The younger the child, the more immediate and short-term the punishment needs to be. Children, especially older ones, respond well to restrictions on things they like to do.

If children do not receive discipline at this age, there is a greater chance of rebellion as a teenager. The secret is to discipline with love. Some discipline is necessary in the earlier years too and it too should be carried out with love. Always tell children what they can do before what they can't do so that the focus is on the positive. With love, every child can learn right from wrong while feeling safe. This encourages communication with parents, teachers, and friends. Parents need to have abundant patience during this time and learn to talk to their children positively. A child who is not disciplined at this age loses a sense of boundaries and wanders lost in the world as an adult.

AGES 12 TO 16: CHARACTER

The ages of 12 to 16 is the age of character. These children want to know more about what is happening in the world and what they can do to help. They are questioning what they see and want to become part of the solution. It is an age when children are interested in social change and learning about lives of people who have a good legacy. They want to carry out service activities to help others and will become involved in projects in their schools and with religious programs that work for humanitarian relief. If there is love in the parental relationship, they will even want to do service in their homes. When character is not the focus during this age, the children lack a foundation for ideals to strive for and lose some of their purpose in life. Many of the projects they become a part of will give experiences that help develop career choices in college.

This is an age when parents need to have trust and faith in their children. The children at this stage are becoming much more independent and need to have the experience of making some of their own decisions. They love being praised for their good actions and accomplishments. If a child needs to be punished at this age, at least try to avoid doing so in front of his friends, for that is humiliating and deeply damages self-esteem. Children at this age are still tender souls and praise is needed instead of criticism so they can increase confidence in themselves.

AGES 17 TO ADULT: FRIENDSHIP

From age 17 on into adulthood is the time of friendship. At some point, even though our children will always be our children, they are grown up and the relationship needs to change to one of being friends, having mutual love and respect. There will be tremendous resistance treating an 18-year-

old like a child. Those who have their mother and father as their best friends through life truly are fortunate. This kind of relationship will be modeled by their children and their children to come.

When my daughter was 11, I sat down and talked with her. I told her that when we come into the world as babies, we are completely dependent on our mothers. Slowly, we test our limits to become more independent. It is important, I told her, because at some point she will need to be able to take care of herself. I told her gradually she will feel a need to test me and do things I wouldn't approve of and that when that happened, we should both realize why it was happening so we could laugh about it. Well, one day when she was about 16 years old, I found her eating cake before dinner, openly, right in front of me! I said, "We never do that in our family. That is dessert!" She kept on eating the cake anyway saying, "Mom, you really don't think I'll eat my dinner?" Then we both realized what was happening and laughed about it. Believe it or not, that was the most rebellion I ever experienced from her. With understanding, there is nonviolence, and we understood what was happening. I recommend highly having this talk with your children just before they become teenagers.

When she turned 14, I wrote a Rite of Passage ceremony that honored her entering the stage of womanhood. A copy of the ceremony is available from the Birth Works® International office for a nominal fee.

The importance of implementing the stages of parent-child relationships is that each lays the foundation for the next. Love, discipline, and character must all be present for a good friendship to evolve. I've met too many parents estranged from their children for various reasons. As parents age, there are issues of financial dependency, health, and the desire to still feel needed. This is happening at a time when our children are ready to go out on their own, in the prime of their lives. The world is open to them. They need independence to find themselves in this big world. But those who grow up in comfortable, loving, and safe homes love coming back to visit their families for they crave the warmth, memories, and intimacy that is in a loving family. A family that knows how to give the children wings so they can fly but still provide the roots of nurturing as they also age is a good family. Family gives children a sense of belonging that continues into adulthood.

I have developed the following steps to becoming a good parent that are a summary of what I remember doing instinctively as I raised my children, and which I believe lead to successful parenting. My children are in their twenties now and people often ask me, "What did you do? What was your secret?" I respond, "I brought them up with human values, a belief that they are special, and knowing that God had an important reason for them being here on the earth." Although they do have their ups and downs, I believe that they are very grounded and have motivation to contribute in a positive way to society and the world.

STEPS TO BECOMING A GOOD PARENT

1. Believe in the power of love and practice it. Remember, love is a verb. Believe that there is nothing that love can't heal.
2. Believe that the consciousness in you can be trusted and listen to it. Allow it to be your guide, just as you did when you were in labor.
3. Believe that your thoughts, words, and actions all affect the fetus as it grows in the womb. See only what is good. Hear only what is good. Do only what is good.
4. Believe that all that is taken in through the five senses is your "food." Feed your children good "food" by teaching them to see good, do good, and be good, and to eat healthily. Set an example yourself and explain why you are eating the foods you eat. This is educational.
5. Believe that all human values are born within you. Put the human values of truth, right action, peace, love, and nonviolence into practice. You will be a remarkable parent.
6. Discipline with love. Let love be your primary thought.
7. Praise your children and let them know they are special.
8. Always tell children what they can do before you tell them what they can't do. In other words, be positive and then teach them what they need to know.
9. Teach them how to place limits on their desires. Show them how to use their time, food, energy, and money wisely.
10. Have a respectful and loving relationship with your own parents. This is how your children may treat you some day.
11. Teach your children tolerance for those of other cultures and faiths.
12. Let your children follow their life dreams.
13. Spend time with your children before they go to sleep at night. With lights off, it is a good chance to talk about how they are feeling, what they need, or just to discuss something that happened that day that they want to talk about.
14. Make their friends welcome in your home.
15. Get them involved with activities early on that will help them build relationships with friends you consider good company.
16. Treat all your children with equal affection but parent them as individuals as each has different needs.
17. Do not quarrel in front of your children.
18. Be truthful to each other. Whatever you say, do it. They will learn to trust you.
19. Never lie to your children. They will learn to lie and they will lose friends.
20. Always take time to answer their questions.
21. Do not punish them in the presence of others. Humiliation cuts to the soul and causes deep wounds. The punishment must be immediate, however. Take him aside and trust your

inclination to either talk it out or leave space until emotions settle down. Only then will there be effective listening and communication.

22. Be constant in your moods and affections. If you can't, at least explain why. They will understand.

23. Keep close to your children. Give them hugs and tell them you love them over and over again. It is never too much.

24. Read to your children. Snuggling in bed each night and reading a story or a chapter of a longer book are times of intimacy that won't be forgotten. A few books I read to my children were *The Wind in the Willows*, *The Story of Heidi*, and *The Hobbit*.

25. Concentrate on their good points and not on their failures.

26. Encourage curiosity.

27. Exercise patience.

28. Limit the number of activities in which they are involved, especially as they grow older. Spreading them too thin decreases their time for creative play and puts them under too much stress with performance anxiety.

29. Find special times alone with your children such as a father and daughter going on "Indian Princess" trips or giving them a special trip on a special birthday. Being in a family of six children, my parents gave each of us one weekend alone with them on our thirteenth birthday.

30. Give the children a special day in which they can make the decisions about what they want to do. We did this with my children when they were young. One day I remember spending the entire day on the Wildwood boardwalk because that's what one of my children wanted to do.

31. Send them surprise packages at camp and do other things that make them feel special. This is still appropriate even when they go onto further schooling or college.

32. Cheerfully help them with their homework as needed to guide them through the process. Consider it special time together and praise them for good work that they do. In time, they won't need your help anymore.

33. One day your children will be ready to leave home and begin their own lives and your home will be an empty nest. Continue to stay in close touch with them. Accept the fact that they are developing into their own people just like you did, and that some of their ways may be different from yours, just like some of your ways were different from those of your mother and father. Love them anyway.

34. Love your children. Love them before they are born. Love them when they are babies. Love them as they grow up. Love them as teenagers. Love them as adults. Love them until the day you die. Love is all. And tell them you love them!

And all else will be given unto you.

Little One

Little one, precious treasure, miracle of life.
Little eyes, gazing into mine, what could they be saying.
Come to me, come to me, always be there when I need you
Care for me, care for me, let me know you love me too
Smile for me, whenever I'm sad
Smile for me, whenever I'm glad,
In easy times, in hard times, to eternity.
As I grow, see me changing, give me freedom to change.
As I mature, let decisions be mine, then I'll always be fine
It's okay, let me go, let me find my own way through life, but
Be my friend, be my guide, open your arms to me always
Life is a song, sing it with me
Life is a game, play it with me
In easy times, in hard times, to eternity.
Little one, precious treasure, miracle of life.

—From the CD "Believe" by Cathy Daub

CHAPTER 30

Improving Birth in America and Around the World

I don't know what your destiny will be, but one thing I know;
the only ones among you who will be really happy are
those who will have sought and found how to serve.

DR. ALBERT SCHWEITZER

There are a number of initiatives working to improve birth outcomes in America and abroad. Here I will give a brief overview of five of them: Healthy People 2010, the Coalition for Improving Maternity Services (CIMS), which also incorporates the World Health Organization WHO-UNICEF Ten Steps of the Baby Friendly Hospital Initiative, the Childbirth Connection, formerly known as the Maternity Center Association (MCA) and the Safe Motherhood Initiative (SMI). I've also included a poem by Mother Teresa who in her own way set an example of how each of us can make the world a better place in which to live, and a better place to birth as well.

HEALTHY PEOPLE 2010

The Healthy People 2010 co-lead agencies are the Centers for Disease Control and Prevention and the Health Resources and Services Administration. A report monitoring the progress of their goal to improve the health and well-being of women, infants, children, and families was published by the Morbidity and Mortality Weekly Report (MMWR) through a Pregnancy Risk Assessment Monitoring System (PRAMS).[1] Their objectives are to increase the quality and years of healthy life and to eliminate health disparities among people living in the United States through a range of objectives, eight of which are pregnancy intention, preventing physical abuse, reducing cigarette smoking during pregnancy, reducing drinking alcohol during pregnancy, cigarette smoking

cessation, breastfeeding initiation, encouraging multivitamin use, and teaching about good infant sleep positions. The first four represent maternal behaviors that have risks which are preventable:[2]

- *Pregnancy intention*: delayed prenatal care, poor maternal nutrition, alcohol use during pregnancy
- *Physical abuse*: increased risk for low birth weight and increased mortality and morbidity for mothers and infants
- *Cigarette smoking*: before delivery causes increased incidence of placenta previa, abruption placentae, preterm birth, low birth weight, and sudden infant death syndrome (SIDS), and after delivery means increased risk for respiratory tract infections
- *Alcohol consumption*: during pregnancy is associated with multiple birth defects including fetal alcohol syndrome (FAS), mental retardation, neurodevelopment disorders, and increased spontaneous abortion

The use of multivitamins is important so women can receive folic acid and reduce by 50 percent the incidence of neural tube defects (NDTs). The United States Public Health Service recommends that all women of childbearing age consume 400 ug of folic acid daily through supplements or fortified foods.[3]

Infant mortality is a marker of a nation's state of health, and worldwide it is an indicator of the health status and social well-being of any country. As of 1995, the U.S. ranked twenty-fifth for infant mortality amongst industrialized nations of the world.[4] A great disparity in the rates of infant mortality between whites and specific racial and ethnic groups persists, and although the overall infant mortality rate has reached record low levels, the rate for African-Americans remains twice that of whites.[5]

The results of PRAMS in 2003 showed variability in progress among the states monitored, with more progress being made in the areas of smoking cessation and infant sleep positions, and less progress made in achieving objectives of pregnancy intention and multivitamin use related to behaviors and experiences in the preconception period.

In April of 2006, PRAMS added nine additional sites for a total of 39 where data is being collected. This represents approximately 75 percent of all U.S. live births.

CIMS (COALITION FOR IMPROVING MATERNITY SERVICES)

The Coalition for Improving Maternity Services (CIMS and pronounced "kims") was established in 1966 to bring together a large number of professionals in the realm of childbirth, including midwives, birth and postpartum doulas, physicians, nurses, childbirth educators, lactation consultants, authors, and other maternity service providers. During its first five years, CIMS developed and reached a consensus on its evidence-based Mother-Friendly Childbirth Initiative (MFCI) with the purpose of identifying those birth sites, whether hospital, birthing center, or home birth services, which qualify to meet the ten steps for mother-friendly care.

Today, more than 90,000 birthing professionals have endorsed the MFCI and they represent a broad spectrum of organizations including the Midwives Alliance of North America (MANA), the Association for Pre- and Perinatal Psychology and Health (APPPAH), the American Collage of Nurse Midwives (ACNM), the Association of Women's Health, Obstetrical and Neo-Natal Nurses (AWHONN), Birth Works® International (BWI), Lamaze International, the International Childbirth Education Association (ICEA), The American Academy of Husband Coached Childbirth (the Bradley® Method), the Association of Labor Assistants & Childbirth Educators (ALACE), DONA International, La Leche League, Midwifery Today, and the International Lactation Consultants Association (ILCA). At the time of this writing, the only two birthing facilities that had been designated as mother and baby friendly have lost this status due to a change of doctors.

The CIMs Initiative is an important document that, when implemented in communities, will have pregnant women asking, "Are you a mother-baby friendly hospital?" If the answer is no, they may choose one that is. This is a powerful way to effect change in medical institutions. The CIMS Mother-Friendly Childbirth Initiative can be found in the Appendix on page 350.

THE WORLD HEALTH ORGANIZATION (WHO)

The World Health Organization, established in 1948, is the United Nations specialized agency for health. Its objective as set out in its Constitution is the attainment by all peoples of the highest possible level of health. Health is defined in WHO's Constitution as a state of complete physical, mental, and social well-being, and not merely the absence of disease or infirmity. It is governed by 193 Member States through the World Health Assembly, and the Health Assembly is composed of representatives from Member States.

Major health issues that WHO is concerned about range widely to all aspects of health for human beings from Avian Influenza to female genital mutilation (FGM) and the eradication of polio, malaria, and tuberculosis.[6] Two major health issues related to the health of mothers and their babies were added to their list for 2006: (1) New international growth standards, and (2) decreasing tobacco smoking. Regarding growth standards WHO states that, "Child growth up to the age of five is influenced by nutrition, feeding practices, environment, and health care rather than by genetics or ethnicity."[7]

For information on maternal and neonatal standards of care, visit:

http://www.who.int/making_pregnancy_safer/publications/standards/en/index.html/.

SAFE MOTHERHOOD INITIATIVE (SMI)

The Safe Motherhood Initiative is a global movement of activists, researchers, health experts, development professionals, and policy-makers that began at a 1987 conference in Nairobi, Kenya. Their goal was to decrease maternal deaths worldwide in half by the year 2000. Researchers

generated a wealth of studies, reports, publications, and fact sheets, and numerous national and regional conferences were held to raise awareness about safe motherhood and to identify priorities and define goals for action. Still, the Initiative reports that one woman dies every minute somewhere in the world from complications of pregnancy and childbirth with more than 530,000 needless deaths each year.[8]

CHILDBIRTH CONNECTION

Childbirth Connection, formerly Maternity Center Association, is a national non-profit organization founded in 1918 to reduce maternal and infant mortality. It has grown to be a nationally recognized advocacy organization with a mission to promote safe, effective, and satisfying maternity care for all women and their families through research, education, and advocacy. In 2006, Childbirth Connection released results of *Listening to Mothers II: The Second National U.S. Survey of Women's Childbearing Experiences,* in collaboration with Lamaze International. The survey was conducted by Harris Interactive and offers an unprecedented view of women's experiences giving birth in U.S. hospitals in 2005. The survey covers the time from planning pregnancy through the postpartum period and sheds light on women's attitudes, beliefs, preferences, and knowledge, as well as family and employment life and maternity care practices. This survey gave voice to those who care most about maternity care: mothers themselves. Policy makers, administrators, clinicians, educators, and others with responsibility for mothers and babies can use survey results to understand and improve childbirth practices and the quality of women's maternity experiences.

I would like to end my book with a quotation from Mother Teresa who devoted her life to spirituality, helping people from all castes and all religions. She believed that practicing values is the way to make change in the world. If everyone were to put her wisdom into practice, truly the world would be a better place in which to live, and birth would become the empowering, beautiful, and wondrous event that the spirit intended it to be.

Poem by Mother Teresa

People are often unreasonable, illogical, and self-centered;

…Forgive them anyway!

If you are kind, people may accuse you of selfish, ulterior motives;

…Be kind anyway!

If you are successful, you will win some false friends and some true enemies;

…Succeed anyway!

If you are honest and frank, people may cheat you;

…Be honest and frank anyway!

What you spend years building, someone could destroy overnight;

… Build anyway!

If you find serenity and happiness, they may be jealous;

…Be happy anyway!

The good you do today, people will often forget tomorrow;

…Do good anyway!

Give the world the best you have, and it may never be enough;

… Give the world the best you've got anyway!

You see, in the final analysis, it is between you and God;

…It was never between you and them anyway.

Endnotes

INTRODUCTION

1. Shy, K. K., Luthy, D. A., Bennett, F. C., Whitfield, M., Larson, E. B., van Belle, G., et al (1990). Effects of electronic fetal-heart-rate monitoring, as compared with periodic auscultation, on the neurologic development of premature infants. *New England Journal of Medicine*, 322, 588-593.
2. Declercq, E. R., Sakala, C., Corry, M. P. & Applebaum, S. (2006). *Listening to Mothers Survey II: Report of the Second National U.S. Survey of Women's Childbearing Experiences.* New York, NY: Childbirth Connection.
3. Hamilton, B. E., Martin, J. A. & Ventura, S. J. (2006). Births: Preliminary data for 2005. *National Vital Statistics Reports*, 55, 1-18.
4. Dosa, L. (2001). Caesarean section delivery, an increasingly popular option. *Bulletin of the World Health Organization*, 79, 1173-1173.
5. Wax, J. R., Cartin, A., Pinette, M. & Blackstone, J. (2004). Patient Choice Cesarean: An Evidence-Based Review. *Obstetrical and Gynecological Survey*, 59, 602.
6. Declercq E. R., Sakala, C., Corry, P., & Applebaum, S. (2006). *Listening to Mothers Survey II: Report of the Second National U.S. Survey of Women's Childbearing Experiences.* New York, NY: Childbirth Connection.
7. Ibid.
8. Ibid.
9. Goodman, P., Mackey, M. & Tavakoli, A. (2004). Factors related to childbirth satisfaction. *Journal of Advanced Nursing*, 46, 212-219.
10. Chopra, D. (1977). *The Path to Love* (p 286). New York, NY: Harmony Books.

CHAPTER 1

1. Morrison, P. & Morrison, P. (1982). *The Powers of Ten*. San Francisco, CA: W.H. Freeman and Company.
2. Kitzinger, S. (1986). *Being Born* (p 48). New York, NY: Grosset & Dunlap.
3. Ibid, p 51.

CHAPTER 2

1. Clay, K. *A Night on the Beach…with Some Busy Turtles.* Retrieved April 25, 2007 from http://www.cdnn.info/news/article/a041008.html.

CHAPTER 3

1. Definition of "spirit" (2003). In *The American Heritage Dictionary of the English Language, Fourth Edition*. Boston, MA: Houghton Mifflin Company.
2. Robinson, S. K. & Brown, A. (2003). *Spirituality and the Practice of Healthcare* (p 20-21). Basingstoke, UK: Palgrave Macmillan.
3. Blavatsky, H. P. (1889). *The Key to Theosophy* (p 90-93). Retrieved April 25, 2007 from http://www.theosociety.org/pasadena/key/key-hp.htm.
4. Willard, D. (1998). Spiritual disciplines, spiritual formation and the restoration of the soul. *Journal of Psychology and Theology*, 26, 101-109.
5. Definition of "spirit" (1966). In *Webster's Unabridged Dictionary*. Springfield, MA: G & C Merriam Company.
6. Jones, D. A. (2004). *The Soul of the Embryo* (p 21). London, UK: Continuum.
7. Eberl, J. T. (2000). The beginning of personhood: A Thomistic biological analysis. *Bioethics*, 14, 134-157.
8. Hall, J. (2006) Spirituality at the beginning of life. *Journal of Clinical Nursing*, 15, 805-810.
9. Stockley, S. (1986). Psychic and spiritual aspects of pregnancy, birth, and life. In R. Claxton (Ed.), *Birth Matters*. London, UK: Unwin Paperbacks.
10. Nursing and Midwifery Council (2004). *Standards of Proficiency For Pre-registration Midwifery Education*. London, UK: Nursing and Midwifery Council.
11. McGeary, K. (1994). The influence of guarding on the developing mother-unborn relationship. In Field, P. A. & Marck, P. B. (Eds.), *Uncertain Motherhood: Negotiating the Risks of the Childbearing Years*. London, UK: Sage Publishing.

CHAPTER 5

1. Harper, B. (1994). *Gentle Birth Choices* (p 6). Rochester, VT: Healing Arts Press.
2. Ibid, p 14.
3. Wax, J. R., Cartin, A., Pinette, M. G. & Blackstone, J. (2004). Patient Choice Cesarean: An Evidence-Based Review. *Obstetrical and Gynecological Survey*, 59, 601-616.
4. Ibid, p 603.
5. Ibid, p 603.
6. Saisto, T., Salmela-Aro, K., Nurmi, J. E., Konoen, T. & Halmesmaki, E. (2001). A randomized controlled trial of intervention in fear of childbirth. *Obstetrics and Gynecology*, 98, 820-826.
7. Schindi, M., Birner, P., Reingrabner, M., Journa, E. A., Hussiein, P. & Langer, M. (2003). Elective cesarean section vs spontaneous delivery: A comparative study of birth experience. *Acta Obstetricia et Gynecologica Scandinavica*, 82, 834-840.
8. Fenwick, J., Gamble, J. & Hauck, Y. (2006). Reframing birth: A consequence of cesarean section. *Journal of Advanced Nursing*, 56, 121-132.

9. Goer, H. (1999). *The Thinking Woman's Guide to a Better Birth* (p 246). New York, NY: The Berkley Publishing Group.

10. *Birth Works International Childbirth Educator Training Manual* (2006). Medford, NJ: Birth Works Press, p 238.

11. College of Physicians and Surgeons of Ontario (2001). *Reports from council. Home birth policy rescinded.* Toronto, Canada: CPSO.

12. Society of Obstetricians and Gynecologists of Canada (2003). Policy statement No 126. Midwifery. *Journal of Obstetrics and Gynaecology Canada*, 25, 5.

13. American Public Health Association (2002). 2001-3: Increasing access to out-of-hospital maternity care services through state-regulated and nationally-certified direct-entry midwives. *American Journal of Public Health* 92, 453-455.

14. ACOG Executive Board (2006). *Statement of Policy: Out of hospital births in the United States.* Washington, DC: American College of Obstetricians and Gynecologists.

15. Ackermann-Liebrich, U., Voegeli, T., Gunter-Witt, K., Kunz, I., Zullig, M., Schindler, C., et al. for the Zurich Study Team (1996). Home versus hospital deliveries: Follow up study of matched pairs for procedures and outcome. *British Medical Journal,* 313, 1313-1318.

16. Wiegers, T. A., Keirse, M. J. N. C., Zee, J. V. & Berghs, G. A. H. (1996). Outcome of planned home and planned hospital births in low risk pregnancies: Prospective study in midwifery practices in the Netherlands, *British Medical Journal*, 313, 1309-1313.

17. Johnson, K. C. & Daviss, B. (2005). Outcomes of planned home births with certified professional midwives: Large prospective study in North America, *British Medical Journal*, 330, 1416.

18. Schlenzka, P. (1999). Safety of alternative approaches to childbirth. Doctoral dissertation, Stanford University, 1999.

19. American Public Health Association (2002). 2001-3: Increasing access to out-of-hospital maternity care services through state-regulated and nationally-certified direct-entry midwives. *American Journal of Public Health*, 92, 453-455.

CHAPTER 6

1. *Baba Yaga- Witch, Crone and Archetype* (2002). Retrieved April 25, 2007 from http://www.bbc.co.uk/dna/h2g2/A823402. (*Vasilisa the Fair* and *Vasilisa the Wise,* two variations of Russian folktale, the Baba Yaga)

CHAPTER 7

1. Odent, M. (1999). *The Scientification of Love* (p 30, 112). London, UK: Free Association Books.

CHAPTER 8

1. Odent, M. (2004). *The Caesarean* (p 111-112). London, UK: Free Association Books.
2. Sathya Sai Baba (Sept. 1996). Discourse: India.
3. Northrup, C. (2003). From Conception to Birth. *Health Wisdom for Women*, 10 (7).
4. Beilin, Y., Bodian, C. A., Weiser, J., Hossain, S., Arnold, I., Feierman, D. E., et al (2005). Effect of labor epidural analgesia with and without fentanyl on infant breast-feeding: A prospective, randomized, double-blind study. *Anesthesiology*, 103, 1211-1217.

CHAPTER 9

1. Tsiaras, A. (2002), *From Conception to Birth* (p 6-7). New York, NH: Doubleday.
2. Ibid, p 7.
3. Ibid, p 7.
4. Ibid, p 232.
5. Nash, J. M. (1997 Feb 3) Fertile Minds. *Time*, 149 (5), 51.
6. Ibid, p 55.
7. Ibid, p 55.
8. Ibid, p56.
9. Ibid, p 51.
10. Ibid, p 51.
11. Mermer, C. A. (April 2000), Potential dangers of childbirth interventions. Early clamping of the umbilical cord: Cutting the ties that bind. PLACE OF PUBLICATION: *Townsend Letter for Doctors and Patients*.
12. Nash, J. M. (1997). Fertile Minds, *Time Magazine*, 149 (5), 54-55.
13. Raveill,G. P., Stein, Z. A. & Susser, M. W. (1976). Obesity in younger men after famine exposure in utero and early pregnancy, *New England Journal of Medicine*, 295, 349-390.
14. Jacobson, B. & Nyberg, K. (1990). Opiate addiction in adult offspring through possible imprinting after obstetric treatment. *British Medical Journal*, 301, 1067-1070.
15. Odent, M. (2002). *Primal Health* (p173), London, UK: Clairview Books.
16. Rizzolatti, G., Fogassi, L. & Gallese, V. (Nov 2006). Mirrors in the Mind. *Scientific American*, 54-61.
17. Rutter, M. (2005), Incidence of autism spectrum disorder: Changes over time and their meaning. *Acta Paediatrica*, 94, 2-15.
18. Chamberlain, D. B. (March 1998), The Prenatal Psyche: New Perspectives. Paper presented to the 3rd International Congress of the World Organization of Associations for Prenatal Education (OMAEP), Rome, Italy.

CHAPTER 10

1. Uvnas-Moberg, K. (2003). *The Oxytocin Factor* (p 65). Cambridge, MA: Da Capo Press.
2. Ibid, p 8.
3. Ibid, p 99.
4. Ibid, p 67.
5. [No authors listed] (1992). Oxytocin in maternal, sexual and social behaviors. Conference of the New York Academy of Sciences. Arlington, VA, May 19-22, 1991. *Annals of the New York Academy of Sciences*, 652, 1-492.
6. Uvnas-Moberg, K. (1989). Hormone release in relation to physiological and psychological changes in pregnant and breastfeeding women. In Van Hall, E. V. & Everaerd, W. (Eds.), *Women's Health in the 1990s*. Carnforth, UK: Parthenon.
7. Kennell, J. H. & Klaus, M. H. (1998). Bonding: Recent observations that alter perinatal care. *Pediatrics in Review*, 19(1), 7.
8. Odent, M. (1999). *The Scientification of Love* (p 35). London, UK: Free Association Books.
9. Ibid, p 93.
10. Steingraber, S. (2001). *Having Faith* (p 180). Cambridge, MA: Perseus Publishing.
11. Gaskin, I. M. (2003). *Ina May's Guide to Childbirth* (p 179). New York, NY: Bantam Books.
12. Ibid, p 172.
13. Declercq, E. R., Sakala, C., Corry, P. & Applebaum, S. (2006). *Listening to Mothers Survey II: Report of the Second National U.S. Survey of Women's Childbearing Experiences.* New York, NY: Childbirth Connection.
14. Odent, M. (1999). *The Scientification of Love* (p 30). London, UK: Free Association Books.
15. Ibid, p 30.
16. Shapiro B.A., Harrison R.A., Walton J.R., (1977) Clinical Application of Blood Gases, second edition, (p 81-83). Chicago, IL, Year Book Medical Publishers, Inc.
17. Klaus, M. verbal communication, *Birth Works International*
18. Odent, M. (1999). *The Scientification of Love* (p 32-33). London, UK: Free Association Books.
19. Ibid, p 29-32.
20. Johnson, J., & Odent, M. (1995). *We Are All Water Babies* (p 56-60). Berkeley, CA: Celestial Arts Publishing.

CHAPTER 11

1. The Five Human Sheaths (2005). Retrieved April 25, 2007 from http://www.yogawiz.com/yoga-therapy/the-five-sheaths.html.
2. Baba, S. S. (1977). Summer Course, 6/16/77. *Sathya Sai Speaks* 10 (23), 146-148.

3. Bentov, I. (1988). *Stalking the Wild Pendulum* (p 29). Rochester, NH: Destiny Books.

4. Ibid, p 24.

CHAPTER 12

1. Tsiaras, A. (2002). *From Conception to Birth* (p 124). New York, NY: Doubleday.

2. Ferrel, F. (Producer), & Paul, D. (Director). (2007). *Birth Day* [Motion Picture]. (Available from www.homebirthvideos.com)

CHAPTER 13

1. Gladwell, M. (2005). *Blink* (p 14). New York, NY: Little Brown and Company.

2. Ibid, p 23.

3. Wilson, T. D. (2004). *Strangers to Ourselves*. Cambridge, MA: Harvard University Press.

4. Gaskin, I. M. (2003). *Ina May's Guide to Childbirth* (p 149), New York, NY: Bantam Books.

5. Davis-Floyd, R. & Arvidson, P. S. (Eds.). (1997). *Intuition, A Collaborative Project of the Academy of Consciousness Studies, Princeton University* (p 157). New York, NY: Routledge.

6. Ibid, p 162.

7. Ibid, p 163-164.

8. Ibid, p 166.

CHAPTER 14

1. Cutler, H. C. & His Holiness the Dalai Lama (1998). *The Art of Happiness* (p 195). New York, NY: Riverbead Books.

2. McCullough, M. (2005, March 20), More women turn to cesarean section. *The Philadelphia Inquirer.*

3. Hamilton, B. E., Martin, J. A. & Ventura, S. J. (2006). Births: Preliminary data for 2005. *National Vital Statistics Reports*, 55, 1-18.

4. Students in the Associate Degree of Nursing program at Hawaii Community (Sept 2005). *College Chinese Cultural Beliefs*. Retrieved April 25, 2007 from http://www.hawcc.hawaii.edu/nursing/RNChinese02.html

5. Lefeber, Y. & Voorhoever, H. (1997). Practices and beliefs of traditional birth attendants: Lessons for obstetrics in the north? *Tropical Medicine and International Health*, 2, 1175-1179.

6. Traditional Health Beliefs, Hispanic: Pregnancy and Childbirth, Transcultural Index, updated October 2005. Retrieved April 25, 2007 from http://www.hawcc.hawaii.edu/nursing/RNHispanic_04.html

7. Wetzel, L. & Huong, J. (July 2005). *Cambodian Cultural Profile*. University of Washington Harborview Medical Center, Retrieved April 25, 2007 from http://ethnomed.org/cultures/cambodian/camb_cp.html

8. Abu-Rabia, A. (Dec 2005). The evil eye and cultural beliefs among the Bedouin tribes of the Negev, Middle East, Folklore, Retrieved April 25, 2007 from http://www.findarticles.com/p/articles/mi_m2386/is_3_116/ai_n15924428/pg_7

9. Bhungalia, S., Kelly, T., Van De Keift, S., & Young, M. Indian Health Care Beliefs and Practices. Retrieved April 25, 2007 from http://www3.baylor.edu/~Charles_Kemp/indian_health.htm.

CHAPTER 15

1. Sutton, J. (2001). *Let Birth Be Born Again* (p 35). London, UK: Birth Concepts.

2. Ibid.

CHAPTER 16

1. Somer, E. (1999). *Food and Mood* (p 194). New York, NY: Henry Holt and Company.

2. [No authors listed]. (Nov 2006). Are You D Deficient? Nutrition Action Health Letter. *Center for Science in the Public Interest*, 33 (9).

3. Kantrowitz, B. & Kalb, C. (2006, March 13). Diet Hype: Food News Blues, *Newsweek*, 44.

4. [No authors listed]. (Dec 2006). The Devil Made Us Ignore That Nutrition Label! *Tufts University, Health & Nutrition Letter*, 24 (8), 4.

5. Schlosser, E. (2002). *Fast Food Nation* (p 7). Boston, MA: Houghton Mifflin Company.

6. Jacobson M.F., (Mar 2006). Trans Traps. *Nutrition Action Health Letter.* 33 (22), 10-11.

7. Mozaffarian, D., Katan, M. B., Ascherio, A., Stampfer, M. J., & Willett, W. C. (2006). Trans fatty acids and cardiovascular disease. *The New England journal of medicine, 354*(15), 1601-1613.

8. Somer, E. (1999). *Food & Mood: The Complete Guide to Eating Well and Feeling Your Best* (p 179). New York, NY: Henry Holt and Company.

9. Srinivasan, M., Katewa, S. D., Palaniyappan, A., Pandya, J. D. & Patel, M. S. (2006). Maternal high-fat diet consumption results in fetal malprogramming predisposing to the onset of metabolic syndrome-like phenotype in adulthood, *American Journal of Physiology. Endocrinology and Metabolism*, 291, E792-2799.

10. Napoli, C., D'Armiento, F. P., Mancini, F. P., Postiglione, A., Witztum, J., Palumbo, G., et al. (1997). Fatty Streak Formation Occurs in Human Fetal Aortas and is Greatly Enhanced by Maternal Hypercholesterolemia. *Journal of Clinical Investigations,* 100, 2680-2690.

11. Schlosser, E. (2002). *Fast Food Nation* (p 240). Boston, MA: Houghton Mifflin Company.

12. Kapoor, R. & Shrivastava, S. (2002). Prevention of coronary artery disease from childhood. *Indian Heart Journal*, 54, 726-730.

13. Asher, P. (1966). Fat babies and fat children. The prognosis of obesity in the very young. *Archives of Disease in Childhood*, 41, 672-673.

14. Ekelund, U., Ong, K., Linne, Y., Neovius, M., Brage, S., Dunger, D. B., et al. (2006). Upward

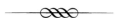

weight percentile crossing in infancy and early childhood independently predicts fat mass in young adults: The Stockholm Weight Development Study (SWEDES). *The American Journal of Clinical Nutrition*, 83, 324-330.

15. Armitage, J. A., Khan, I. Y., Taylor, P. D., Nathanielsz, P. W. & Poston, L. (2004). Developmental programming of the metabolic syndrome by maternal nutritional imbalance: How strong is the evidence from experimental models in mammals? *The Journal of Physiology*, 561, 355.

16. Price, J. H. (2000, January 30). Fat Chance: The Government's War on Obesity, *Washington Post*.

17. Schlosser, E. (2002). *Fast Food Nation* (p 242). Boston, MA: Houghton Mifflin Company.

18. Ibid, p 243.

19. Liebman, B. & Schardt, D. (Jan-Feb 2001). Diet & Health: Ten Megatrends. *Nutrition Action Health Letter*, p 4.

20. Liebman, B. (Nov 1998). Sugar, the Sweetening of the American Diet. *Nutrition Action Health Letter*, 25 (9), p 5.

21. Ibid, p 4.

22. Schlosser, E. (2002). *Fast Food Nation* (p 54). Boston, MA: Houghton Mifflin Company.

23. Ibid.

24. Ibid.

25. Jiang, R., Manson, J. E., Stampfer, M. J., Liu, S., Willett, W. C. & Hu, F. B. (2002). Nut and Peanut Butter Consumption and Risk of Type 2 Diabetes in Women. *Journal of the American Medical Association*, 288, 2554-2560.

26. Jacobson, M.F., (Dec 2006). Fear of Fresh. *Nutrition Action Health Letter*, 33 (10).

27. From the School of Public Health, (May 1998). Are fruits and vegetables less nutritious today? *University of California, Berkeley Wellness Letter*, p 1.

28. Whole Foods Market:Company, Whole Foods Market Offers Heart-Friendly Food Ideas for Heart Health Month, Retrieved April 25, 2007 from http://www.wholefoodsmarket.com//company/pr_02-01-05.html

29. Klausner, A., From Avocados to Yogurt: 15 Super Foods for Super Health, (2004 April). 27: Issue 4, Environmental Nutrition

30. Underwood, A. (Sep 2002). Eat Your Color. *Health*, 126-129.

31. Environmental Protection Agency. Should I Eat the Fish I Catch? A guide to healthy eating of fish you catch. Retrieved April 25, 2007 from www.epa.gov/ost/fish (or call 1-800-490-9198 and request document number EPA 823-B-97-009).

32. Chen, L. & Nyomba, B. L. (2003). Effects of prenatal alcohol exposure on glucose tolerance in the rat offspring, *Metabolism*, 52, 454-462.

33. Ramsey, D. S., Bendersky, M. I. & Lewis, M. (1996). Effect of prenatal alcohol and cigarette exposure on two and six-month-old infants' adrenocortical reactivity to stress. *Journal of Pediatric Psychology*, 21, 833-840.

34. Chen, L. & Nyomba, B. L. (2003). Effects of prenatal alcohol exposure on glucose tolerance in the rat offspring, *Metabolism*, 52, 454-462.

35. Higdon, J. V. & Frei, B. (2006). Coffee and health: A review of recent human research. *Critical Reviews in Food Science and Nutrition*, 46, 101-123.

36. Franklin D: The healthiest women in the world. *Health* 9:57-63, 1996

37. Daub, H. & Daub, C. (2000). *Common Sense Nutrition*. Medford, NJ: Birth Works Press.

CHAPTER 17

1. Sharma, S. & Franco, R. (2004). Sleep and Its Disorders in Pregnancy. *Wisconsin Medical Journal*, 103 (5), 48.

2. Dement, W. C. & Vaughn, C. (1999). *The Promise of Sleep* (p 3-4). New York, NY: Dell Publishing.

3. Ibid, p 229.

4. Ibid, p 230.

5. Ibid, p 54.

6. Ibid, p 9.

7. Ibid, p 72.

8. Ibid, p 75.

9. Langone, J. (2000). The Mystery of Time. *National Geographic*, Ch 1 Cycles of Nature, p 61.

10. Dement, W. C. & Vaughn, C. (1999). *The Promise of Sleep* (p 76). New York, NY: Dell Publishing.

11. Ibid, p 96.

12. Sharma, S. & Franco, R. (2004). Sleep and Its Disorders in Pregnancy. *Wisconsin Medical Journal*, 103 (5), 48.

13. Ibid, p 48.

14. Dement, W. C. & Vaughn, C. (1999). *The Promise of Sleep* (p 104). New York, NY: Dell Publishing.

15. Ibid, p 107.

16. Ibid, p 107-108.

17. Klaus M.H., Klaus P.H.,(1998) Amazing Talents of the Newborn, (p 23), Reading, MA: Perseus Books.

18. Dement, W. C. & Vaughn, C. (1999). *The Promise of Sleep* (p 253). New York, NY: Dell Publishing.

19. Cornwell, A. C. & Feigenbaum, P. (2006). Sleep biological rhythms in normal infants and those at high risk for SIDS, *Chronobiology International*, 23, 935-961.

20. Dement, W. C. & Vaughn, C. (1999). *The Promise of Sleep* (p 253-256). New York, NY: Dell Publishing.

21. Kennell, J. H. & Klaus, M. H. (1998). Bonding: Recent observations that alter perinatal care. *Pediatrics in Review*, 19, 7.

22. Dement, W. C. & Vaughn, C. (1999). *The Promise of Sleep* (p 374). New York, NY: Dell Publishing.

23. Jones, M. W. (2004). Supine and Prone Infant Positioning: A Winning Combination, *The Journal of Perinatal Education*. 13 (1), 10-20.

24. Dement, W. C. & Vaughn, C. (1999). *The Promise of Sleep* (p 111). New York, NY: Dell Publishing.

25. Ibid, p 408.

26. Smaldone, A., Honig, J. C. & Byrne, M. W. (2007). Sleepless in America: Inadequate sleep and relationships to health and well-being of our nation's children. *Pediatrics*, 119 (Suppl 1), 529-537.

27. Spiegel, K., Leproult, R., & Van Cauter, E. (1999). Impact of sleep debt on metabolic and endocrine function. *Lancet*, 354, 1435-1439.

28. Cornwell, A. C. & Feigenbaum, P. (2006). Sleep biological rhythms in normal infants and those at high risk for SIDS, *Chronobiology International*, 23, 935-961.

CHAPTER 18

1. Alexander, C. N. (1992). Peaceful Body, Peaceful Mind, Peaceful World, Modern Science and Vedic Science, Volume 5, Numbers 1-2, 1992 Maharishi International University,

2. Ibid, p 3.

3. Bishop, J.P. (2003). Prayer, science, and the moral life of medicine. *Archives of Internal Medicine*, 163, 1405-1408.

CHAPTER 19

1. Peterson, G. & Mehl, L. (1984). *Pregnancy as Healing* (p 155), Berkeley, CA: Mindbody Press.

2. McGlade, M. S., Saha, S., & Dahistrom, M. A. (2004). The Latina paradox: An opportunity for restructuring prenatal care delivery. *American Journal of Public Health,* 94, 2062-2065.

3. Ornish, D. (1977). *Love and Survival* (p 19). New York, NY: Harper Collins.

4. Moberg, K. U. (2003). *The Oxytocin Factor* (p 99). Cambridge, MA: Da Capo Press.

5. Ibid, p 99.

6. Odent, M. (2004). *The Caesarean* (p 67). London, UK: Free Association Books.

7. Nissen, E., Uvnas-Moberg, K., Svensson, K., Stock, S., Widstrom, A. M. & Winberg, J. (1996). Different patterns of oxytocin, prolactin but not cortisol release during breastfeeding in women delivered by caesarean section or by the vaginal route. *Early Human Development*, 5, 103-118.

8. Moberg, K. U. (2003). *The Oxytocin Factor* (p 48). Cambridge, MA: Da Capo Press.

9. Ibid, p 176.

10. Odent, M. (2002). *Primal Health* (p 176). London, UK: Clairview Books.

11. Ibid, p 42.

12. Declercq, E. R., Sakala, C., Corry, M. P. & Applebaum, S. (2006). *Listening to Mothers Survey II: Report of the Second National U.S. Survey of Women's Childbearing Experiences.* New York: Childbirth Connection.

13. Boudarene, M., Legros, J. J. & Timsit-Berthier, M. (2002). Study of stress response: Role of anxiety, cortisol, and DHEAs. *Encephale, 28,* 139-146.

14. Enkin, M., (2000). *A Guide to Effective Care in Pregnancy and Childbirth, Third Edition* (p 367). New York, NY: Oxford University Press.

15. Ornish, D. (1977). *Love and Survival* (p 14). New York, NY: Harper Collins.

CHAPTER 20

1. Ornish, D. (1977). *Love and Survival* (p 15). New York, NY: Harper Collins.

CHAPTER 21

1. Bentov, I. (1988). *Stalking the Wild Pendulum* (p 32). Rochester, VT: Destiny Books.

CHAPTER 22

1. Krystal, P. (1993). *Cutting the Ties That Bind,* York Beach, ME: Samuel Weiser Inc.

CHAPTER 23

1. Ornish, D. (1977). *Love and Survival.* New York, NY: Harper Collins.

2. Russek, L. G., & Schwartz, G. E. (1997). Perceptions of parental caring predict health status in midlife: A 35 year follow-up of the Harvard Mastery of Stress Study. *Psychosomatic Medicine, 59,* 144-149.

3. Funkenstein, D., King, S., & Drolette, M. (1957). *Mastery of Stress.* Cambridge, MA: Harvard University Press.

4. Ornish, D. (1977). *Love and Survival* (p 35). New York, NY: Harper Collins.

5. Ibid.

6. Thomas, C. B., & Duszynski, K. R. (1974). Closeness to parents and the family constellation in a prospective study of five disease states: Suicide, mental illness, malignant tumor, hypertension, and coronary heart disease. *Johns Hopkins Medical Journal,* 134, 251.

7. Ornish, D. (1977). *Love and Survival* (p 36). New York, NY: Harper Collins.

CHAPTER 24

1. Ornish, D. (1998). *Love and Survival* (p 2-3). New York, NY: Harper Collins.

2. Definition of "love". In Wikipedia, The Free Encyclopedia, Retrieved April 25, 2007 from http://en.wikipedia.org/wiki/Love.

3. Chopra, D. (1997). *The Path of Love* (p 49). New York, NY: Harmony Books.

4. Odent, M. (1999). *The Scientification of Love.* New York, NY: Free Association Books.

5. Moberg, K. U. (2003). *The Oxytocin Factor.* Cambridge, MA: Da Capo Press.

6. Chopra, D. (1997). *The Path of Love.* New York, NY: Harmony Books.

7. Kitzinger, S. (2000). Rediscovering Birth. New York, NY: Pocket Books.

8. Gaskin, I. M. (2003). *Ina May's Guide to Childbirth.* New York, NY: Bantam Books.

9. Ibid, p 51.

10. Hicks, E. & Hicks, J. (2004). *Ask and It Is Given.* Carlsbad, CA: Hay House, Inc.

11. Moberg, K. U. (2000). *The Oxytocin Factor* (p 53-103). Cambridge, MA: Da Capo Press.

12. Ibid, p 80.

13. Northrup, C. (2004). Creating your own health. [Audio Tape].

14. Gibran, K. (2003). *The Prophet* (p 12). Surrey, UK: Merchant Book Company Ltd.

15. Ibid, p 10.

CHAPTER 26

1. Kelley, K. W. (1988). *The Home Planet,* New York, NY: Addison-Wesley Publishing Company.

2. Ibid, p.10

3. Ibid.

4. Odent, M. (2004), *The Caesarean* (p 22), London, UK: Free Association Books.

CHAPTER 28

1. Langone, J. (2000). *The Mystery of Time* (p 9). Washington, DC: National Geographic.

2. Ibid, p 47.

3. Ibid, p 61-64.

4. Bentov, I. (1988). *Stalking the Wild Pendulum* (p 30). Rochester, VT: Destiny Books.

5. Gauquelin, M. (1983). *Birth Times.* New York, NY: Hill and Wang.

6. Ibid, p 13.

7. Ibid, p 19.

8. Ibid, p 21.

9. Ibid, p 24.

10. Ibid, p 27.

11. Ibid, p 32.

12. Ibid, p 43.

13. Ibid, p 46.

14. Ibid, p 46.
15. Ibid, p 58.
16. Ibid, p 63.
17. Ibid, p 78.
18. Ibid, p 78.
19. Ibid, p 116.
20. Ibid, p 126.
21. Ibid, p 158.
22. Ibid, p 129.
23. Ibid, p 144.
24. Ibid, p 144.
25. Professor Robert Debre, France-Soir, (1975 April 12). Retrieved from p145 Birth Times by Gauquelin)
26. Liggins G.C.(1971, October 25). The Baby's Role in Timing Birth. *Medical News Tribune.* Auckland University, New Zealand. Retrieved from p 145 Birth Times by Gauquelin.
27. Ibid.
28. Macfarlane, A., (1977) The Psychology of Childbirth. Cambridge, MA: Harvard University Press.
29. Malek, J., Gleich, J., & Maly, V. (1962). Characteristics of the daily rhythm of menstruation and labor. *Annals of the New York Academy of Sciences,* 98, 1042.
30. Gauquelin, M. (1983). *Birth Times* (p 164). New York, NY: Hill and Wang.
31. Ibid.
32. Gauquelin, M. & Gauquelin, F. (1976). Replication of the Planetary Effect in Heredity. In *Cosmic Influences on Human Behaviour.* London, UK: Futura.
33. Gauquelin, M. (1983). *Birth Times* (p 170). New York, NY: Hill and Wang.
34. Sureau, C. (1978). Comment naitre sans danger. *Parents* 118, Retrieved from p 169 Birth Times by Gauquelin)
35. Laing, R. D. (1977). *The Facts of Life* (p 64). London, UK: Penguin Books.
36. Leboyer, F. (1975). *Birth without Violence,* New York, NY: Knopf.
37. Kloosterman, G. J. (1972). Obstetrics in the Netherlands: A survival challenge? 50th Anniversary of the International Confederation of Midwives.
38. Kelley, T. (2007, March 15). New Jersey Assembly Considers Legislation on Autism, Seen as Prevalent in the State. *New York Times.*

CHAPTER 29

1. Jumsai, A. (1999). Parenting Conference, India [Lecture].
2. DeCasper, A. J. & Fifer, W. P. (1980). Of human bonding: Newborns prefer their mothers' voices. *Science* 208, 1174-1176.

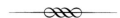

3. Klaus, M. J. & Klaus, P. H. (1998). *Your Amazing Newborn* (p 47). Reading, MA: Perseus Books.

4. Amato, P. R., Johnson, D. R., Booth, A. & Rogers, S. (2003). Continuing changes in marital quality between 1980 and 2000. *Journal of Marriage and Family*, 65,1-22.

5. Teachman, J. D. (2002). Childhood living arrangements and the intergenerational transmission of divorce. *Journal of Marriage and Family*, 64, 717–729.

6. Bramlett, M., & Mosher, W. (YEAR). *First marriage dissolution, divorce, and remarriage: United States. Advance Data From Vital and Health Statistics*; No.323. Hyattsville, MD: National Center for Health Statistics, 21.

7. Kreider, R. M. & Fields, J. M. (Feb 2002). *Number, timing, and duration of marriages and divorces: 1996* (p 18). U.S. Census Bureau Current Population Reports.

CHAPTER 30

1. Suellentrop, K., Morrow, B., Williams L. & D'Angelo, D. (2006). Monitoring Progress Toward Achieving Maternal and Infant Healthy People 2010 Objectives – 19 States, Pregnancy Risk Assessment Monitoring System (PRAMS), 2000-2003. Morbidity and Mortality Weekly Report (MMWR). 55, SS-9.

2. Ibid, p 2.

3. Center for Disease Control (1992). *Recommendations for the use of folic acid to reduce the number of cases of spina bifida and other neural tube defects*. Morbidity and Mortality Weekly Report (MMWR) 41, RR-14.

4. National Center for Health Statistics (1999). *Health*, Hyattsville, MD: U.S. Department of Health and Human Services.

5. Ventura, S. J., Anderson, R. N., Martin, J. A., et al. (1999). Births and deaths: Preliminary data for 1997. *National Vital Statistics Report*, 47(4), 1-42.

6. World Health Organization. Retrieved April 25, 2007 from info@who.int.

7. Ibid.

8. Safe Motherhood Initiative, http://www.womendeliver.org

Appendix

RESOURCE AND SUPPORT ORGANIZATIONS FOR CHILDBIRTH

BEDREST

Sidelines National Support Network
PO Box 1808
Laguna Beach, CA 92652
www.sidelines.org

BREASTFEEDING

The International Board of Lactation Consultant
    Examiners (IBLCE)
Suite 300
7309 Arlington Blvd
Falls Church, VA 22042-3215 USA
www.iblce.org

The International Lactation Consultant Association
    (ILCA)
Suite 102
1500 Sunday Drive
Raleigh, NC 27607
http://users.erols.com/ilca

La Leche League International
1400 N. Meacham Road
PO Box 4079
Schaumburg, IL 60173
847-519-7730
800-LALECHE
www.lalecheleague.org

BIRTH CENTERS

The National Association of Childbearing Centers/
    Birth Centers Online (NACC)
3123 Gottschall Road
Perkiomenville, PA 18074-9546
www.birthcenters.org

CHILDBIRTH EDUCATION AND DOULAS

Birth Works® International
PO Box 2045
Medford, NJ 08055
1-888-TO BIRTH(862-4784
www.birthworks.org

Association of Labor Assistants and Childbirth
    Educators (ALACE)
PO Box 382724
Cambridge, MA 02238-2724
888-222-5223
www.alace.org

HypnoBirthing Institute
PO Box 810
Epsom, NH 03234
603-798-4781
www.hypnobirthing.com

The Bradley Method of Natural Childbirth
PO Box 5224 Sherman Oaks, CA 91413-5224
1-800 4-A-Birth
www.bradleybirth.com

Birthing from Within
PO Box 4528
Albuquerque, NM 87196
505-254-4884
www.birthingfromwithin.com

Lamaze International
1200 19th St. NW, Suite 300
Washington, DC 20036-2422
202-857-1128
www.lamaze-childbirth.com

ICEA
PO Box 20048
Minneapolis, MN 55420
612-854-8660
www.icea.org

Childbirth Enhancement Foundation
1004 George Ave.
Rockledge, FL 32955
321-631-9977
www.cefcares.org

DONA International
1100 23rd Ave. East
Seattle, WA 98112
801-756-7331
www.DONA.org

CIRCUMCISION

Circumcision Resource Center
PO Box 232
Boston, MA 02133
www.circumcision.org

National Organization of Circumcision Information
    Resource Centers (NOCIRC)
PO Box 2512
San Anselmo, CA 94979-2512
www.nocirc.org

FERTILITY/INFERTILITY

RESOLVE The National Infertility Association
1310 Broadway
Somerville, MA 02144
www.resolve.org

GAY AND LESBIAN PARENTING SUPPORT

Family Pride Coalition
PO Box 34337
San Diego, CA 92163
www.familypride.org

GRIEF AND LOSS SUPPORT

The National Association of Childbearing Centers/
    Birth
The Compassionate Friends (TCF) Inc.
PO Box 3696
Oak Brock, IL 60522
www.compassionatefriends.org

SHARE Pregnancy and Infant Loss Support, Inc.
St. Joseph Health Center
300 First Capitol Drive
St. Charles, MO 63301-2893
www.NationalSharecE.com

MIDWIFERY

American College of Nurse Midwives (ACNM)
818 Connecticut Avenue, NW, Ste. 900
Washington, D.C. 20006
www.midwife.org

Citizens for Midwifery (CFM)
PO Box 82227
Athens, GA 3068-2227
888-CFM-4880
www.cfmidwifery.org

Midwife Info.com
www.midwifeinfo.com

Midwifery Today, Inc.
PO Box 2672
Eugene, OR 97402
www.midwiferytoday.com

Midwives Alliance of North America (MANA)
PO Box 175
Newton, KS 67114
www.mana.org

MOTHERS SUPPORT

Matching Moms
www.matchingmoms.com

International MOMS Club
www.momsclub.org

Mothers At Home
9493-C Silver King Court
Fairfax, VA 22031
www.mah.org

Mothers of Preschoolers (M.O.P.S.) MOPS
    International
PO Box 102200
Denver, CO 80250-2200
www.gospelcom.net/mops

Mothers and More
PO Box 31
Elmhurst, IL 60126
www.mothersandmore.org

Women, Infants, and Children Program (WIC)
Supplemental Food Programs Division
Food and Nutrition Service – USDA
3101 Park Center Drive

Alexandria, VA 22302
www.fns.usda.gov/wic

PARENTING

Attachment Parenting International (API)
1508 Clairmont Place
Nashville, TN 37215
www.attachmentparenting.org

The Natural Child Project
PO Box 55002
Victoria, BC V8N 6L8
www.naturalchild.org

PREGNANCY AND BIRTH

Birthing the Future
PO Box 1040
Bayfield, CO 81122
www.birthingthefuture.com

Coalition for Improving Maternity Services (CIMS)
The Mother Friendly Childbirth Initiative
CIMS National Office
PO Box 2346
Ponte Vedra Beach, FL 32004
www.motherfriendly.org

The Childbirth Connection
281 Park Avenue South, 5th floor
New York, NY 10010
www.childbirthconnection.org/listeningtomothers/

Group B Strep Association (GBSA)
PO Box 16515
Chapel Hill, NC 27516
www.GroupBStrep.org

Plus Size Pregnancy
www.plus-size-pregnancy.org

Postpartum Support International
927 North Kellogg Ave
Santa Barbara, CA 93111
805-967-7636
www.postpartum.net

National Association of Postpartum Care Services
(NAPCS)
800 Detroit St.
Denver, CO 80206
800-45-DOULA
www.napcs.org

VACCINE SAFETY AND INFORMATION

Institute for Vaccine Safety
Johns Hopkins University
Bloomberg School of Public Health
615 N. Wolfe Street, Suite 5515
Baltimore, MD 21205-2179
www.vaccinesafety.edu

National Vaccine Information Center
512 W. Maple Avenue, Suite 206
Vienna, VA 22180
www.909shot.com

VBAC SUPPORT AND CESAREAN PREVENTION

ICAN (International Cesarean Awareness Network)
1304 Kingsdale Avenue
Redondo Beach, CA 90278
310-542-5368
www.ican-online.org

WATERBIRTH

Waterbirth International Resources and Referral
Service
PO Box 1400
Wilsonville, OR 97070
www.waterbirth.org

Overview of Fetal Development

Week 3
- the brain, spinal cord, and heart begin to develop
- beginning development of the gastrointestinal tract
- one month (4-5 weeks)
- formation of tissue that develops into the vertebra and other bones
- further development of the heart which now beats at a regular rhythm
- movement of rudimentary blood through the main vessels
- beginning of the structures of the eye and ears
- the brain develops into five areas and some cranial nerves are visible
- arm and leg buds are visible

Week 6
- beginning of formation of the lungs
- further development of the brain
- arms and legs have lengthened with foot and hand areas distinguishable
- hands and feet have digits, but may still be webbed

Week 7
- nipples and hair follicles form
- elbows and toes visible
- all essential organs have at least begun to form
- two months (week 8)
- rotation of intestines
- facial features continue to develop
- the eyelids are more developed
- the external features of the ear begin to take their final shape
- The end of the eighth week marks the end of the "embryonic period" and the beginning of the "fetal period".

Three months (9-12 weeks)
- the fetus reaches a length of 3.2 inches
- the head comprises nearly half of the fetus' size
- the face is well formed

- eyelids close and will not reopen until about the 28th week
- tooth buds appear for the baby teeth
- limbs are long and thin
- the fetus can make a fist with its fingers
- genitals appear well differentiated
- red blood cells are produced in the liver

Four months (13-16 weeks)
- the fetus reaches a length of about 6 inches
- a fine hair develops on the head called lanugo
- fetal skin is almost transparent
- more muscle tissue and bones have developed, and the bones become harder
- the fetus makes active movements
- Sucking motions are made with the mouth
- meconium is made in the intestinal tract
- the liver and pancreas produce their appropriate fluid secretions

Five months (20 weeks)
- the fetus reaches a length of 8 inches
- lanugo hair covers entire body
- eyebrows and lashes appear
- nails appear on fingers and toes
- the fetus is more active with increased muscle development
- "quickening" usually occurs (the mother can feel the fetus moving)
- fetal heartbeat can be heard with a stethoscope

Six months (24 weeks)
- the fetus reaches a length of 11.2 inches
- the fetus weighs about 1 lb. 10 oz.
- eyebrows and eyelashes are well formed
- all the eye components are developed
- the fetus has a hand and startle reflex
- footprints and fingerprints forming
- alveoli (air sacs) forming in lungs

Seven months (25-28 weeks)
- the fetus reaches a length of 15 inches
- the fetus weighs about 2 lbs. 11 oz.
- rapid brain development

- nervous system developed enough to control some body functions
- eyelids open and close
- respiratory system, while immature, has developed to the point where gas exchange is possible
- a baby born at this time may survive, but the possibilities for complications and death remain high

Eight months (29-32 weeks)
- the fetus reaches a length of about 15-17 inches
- the fetus weighs about 4 lbs. 6 oz.
- rapid increase in the amount of body fat
- rhythmic breathing movements occur, but lungs are not fully mature
- bones are fully developed, but still soft and pliable
- fetus begins storing iron, calcium, and phosphorus

Nine months (36 weeks)
- the fetus reaches a length of about 16-19 inches
- the fetus weighs about 5 lbs. 12 oz. to 6 lbs. 12 oz.
- lanugo begins to disappear
- increase in body fat
- fingernails reach the end of the fingertips
- a baby born at 36 weeks has a high chance of survival, but may require some medical interventions

Weeks 37 to 40
- considered full-term at 37 weeks
- may be 19 to 21 inches in length
- lanugo is gone except for on the upper arms and shoulders
- fingernails extend beyond fingertips
- small breast buds are present on both sexes
- head hair is now coarse and thicker

FROM *CONCEPTION TO BIRTH* BY ALEXANDER TSIARAS

The Ten Steps of the Mother-Friendly Childbirth Initiative for Mother-Friendly Hospitals, Birth Centers, and Home Birth Services

Copyright © 1996 by The Coalition for Improving Maternity Services (CIMS).

To receive CIMS designation as "mother-friendly," a hospital, birth center, or home birth service must carry out our philosophical principles by fulfilling the Ten Steps of Mother-Friendly Care:

A mother-friendly hospital, birth center, or home birth service;
1. Offers all birthing mothers:
    a. unrestricted access to the birth companions of her choice, including spouse, partners, children, family members, and friends;
    b. unrestricted access to continuous emotional and physical support from a skilled woman—for example, a doula, or labor-support professional;
    c. access to professional midwifery care.

2. Provides accurate descriptive and statistical information to the public about its practices and procedures for birth care, including measures of interventions and outcomes.

3. Provides culturally competent care—that is, care that is sensitive and responsive to the specific beliefs, values, and customs of the mother's ethnicity and religion.

4. Provides the birthing woman with the freedom to walk, move about, and assume the positions of her choice during labor and birth (unless restriction is specifically required to correct a complication), and discourages the use of the lithotomy (flat on back with legs elevated) position.

5. Has clearly defined policies and procedures for:
    a. collaborating and consulting throughout the perinatal period with other maternity services, including communicating with the original caregiver when transfer from one birth site to another is necessary;
    b. linking the mother and baby to appropriate community resources, including prenatal and post-discharge follow-up and breastfeeding support.

6. Does not routinely employ practices and procedures that are unsupported by scientific evidence, including but not limited to the following:
    a. shaving;
    b. enemas;
    c. I.V.s (intravenous drip);
    d. withholding nourishment;
    e. early rupture of membranes;
    f. electronic fetal monitoring;

Other interventions are limited as follows;
    g. Has an induction use rate of 10 percent or less;
    h. Has an episiotomy rate of 20 percent or less, with a goal of 5 percent or less
    i. Has a total cesarean rate of 10 percent or less in community hospitals, and 15 percent or less in tertiary care (high-risk hospitals)
    j. Has a VBAC (vaginal birth after cesarean) rate of 60 percent or more with a goal of 75 percent or more.

7. Educates staff in non-drug methods of pain relief, and does not promote the use of analgesic or anesthetic drugs not specifically required to correct a complication.

8. Encourages all mother and families, including those with sick or premature newborns or infants with congenital problems, to touch, hold, breastfeed, and care for their babies to the extent compatible with their conditions.

9. Discourages nonreligious circumcision of the newborn.

10. Strives to achieve the WHO-UNICEF "Ten Steps of the Baby-Friendly Hospital Initiative" to promote successful breastfeeding:
    a. Have a written breastfeeding policy communicated to all health care staff.
    b. Train all health care staff in skills necessary to implement this policy.
    c. Inform all pregnant women about the benefits and management of breastfeeding.
    d. Help mothers initiate breastfeeding within an hour of birth.
    e. Show mothers how to breastfeed and how to maintain lactation even if they should be separated from their infants.
    f. Give newborn infants no food or drink other than breast milk unless medically indicated.
    g. Practice room in: allow mothers and infants to remain together 24 hours a day.
    h. Encourage breastfeeding on demand.

    i.   Give no artificial teat or pacifiers (also called dummies or soothers) to breastfeeding infants.

    j.   Foster the establishment of breastfeeding support groups and refer mothers to them on discharge from hospitals or clinics.

To view the CIMS documents and services visit their website at www.motherfriendly.org and be sure to read the consumer version called "Having a Baby? Ten Questions to Ask" and the CIMS Self-Assessment Tool.

Index

BIRTHING IN THE SPIRIT

A

Adrenaline 87
Air 234
American College of Obstetrics and Gynecology (ACOG) 27,34
Anger 21-41
Anxiety 35,194,207
Astraunauts 279 (about the earth)
Atma 10,28
Attraction 13, 260
American Public Health Association 35
Alcohol 7,167
Analgesic (fentanyl) 71
Autism 81 (Pervasive Developmental Disorder PDD)
Anesthetic 86.
Atomic power 109 (within body)
Affirmations 137,190,193,207
Artwork 21
Attachment 220
Attitude 130, (Healthy is necessary) 231,281

B

Babies 96 (premature)
Balance 157
Beliefs 130,132 (societal and cultural,132 (Chinese), 133 (African, Asian, Latin American), 134 (Cambodian),134 (Bedouin), 135 (Indian), 137 (changing)
Bells 269 (Tibetan women)

Biological clock 181
Birth 17 (natural), 19,25, 62-63 (as instinctive process, 287 (Times), 289 (moment of), 293 (interference in)
Birth memories 12
Birth positions 64 (upright), 145 (hands and knees), 146 (squatting, dangle squat, supported squat, stranded beetle)
Birthing center 29,31-32
Birthing in the spirit 37,112
Blastocyst 75
Blessing 47
Bliss 51
Blood-oxygen dissociation curve 90
Blood patch 88
Body mass index 159
Bonding and attachment 14, 86
Brain 76 (fetal), 78 (windows of opportunity), 101 (primal/old)
Breastfeeding 85,229 (self-attachment)
Breathing 105 (slow,deep), 146 (to birth a baby), 191 (diaphragm), 192 (pelvic), 311 Biological 176 (clock), 287(rhythms), 288 (diurnal rhythm)

C

Caffeine 167,180-181
Calcium 154
Calories 153

Cataracts 77
Cerebrospinal fluid 88
Cesarean 20,26-28 (reasons for), 32,29 (on demand or by appointment), 69
Chaos, reorganization, refinement 244
Character 51,55,318
Chi 103, (life force) 214
Childbirth education 22,26,29 (emotional preparation), 63,71,130,209
Children 314 (overextended)
Circadian rhythms 176
Conception 2,11
Colostrum 3
Compassion 21
Confidence 15 (natural birth), 37,51,284
Consciousness 10,47,214
Contractions 26,110-111
Cortisol 85,206
Criticizing 315
Crying babies 180
Cultures 202 (Latina paradox)
Curiosity 67
Cycles 3

D

Detachment 219,264
Determination 21
Dharma 127
Diabetes 160
Differentiation 76 (embryonic cells)
Dim lights 92

———∞∞∞———

Discipline 317
Discrimination 274
Divorce 314
Doptone 64
Doubt 71,195
Doula 21,35
Drug addiction 80
Duality 186
Due date 26
Dural sac 88

E

Earth 234
Educare 17,21
Education 17
Ego and desire 188
Electronic age 65, (post) 295
Elements 230 (five of), 230 (earth,
    water, fire, air), 232(ether/
    space), 288 (in body)
Embarrassment 199
Endorphins 83,86
Energy 96,262 (field)
Entrainment 103
Equanimity 186
Envy 21
Epidural 26,29,80,87,89
Ether 234
Exercise 210
Experience 47 (importance of
    experiencing it)
Expression of depression 241
External fetal monitor 26,6,91,32
Eyes 28 (babies), 95

F

Family 312
Fatty streaks 158 (fetal aortas)
Fear 27 (of childbirth), 197
    (primal), 201(nature of), 206

(healthy), 206 (physiological
    effects of), 215 (moving out
    of), 315 (fear vs love-based
    parenting)
Fetascope 64
Figure 8 exercise 245
Fire 234
Five D's 271,272 (duty
    and devotion), 272-273
    (discipline), 273
    (determination), 274
    (discrimination)
Fish 80,166
Flaxseed oil 168
Focus 47
Folic acid 154
Forceps 26
Forgiveness 140,242
Friendship 318
Fruits and vegetables 163-166,166
    (color coding)
    (High Power foods)

G

Genetic engineering 156
Glial cells 76
God 10
Grace 190 (of God)
Grief 238,240 (social and physical
    aspects and stages of)
Growth cones 76
Growth hormone 85
Guilt 241

H

Habituation 57
Hands 95,193
Head, heart, hands (3HV),121
Heartburn 168
Heart center 135,222

Hemoglobin 90,153
Holistic 10,11,169
Home 29, 31-35 (home birth-
    safety of)
Homeostasis 152
Honesty 66
Heredity 290 (planetary)
Hospitals 29-31,35
Human potential 50-51
Human values 21,50-51,55
    (interconnectedness), 72
    (breakdown of)
Humility 283
Hypnotic effect 129
Hypothalamus 84

I

Ice 192
Imitation 308
Induction 26
Infection 76
Initiatives 373 (Healthy People
    2010), 324 (CIMS), 325
    (WHO and Safe Motherhood
    Initiative SMI), 326
    (Childbirth Connection)
Insomnia 181
Integrity 66-67,189
Internal fetal monitor 26
Intimacy 84, 312 (family)
Intimidation 200
Intravenous 64-88
Intuition 47-47,118,119
    (blocks to), 120-121
    (characteristics of), 123,125
    (losing of), 63 (instinctive),
    71
Ion channels 81
Iron 153

J

Jealousy 21

J-point 201

Judgment 29

K

Kindness 21, 282 (random acts of)

Kloosterman 294

Knowledge 17 (worldly and creative), 21

L

Labor 110,123,178 (false), 213 (sounds)

Leboyer, F 294

Lifestyles 143 (traditional vs modern), 308 (life experiences)

Love 13,21,51,53,85,113,217 (pouring love exercise), 23,13 (attachment), 54,250 (for mothers), 257 (power of), 258 (as thought is truth), 259 (as feeling is peace), 259 (as understanding is nonviolence), 260 (in action is right action; faith), 262 (oxytocin), 263 (powerful force), 270-271 (as verb), 274 (unconditional), 275(circle exercise)

M

Magneticism 13-14,260,298-299

Mantras 129,269

Massage 96

Matter 39,61

Medial world 39,46,47

Meditation 52,129,264

Metamessage 122

Midwives 33 (types of)

Milky Way 2,177

Mind 13,105,128 and 189 (steadying of), 129 (concept)

Mindfulness 168 (in eating)

Miscarriage 238

Moon 26

Morning sickness 168

Morphine 86

Mother nature 46

Mothers and fathers 252-253 (effects of unhealthy relationships), 309 (mother as child's first teacher), 313 (working mother and father)

Multiple births 155

N

Naturalness 69

Nature 222 (connecting with)

Neocortex 26,71,87,91-92,93 (stimulation of), 211

Neuron 77 (mirror), 81,308 (imitation)

Nicotine 167

Nocebo effect 62-63

Nonviolence,51,54,234,280

Nutrition 151,169 (holistic),171 (Common Sense Nutrition)

Nuts 162-163

O

Obesity 80-160

Odent, Michel 294

Omega-3 polyunsaturated fatty acids (DHA) 80

Ovum 1

Oxygen 90

Oxygen supplementation 26

Oxytocin 84,86,262

P

Pain 211(healthy), 6

Parantese (talking to babies), 79

Parenting 307,320 (Steps to Becoming a Good Parent)

Partial pressure of oxygen 90

Peace 51-52,104,185-187,233

Pelvic floor 25

Perseverance 21

Patience 21,26,52

Pelvis 62 (female), 143 (importance of anterior)

Pelvic bodywork 143

Pelvic outlet 144

Physiology of birth 83

Pitocin (synthetic oxytocin) 89,293

Place of birth 29

Posterior pituitary gland 84

Power within 109

Prana 103

Prayer 193, (mother's prayer) 94,269

Pride 21

Primal Health Research 79,160

Primal period 80

Privacy 71,92

Prolactin 85

Prostaglandins 86,206

Protein 153

Planets 290

R

Rabbits (and love) 264

Radiation 76

Reaction, reflection, resounding 81,111

Reframing 138,212

Relaxation 192

Religion 284 (word comes from)

Repression and denial 223
Resonance 9,103,121
Respect 21,29,82,279,307 (for parents)
Rest 210
Rhombus of Michaelis 147
Right action 37,51-52,182,234
Role change 312, (men and women)

S

Safe(feeling) 29,30 97 (safe birth place), 193,207 (with birth team), 316 (parents love for children), 32 (home birth), 34
Salt 167
Scopolomaine anesthesia 29
Sensory stimulation (on fetal brain) 77,79
Self confidence 21,55
Self realization 51,56
Self sacrifice 51,56
Self satisfaction 51,55
Self inquiry 68
Senses 227 (five), 228-229 (hearing, smell, touch), 230 (taste)
Service 282 (selfless)
Sheaths 101,102 (food), 102 (gross, subtle, causal), 103 (vital air), 104 (mind), 105 (intelligence and bliss)
Shock and disbelief 240
Singing 311

SIDS (Sudden Infant Death Syndrome) 176
Silence 26, 94
Smell 229
Sleep 178 (REM and non-REM), 180 (cycles)
Sleep debt 175,177,181
Soda 161
Soul 10,11,12,68-69,264
Sphincters 86
Spirit 10 (Holy Spirit), 13,39,46,51,223
Spiritus 9
Squatting 146
Star Wars 296
Sugar 161
Surrender 111
Symbolic language 46

T

Technology 67 (age of)
Thoughts (positive) 111, (immune system effects) 113
Time periods 65
Tocophobia 27
Tone of voice 70
Touching 310
Trust and faith 26
Truth 37,51,61-62,71,234
Turtle 5,7
Twilight sleep 29

U

Umbilical cord (cutting) 79,110

Unassisted birth 29
Unconditional love 274
Unity of thought, word, and deed 67
Unity in diversity 279,280-281,283
Uterine inertia 90
Uterus 111

V

Vacuum extraction 26
Vaginal delivery 27
VBAC 29,32,67
Vibration 68
Violence 80, uterine inertia 90
Vocalization 94,190,265
Visualization 97,99 (safe birth), 210
Vitamins 154,167, (vitamin D)

W

WATCH 140 (words, actions, thoughts, character, heart)
Water 25,32,83 (pools for labor), 26 (water birth), 233
White coat hypertension 104
Who am I? 49
Witness 222 (detachment), 242 (writing)
Worrying 205

Z

Zygote 75

Printed in the United States
81041LV00006BA/1-46